GCSE

Com**hed Science**

A wise w___d, "There's no combustion without oxygen, and no Grade 9-1 GC___ ___ Science exam success without practice." Truly profound.

Well as luck ___ this super CGP book is simply bursting with realistic exam-style que___ topic. All the required practicals are covered too and there are p___ d analysis questions to test those tricky AO3 skills.

We've also inclu___ mixed questions for Biology, Chemistry and Physics, just like in the real ex___ complete answers to every question at the back. Enjoy!

xam Practice Workbook
Foundation Level

Published by CGP

Editors:
Eleanor Crabtree, Mary Falkner, Katie Fernandez, Emily Garrett, Rob Hayman, Paul Jordin, Chris Lindle,
Duncan Lindsay, Sarah Pattison, Rachael Rogers, Camilla Sheridan, Sarah Williams and George Wright.

Contributors:
Sophie Anderson, Ian Davis, Mark A. Edwards, Bethan Parry, Alison Popperwell and Chris Workman.

With thanks to Luke Molloy and Glenn Rogers for the proofreading.

With thanks to Lottie Edwards, Jan Greenway and Emily Smith for the copyright research.

Data in Figure 1 on page 28 source: Health Survey for England 2018. Licensed under the Open Government Licence v3.0.
http://www.nationalarchives.gov.uk/doc/open-government-licence/version/3/

Data in Figure 2 on page 28 contains information from NHS Digital. Licensed under the Open Government Licence v3.0.
http://www.nationalarchives.gov.uk/doc/open-government-licence/version/3/

Graph on page 153 based on data provided by NOAA ESRL Global Monitoring Division, Boulder, Colorado, USA (http://esrl.noaa.gov/gmd/).
By Dr. Pieter Tans, NOAA/ESRL (www.esrl.noaa.gov/gmd/ccgg/trends/) and Dr. Ralph Keeling, Scripps Institution of Oceanography
(scrippsco2.ucsd.edu/).

Data for the global temperature anomaly and CO_2 concentration in the table on page 154: NOAA National Centers for Environmental
information, Climate at a Glance: Global Time Series, published November 2020, retrieved on November 18, 2020 from
https://www.ncdc.noaa.gov/cag/

Stopping distances data on page 219 from the Highway Code. Contains public sector information licensed under the
Open Government Licence v3.0. http://www.nationalarchives.gov.uk/doc/open-government-licence/version/3/

Table on page 231 contains public sector information licensed under the Open Government Licence v3.0.
http://www.nationalarchives.gov.uk/doc/open-government-licence/version/3/

Clipart from Corel®
Illustrations by: Sandy Gardner Artist, email sandy@sandygardner.co.uk
Printed by Elanders Ltd, Newcastle upon Tyne

Based on the classic CGP style created by Richard Parsons.

Contents

✓ Use the tick boxes to check off the topics you've completed.

Topic P1 — Energy

Topic P2 — Electricity

Topic P3 — Particle Model of Matter

Topic P4 — Atomic Structure

Topic P5 — Forces

Topic P6 — Waves

Topic P7 — Magnetism and Electromagnetism

Mixed Questions

You can find some useful information about What to Expect in the Exams and other exam tips at cgpbooks.co.uk/GCSEScienceFoundation/Exams

How to Use This Book

- Hold the book <u>upright</u>, approximately <u>50 cm</u> from your face, ensuring that the text looks like <u>this</u>, not <u>ʂᴉɥʇ</u>.
- Before attempting to use this book, read the following <u>safety information</u>:

There are warm-up questions for the trickier sub-topics, to ease you in and get you thinking along the right lines.

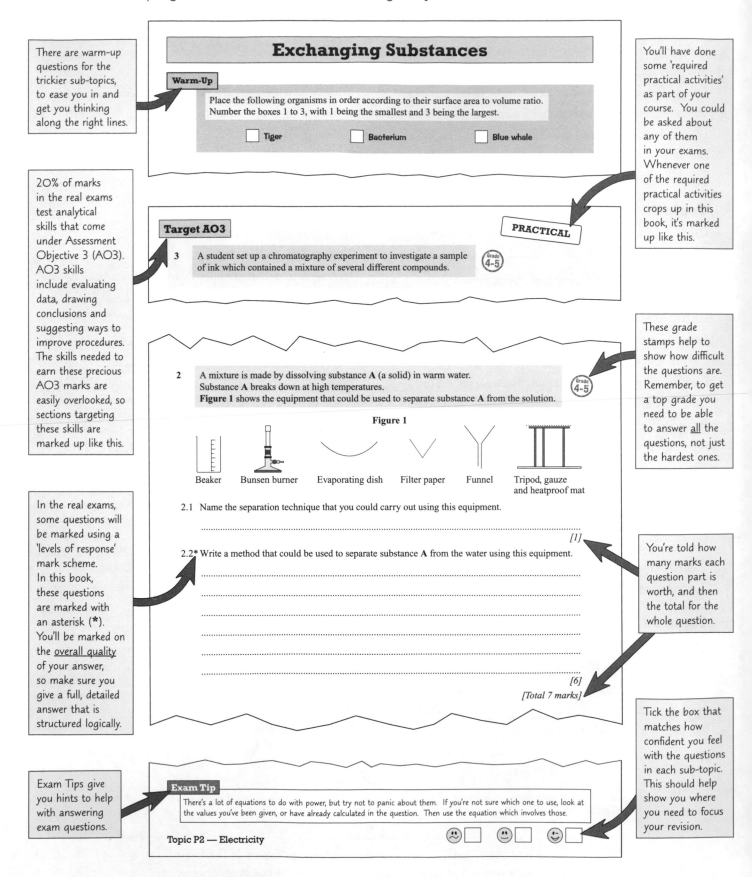

Exchanging Substances

Warm-Up

Place the following organisms in order according to their surface area to volume ratio. Number the boxes 1 to 3, with 1 being the smallest and 3 being the largest.

☐ Tiger   ☐ Bacterium   ☐ Blue whale

You'll have done some 'required practical activities' as part of your course. You could be asked about any of them in your exams. Whenever one of the required practical activities crops up in this book, it's marked up like this.

20% of marks in the real exams test analytical skills that come under Assessment Objective 3 (AO3). AO3 skills include evaluating data, drawing conclusions and suggesting ways to improve procedures. The skills needed to earn these precious AO3 marks are easily overlooked, so sections targeting these skills are marked up like this.

Target AO3

PRACTICAL

3   A student set up a chromatography experiment to investigate a sample of ink which contained a mixture of several different compounds.

Grade 4-5

These grade stamps help to show how difficult the questions are. Remember, to get a top grade you need to be able to answer <u>all</u> the questions, not just the hardest ones.

2   A mixture is made by dissolving substance **A** (a solid) in warm water.
Substance **A** breaks down at high temperatures.
Figure 1 shows the equipment that could be used to separate substance **A** from the solution.

Grade 4-5

Figure 1

Beaker   Bunsen burner   Evaporating dish   Filter paper   Funnel   Tripod, gauze and heatproof mat

2.1   Name the separation technique that you could carry out using this equipment.

....
[1]

In the real exams, some questions will be marked using a 'levels of response' mark scheme. In this book, these questions are marked with an asterisk (*). You'll be marked on the <u>overall quality</u> of your answer, so make sure you give a full, detailed answer that is structured logically.

2.2* Write a method that could be used to separate substance **A** from the water using this equipment.

....
....
....
....
....
....
[6]

[Total 7 marks]

You're told how many marks each question part is worth, and then the total for the whole question.

Tick the box that matches how confident you feel with the questions in each sub-topic. This should help show you where you need to focus your revision.

Exam Tips give you hints to help with answering exam questions.

Exam Tip

There's a lot of equations to do with power, but try not to panic about them. If you're not sure which one to use, look at the values you've been given, or have already calculated in the question. Then use the equation which involves those.

Topic P2 — Electricity   ☹ ☐   ☺ ☐   ☺ ☐

- There's also a Physics Equations List at the back of this book — you'll probably be given these in your exam. You can look up equations on this list to help you answer some of the physics questions in this book.

Cells

Warm-Up

Complete the table to show whether each statement is **true** for
eukaryotic cells or prokaryotic cells. Tick **one** box in each row.

Statement	Eukaryotic cells	Prokaryotic cells
These cells have a nucleus.		
These are the smallest type of cell.		
These cells can be bacteria.		

1 **Figure 1** shows a diagram of an animal cell.

Figure 1

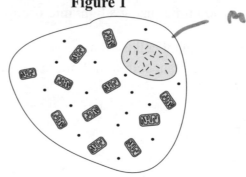

1.1 Label the cell membrane, the nucleus and a mitochondrion on **Figure 1**.

[3]

1.2 Give the function of each part of the cell on **Figure 1**.

Cell membrane ....

Mitochondria ....

Nucleus ....

[3]

1.3 Name **two** other subcellular structures that can be found in an animal cell.

1. ....

2. ....

[2]

1.4 Give **one** reason why the diagram in **Figure 1** does not represent a plant cell.

....

[1]

[Total 9 marks]

Exam Tip

If you get a question in the exam where you need to label a diagram, make sure you draw your label lines very carefully.
If it's not clear what part of the diagram the end of your line is touching, you might miss out on some valuable marks.

Microscopy

1   A student observed blood cells under a microscope. _{Grade} **1-3**
A scale drawing of one of the cells is shown in **Figure 1**.

Figure 1

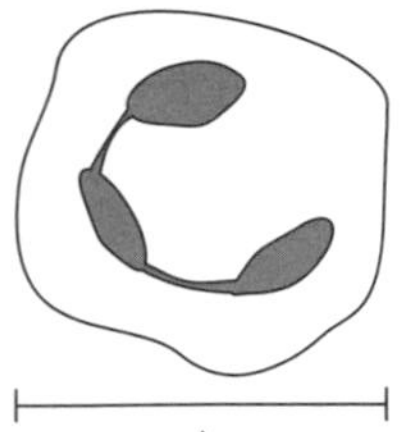

In **Figure 1**, A is the image width.

1.1   Measure the length of A with a ruler.   .... mm
[1]

1.2   The real width of the cell is 0.012 mm.
What is the magnification of the image in **Figure 1**?
Use the formula:

$$\text{magnification} = \frac{\text{image size}}{\text{real size}}$$

magnification = × ....
[1]

[Total 2 marks]

2   A plant cell is magnified 1000 times using a light microscope. _{Grade} **3-4**

2.1   The length of the image of the plant cell is 10 mm.
Calculate the real length of one plant cell in millimetres (mm).
Use the formula:

$$\text{real size} = \frac{\text{image size}}{\text{magnification}}$$

.... mm
[1]

2.2   What is the length of one plant cell in micrometres (μm)?

.... μm
[1]

2.3   How do magnification and resolution compare between electron and light microscopes?
Tick **one** box.

Magnification and resolution are the same for electron microscopes and light microscopes. ☐

Electron microscopes have a lower magnification and resolution than light microscopes. ☐

Electron microscopes have a higher magnification and resolution than light microscopes. ☐
[1]

2.4   Give **one** way in which electron microscopy has increased understanding of subcellular structures.

....
[1]

[Total 4 marks]

Exam Tip

Make sure you know how to convert one unit to another. To go from a bigger unit to a smaller unit (for example, from millimetres to micrometres) your calculation should be a multiplication. To go from a smaller unit to a bigger unit (e.g. from micrometres to millimetres) your calculation should be a division.

Topic B1 — Cell Biology

More on Microscopy

1 A student wants to use a light microscope to view a sample of onion cells. **(Grade 4-5)**

1.1 The student adds a drop of iodine stain to her sample. Which statement best describes why a stain might be used to view a sample of tissue? Tick **one** box.

To make the specimen easier to cut. ☐

To make the specimen easier to see. ☐

To prevent air bubbles forming. ☐

To help the cover slip stick to the slide. ☐

[1]

Figure 1 shows a diagram of the light microscope that the student plans to use.

1.2 The three different objective lenses are labelled in **Figure 1** with their magnification.

Which lens should the student select first when viewing her cells?

....

[1]

Figure 1

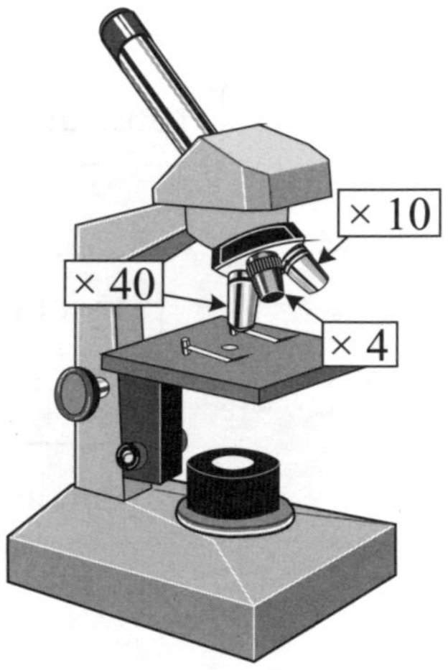

× 10
× 40
× 4

1.3 After she has selected the objective lens, she looks down the eyepiece and uses the adjustment knobs.

Describe the purpose of the adjustment knobs.

....

....

....

[1]

1.4 The student wants to see the cells at a greater magnification.

Describe the steps that she should take.

....

....

....

[2]

1.5 After she has viewed the cells, she wants to produce a scientific drawing of them. Her teacher has told her to use smooth lines to draw the structures she can see.

Give **two** other ways in which she can make sure she produces an accurate and useful drawing.

1. ....

2. ....

[Total

Exam Tip

The number of marks that a question is worth is sometimes a bit like a secret tip from the examiner they want you to write. E.g. if a 'describe' question is worth two marks, you'll usually need to ma

4

Cell Differentiation and Specialisation

Complete the sentence below. Use a word from the box.

specialisation	differentiation	adaptation

The process by which cells change to carry out specific functions is called ....

---

1   Specialised cells have different structures.
     This allows them to carry out different functions.   Grade 1-3

Draw straight lines to match up each type of plant cell with its structure and function.

Plant cell

root hair cell

xylem

phloem

Structure and Function

Long cells joined end to end, with very few subcellular structures. They transport food.

Long hollow cells joined end to end. They transport water.

Long, hair-like shape. They absorb water and mineral ions.

[Total 2 marks]

---

2   A sperm cell is specialised for its function.   Grade 3-4

2.1   What is the function of a sperm cell?

     ....
     [1]

Figure 1 shows a sperm cell.

Figure 1

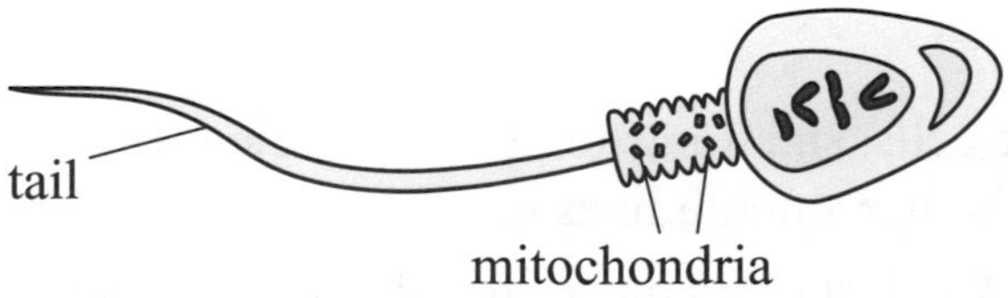

tail

mitochondria

2.2   How does the sperm cell's **tail** help it to carry out its function?

     ....
     [1]

2.3   Describe how **mitochondria** help the sperm cell to carry out its function.

     ....
     [1]

[Total 3 marks]

Chromosomes and Mitosis

1   **Figure 1** shows a cell during the cell cycle.

Figure 1

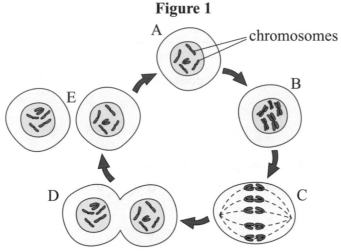

1.1 Cell **A** is preparing to divide. What is happening to the chromosomes in cell A?
Tick **one** box.

The chromosomes are dividing. ☐

The chromosomes are being copied. ☐

The chromosomes are getting longer. ☐

[1]

1.2 What else is happening in cell **A**?
Tick **one** box.

The number of mitochondria is increasing. ☐

The number of ribosomes is decreasing. ☐

The nucleus is dividing. ☐

[1]

1.3 Describe what is happening to cell **D**.

....

....

[2]

1.4 How do the two cells produced at stage **E** compare to cell **A**?
Tick **one** box.

They are genetically different. ☐

They are genetically similar. ☐

They are genetically identical. ☐

[1]

[Total 5 marks]

Exam Tip

In the exam, you might be given photos of real cells undergoing mitosis and asked what's going on. Don't panic
if the cells themselves don't look familiar — the main thing you have to look at is what the chromosomes are doing.

Topic B1 — Cell Biology

Stem Cells

1 Stem cells can be found in the growing areas of plants. (Grade 4-5)

1.1 What is a stem cell?

....

[1]

1.2 What are the growing areas of a plant that contain stem cells called?
Tick **one** box.

cloning zones ☐   meristems ☐   leaves ☐   mesophyll layers ☐

[1]

1.3 You can produce cloned plants from plant stem cells.
Describe **two** benefits of producing cloned plants from stem cells.

1. ....

2. ....

[2]

[Total 4 marks]

2 The technique shown in **Figure 1** could be used to produce cells for some medical treatments. (Grade 4-5)

Figure 1

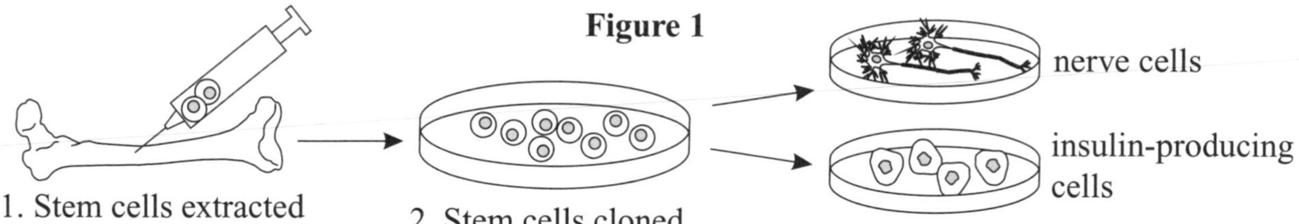

1. Stem cells extracted from bone marrow.

2. Stem cells cloned.

nerve cells

insulin-producing cells

3. Different cell types are produced.

2.1 Name **one** medical condition that may be helped by treatment using stem cells.

....

[1]

2.2 Apart from bone marrow, give **one** other source of stem cells for medical treatments.

....

[1]

2.3 Suggest **one** reason why some people may be **against** using the source of stem cells you named in **2.2**.

....

[1]

2.4 Give **one** potential **risk** of using stem cells in medical treatments.

....

[1]

[Total 4 marks]

Exam Tip

You might be asked to write about the social or ethical issues to do with using stem cells. It's a good idea to know some different points of view, so that you have plenty to write about. You don't have to agree with the opinions.

Topic B1 — Cell Biology

Diffusion

1   **Figure 1** shows glucose molecules diffusing through a cell membrane.

Figure 1

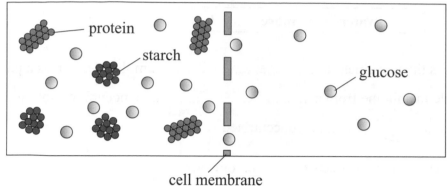

cell membrane

1.1 In which direction will most of the glucose molecules be moving?
Draw an arrow on **Figure 1** to show your answer.

[1]

1.2 Why can't the protein molecules in **Figure 1** diffuse through the membrane?

....

[1]

1.3 As glucose diffuses from one side of the membrane to the other,
its concentration gradient decreases. Which statement is correct?
Tick **one** box.

A decrease in the concentration gradient will have no effect on the rate of diffusion. ☐

A decrease in the concentration gradient will increase the rate of diffusion. ☐

A decrease in the concentration gradient will decrease the rate of diffusion. ☐

[1]

[Total 3 marks]

2   A student adds a drop of ink to a glass of cold water.

2.1 What will the student observe happening to the drop of ink? Explain your answer.

....

....

....

[2]

2.2 How might the observation differ if the ink was added to a glass of warm water?

....

[1]

[Total 3 marks]

Exam Tip

Diagrams showing molecules diffusing through a cell membrane often crop up in the exams. Look at the labels on these sorts of diagrams carefully to check that you're answering about the type of molecule that you're being asked about.

 ☐   ☐   ☐

Topic B1 — Cell Biology

Osmosis

1   Some molecules move by osmosis.

1.1 Use the words in the box to complete the following definition of osmosis:

water	more	less	sugar

Osmosis is the movement of .... molecules across a partially

permeable membrane from a .... concentrated solution

to a .... concentrated solution.

[3]

1.2 In which of these is osmosis occurring? Tick **one** box.

A plant is absorbing water from the soil. ☐

Sugar is being taken up into the blood from the gut. ☐

Water is evaporating from a leaf. ☐

Oxygen is entering the blood from the lungs. ☐

[1]

[Total 4 marks]

PRACTICAL

2   A student did an experiment to see the effect of different salt solutions on pieces of potato.

•   He cut five equal-sized chips from a raw potato and measured the mass of each chip.
•   Each chip was placed in a beaker containing a different concentration of salt solution.
•   The mass of each chip was measured again after 24 hours. The results are shown in **Table 1**.

Table 1

Beaker	1	2	3	4	5
Mass of potato chip at start of experiment (g)	5.70	5.73	5.71	5.75	5.77
Mass of potato chip after 24 hours (g)	6.71	6.58	6.27	5.46	4.63
Percentage change in mass of potato chip (%)	17.7	?	9.81	−5.04	−19.8

2.1 Calculate the percentage change in mass for the potato chip in beaker 2.

.... %

[2]

2.2 Explain why the chips in beakers 4 and 5 lost mass.

....

....

[2]

[Total 4 marks]

3 A student is investigating osmosis. She takes two beakers and puts a different
concentration of sucrose solution into each one. Then she places a length of Visking
tubing (a partially permeable membrane) containing 0.5 M sucrose solution into
each beaker. She places a glass capillary tube in the Visking tubing so that the end
dips into the sucrose solution. A diagram of her experiment is shown in **Figure 1**.

Figure 1

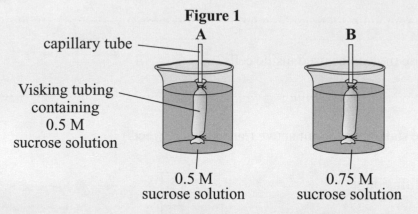

The student records the level of the sucrose solution in each beaker and each capillary tube
at the start of the experiment. She plans to record the level of the solution in each beaker
every 30 minutes for 8 hours.

3.1 Give **two** variables that the student should keep constant in this experiment.

....

....
[2]

3.2 Predict what will happen to the level of the solution in Beaker A after 1 hour. Tick **one** box.

It will increase. ☐   It will decrease. ☐   It will stay the same. ☐
[1]

3.3 The level of the solution in Beaker B increased after one hour because there was a net movement
of water molecules out of the Visking tubing into the beaker.
Explain why there was a net movement of water molecules out of the Visking tubing.

....

....
[1]

3.4 The level of the solution in Beaker B had stopped increasing by the end of the experiment.
Explain why.

....

....
[2]

[Total 6 marks]

Exam Tip

In your exams, you might be given an experiment you've not done before and have to answer questions about it.
If that happens, don't panic. All you need to do is apply what you know about the topic to the new experiment.
If there's any extra information that you need to know, it'll be given to you in the question. What a relief.

 ☐   ☐   ☐

Topic B1 — Cell Biology

Active Transport

1 Glucose molecules can be absorbed from the gut into the blood by active transport. *(Grade 4-5)*

1.1 What is active transport?

....

....

[1]

1.2 How are glucose molecules used inside cells?

....

[1]

1.3 Which of these statements about active transport is correct?
Tick **one** box.

It's a type of diffusion. ☐

It can only occur down a concentration gradient. ☐

It needs energy from respiration. ☐

It needs energy from photosynthesis. ☐

[1]

[Total 3 marks]

2 Plants absorb mineral ions from the soil by active transport. *(Grade 4-5)*

2.1 Why do plants need mineral ions?

....

[1]

2.2 Why do plants need to use active transport to absorb mineral ions from the soil?

....

....

[2]

2.3 State **two** ways in which active transport differs from diffusion.

1. ....

2. ....

[2]

[Total 5 marks]

Exam Tip

Diffusion, osmosis and active transport can be pretty tricky ideas to get your head around, but it's really important that you do. You could try making a list of all the important facts about each of the three processes and then learning it. Like the fact that active transport needs energy from respiration to happen, but diffusion and osmosis don't.

Topic B1 — Cell Biology

Exchanging Substances

Warm-Up

Place the following organisms in order according to their surface area to volume ratio.
Number the boxes 1 to 3, with 1 being the smallest and 3 being the largest.

☐ Tiger   ☐ Bacterium   ☐ Blue whale

1   The cube in **Figure 1** represents a small cell. (Grade 3-4)

Figure 1

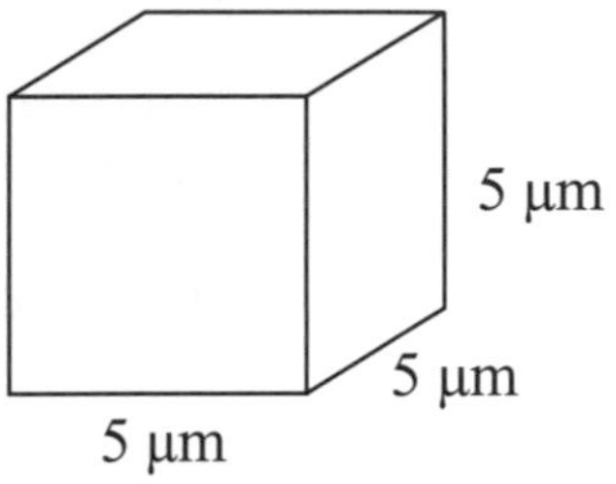

5 μm, 5 μm, 5 μm

1.1 What is the volume of the cube? Tick **one** box.

5 μm³ ☐   15 μm³ ☐

125 μm³ ☐   150 μm³ ☐
[1]

1.2 What is the surface area of the cube? Tick **one** box.

5 μm² ☐   15 μm² ☐   125 μm² ☐   150 μm² ☐
[1]

1.3 Another cell has a surface area of 24 μm². It has a volume of 8 μm³.
What is its surface area to volume ratio? Tick **one** box.

3:1 ☐   2:1 ☐   1:3 ☐   1:2 ☐
[1]

[Total 3 marks]

2   **Figure 2** shows the relative sizes of an Arctic hare and a polar bear. Both animals live in cold, snowy conditions. (Grade 4-5)

Figure 2

polar bear

Arctic hare

Having a large surface area to volume ratio increases the rate at which an organism loses heat.

Which of the organisms in **Figure 2** is more likely to have difficulty keeping warm in the Arctic? Explain your answer.

....

....

....

....

[Total 3 marks]

Topic B1 — Cell Biology

More on Exchanging Substances

Warm-Up

Which of these are adaptations of a gas exchange surface in animals?
One has been circled for you. Circle **three** more.

a thin membrane   a good blood supply   a thick membrane

being flat   a large surface area   being ventilated

1   Digested food is absorbed into the blood from the small intestine. *Grade 1-3*
    Which of the following statements is correct? Tick **one** box.

Villi decrease the blood supply to the small intestine. ☐

A single layer of surface cells increases the surface area of the small intestine. ☐

Villi increase the surface area of the small intestine. ☐

[Total 1 mark]

2   **Figure 1** shows an alveolus in the lungs. *Grade 3-4*

Figure 1

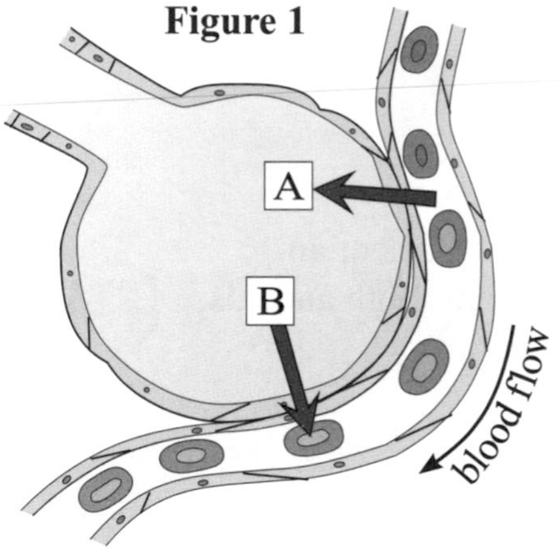

2.1 Name gases A and B.

A ....

B ....

[2]

2.2 By what process do these gases move across the membrane?

....

[1]

2.3 State which feature of the lungs gives:

gases a short distance to move ....

a large surface area ....

[2]

[Total 5 marks]

Topic B1 — Cell Biology

3 **Figure 2** shows a diagram of a fish gill. This is a gas exchange surface.

Figure 2

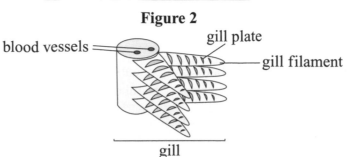

3.1 Describe the movement of gases in a fish gill.

....

....
[2]

3.2 The gill filaments and gill plates have the same purpose. Suggest what this purpose is.

....
[1]

3.3 Give **one** other feature of a fish gill. Explain how it makes gas exchange more efficient.

....

....
[2]

[Total 5 marks]

4* Leaves are adapted for gas exchange. **Figure 3** shows the cross-section of a leaf.

Figure 3

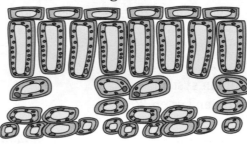

Explain how a leaf is adapted for efficient gas exchange.

....

....

....

....

....
[Total 4 marks]

Exam Tip

There are a fair few exchange surfaces that you need to know about — root hairs and leaves in plants, and gills, villi and alveoli in animals. If you can reel off the ways that exchange surfaces are adapted for exchanging materials, then questions on how the structure of each of these things relates to its function shouldn't catch you out on exam day.

Topic B1 — Cell Biology

Cell Organisation

Warm-Up

Number the boxes 1 to 4 to put the body components in order of size.
Number 1 should be the smallest component. Number 4 should be the largest component.

☐ Organ system ☐ Tissue ☐ Cell ☐ Organ

1 **Figure 1** is a diagram of the human digestive system. Three organs are labelled **X, Y** and **Z**. Grade 4-5

Figure 1

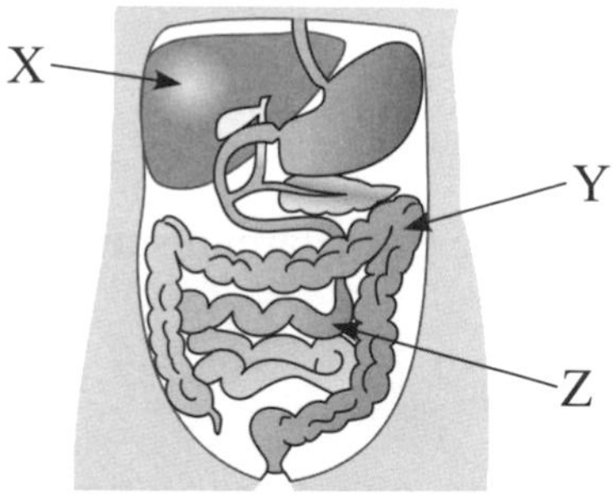

1.1 Draw **one** line to match each letter below to the name of the organ it represents in **Figure 1**.

Letter	Name of organ
X	liver
Y	small intestine
Z	large intestine
	stomach

[3]

1.2 What is an organ?

....

....

[1]

1.3 The digestive system is an organ system.
What is meant by the term 'organ system'?

....

....

[1]

1.4 Organ systems contain multiple types of tissue.
What is a tissue?

....

....

[1]

1.5 What is the role of the digestive system?

....

[1]

[Total 7 marks]

Enzymes

1 The shape of an enzyme is important for its job. **Figure 1** shows an enzyme.

Grade 1-3

Figure 1

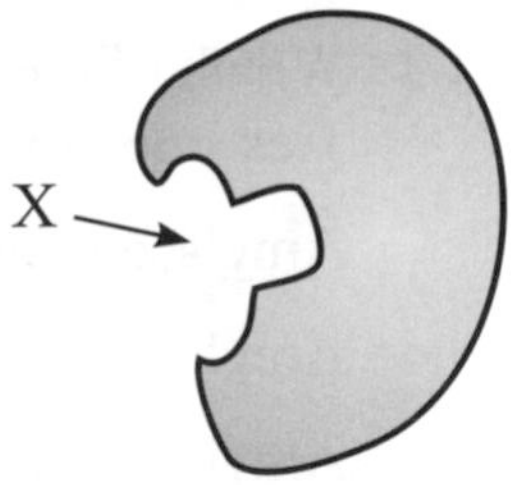

1.1 Name the part of the enzyme labelled **X** in **Figure 1**.

....

[1]

1.2 The enzyme in **Figure 1** catalyses a reaction that breaks apart a substrate.
Which reaction, **A**, **B** or **C**, will the enzyme in **Figure 1** catalyse?
Tick **one** box.

A 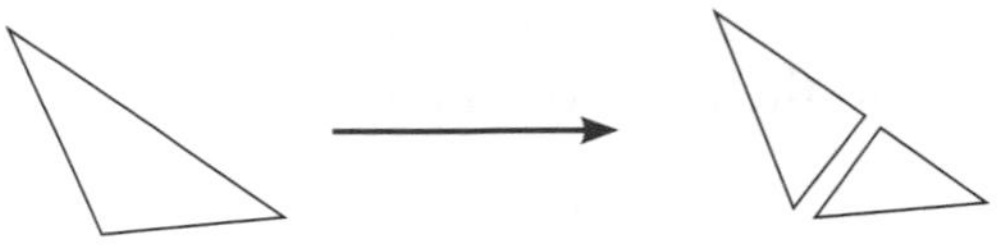 ☐

B  ☐

C 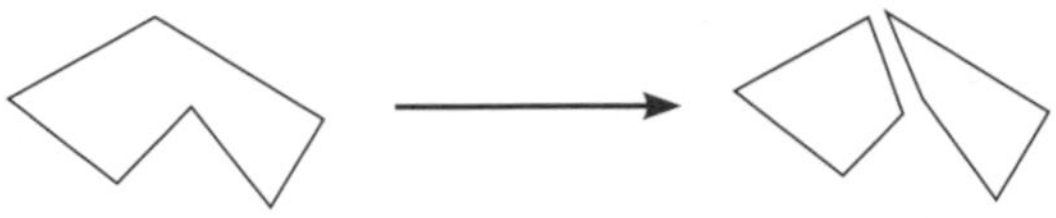 ☐

[1]

[Total 2 marks]

2 A reaction is catalysed by an enzyme. **Figure 2** shows how temperature affects the rate of this reaction.

Grade 4-5

Figure 2

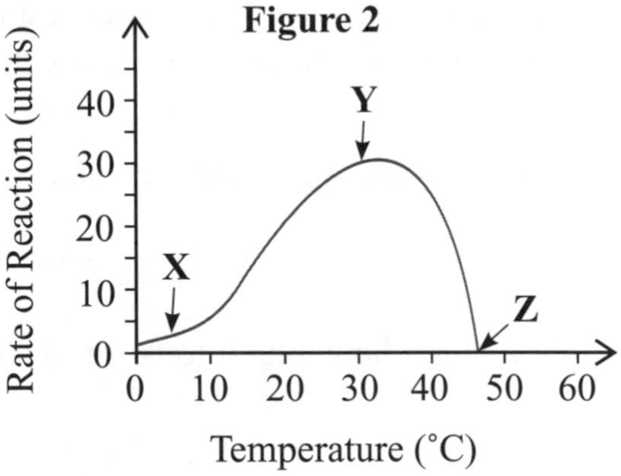

2.1 Look at points **X** and **Y** on **Figure 2**.

Describe the relationship between rate of reaction and temperature between points **X** and **Y**.

....

[1]

2.2 Explain why the reaction has stopped at point **Z**.

....

....

....

[3]

[Total 4 marks]

Exam Tip

Enzymes are important in biology, so it's a pretty good bet that they'll make an appearance on exam day. Make sure you can explain how they work and that you know how temperature and pH affect the rate of enzyme-controlled reactions.

Investigating Enzymatic Reactions

1 Amylase is an enzyme. (Grade 3-4)

1.1 Which of the following statements about amylase is correct?
Tick **one** box.

Amylase joins sugar molecules together to make starch. ☐

Amylase helps to break down sugar into starch. ☐

Amylase helps to break down starch into amino acids. ☐

Amylase helps to break down starch into sugar. ☐

[1]

Iodine solution can be used in investigations into the activity of amylase.

1.2 Describe the colour change that takes place when iodine solution
is added to a solution containing starch.

....

....

[2]

[Total 3 marks]

2 A student investigated the effect of pH on amylase activity. (Grade 4-5)

He added amylase solution to three test tubes, **X**, **Y** and **Z**.
Each test tube contained:
• a starch solution.
• a buffer solution with a different pH.

2.1 Give **one** way that the student could control the temperature in the test tubes.

....

[1]

Table 1 shows how long it took for the reaction in each test tube to finish.

Table 1

Test tube	Time (s)	Rate of reaction
X	110	9.1
Y	40	....
Z	190	....

2.2 Complete **Table 1** to show the rate of the reactions in test tubes **Y** and **Z**.

Use the equation: $\text{Rate} = \dfrac{1000}{\text{time}}$

Give each of your answers to 2 significant figures.

[2]

2.3 What are the units for the 'Rate of reaction' column in **Table 1**? Tick **one** box.

second (s) ☐   per second (s^{-1}) ☐   time (t) ☐

[1]

[Total 4 marks]

Enzymes and Digestion

1 Enzymes are involved in digestion in the human body. *(Grade 1-3)*

1.1 Draw **one or more** lines from each type of molecule to the products of its digestion.

Type of molecule

carbohydrate

lipid

protein

Products of digestion

amino acids

sugars

glycerol

fatty acids

[4]

1.2 Lipases are digestive enzymes.
What type of molecule do lipases break down? Tick **one** box.

Carbohydrates ☐   Lipids ☐   Proteins ☐

[1]

1.3 Give **two** places in the body that produce lipases.

1. ....   2. ....

[2]

[Total 7 marks]

2 Bile is used in the digestion of fats by enzymes. *(Grade 3-4)*

2.1 Complete the sentences below.
Use words from the box.

| gall bladder small intestine alkaline acidic |
| liver neutralises emulsifies |

Bile is produced by the .... It is stored in the ....

It has an .... pH, so it .... acid from the stomach.

It also .... fats.

[5]

2.2 Fats are broken down into tiny droplets before being digested by enzymes.
Why does this make digestion by enzymes happen faster?

....

....

[1]

[Total 6 marks]

Exam Tip

The name of a digestive enzyme usually starts with the same letters as the type of molecule that it breaks down —
e.g. proteases break down proteins. Knowing that should make learning their names, and what they do, much easier.

Topic B2 — Organisation

PRACTICAL

Food Tests

Warm-Up

Put a tick (✓) in the box next to the correct test for **glucose**.

Benedict's test ☐

Iodine test ☐

Biuret test ☐

1 Many food tests involve a colour change. Grade 1-3

Draw **one** line to match each of the following tests to its positive result.

Positive result

Test

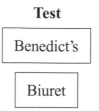

Benedict's

Biuret

turns purple

top layer turns red

turns brick-red

[Total 2 marks]

2* A student has a sample of cooked butter beans. He wants to find out if the beans contain protein. Grade 4-5

Describe how the student could:
- prepare a sample of the beans for testing.
- test for protein in his prepared sample.

....

....

....

....

....

....

....

....

....

....

[Total 6 marks]

Exam Tip

When you get a long-answer question, it's OK to use spare space on your exam paper to jot down the key points you want to make before you start writing. Just remember to cross your jottings out afterwards so they don't get marked.

Topic B2 — Organisation

 ☐ ☐ ☐

The Lungs

1 **Figure 1** shows the structure of the lungs in humans. (Grade 1-3)

Figure 1

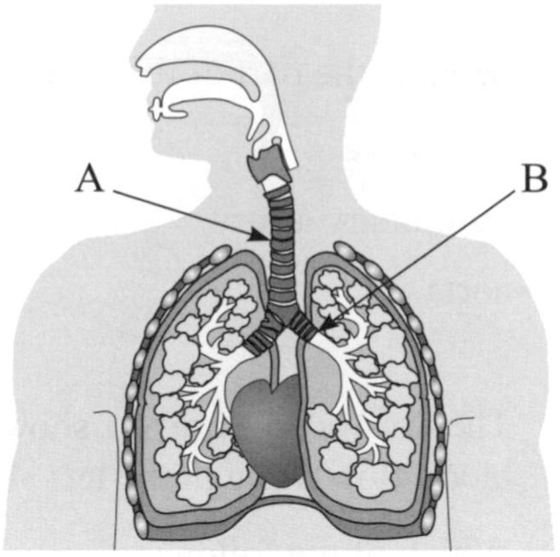

1.1 What is structure **A** on **Figure 1**?
Tick **one** box.

bronchus ☐

trachea ☐

alveolus ☐

[1]

1.2 What is structure **B** on **Figure 1**?
Tick **one** box.

bronchus ☐   trachea ☐   alveolus ☐

[1]

[Total 2 marks]

2 A student ran for 12 minutes.
During this 12 minute run, the student took 495 breaths. (Grade 3-4)

Calculate the student's average breathing rate.
Use the equation: breathing rate = number of breaths ÷ number of minutes

Give your answer to 3 significant figures.

.... breaths per minute

[Total 2 marks]

3 **Figure 2** shows an alveolus surrounded by a capillary.
Table 1 shows the relative concentrations of oxygen
and carbon dioxide at positions **X**, **Y** and **Z** in **Figure 2**. (Grade 4-5)

Complete **Table 1** by writing **high** or **low** in the empty cells.

Figure 2

Table 1

	Oxygen concentration	Carbon dioxide concentration
X	High	Low
Y	Low	....
Z	....	....

[Total 3 marks]

Topic B2 — Organisation

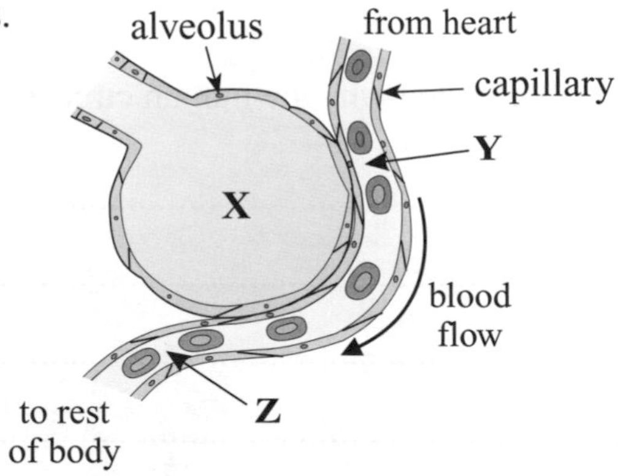

Circulatory System — The Heart

1 **Figure 1** shows a diagram of the heart. Grade 1-3

Figure 1

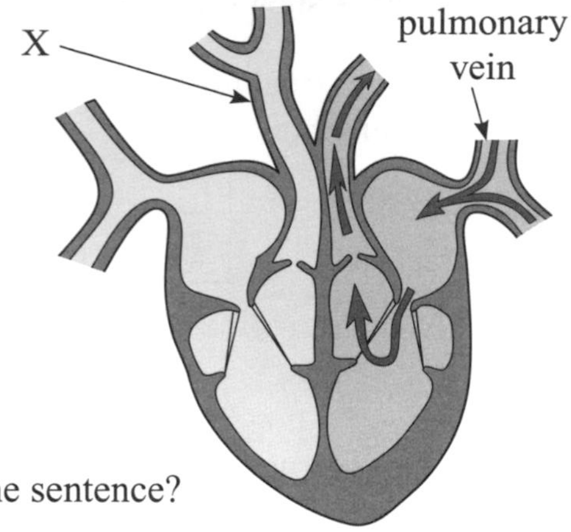

1.1 What is the part of the heart labelled **X**? Tick **one** box.

vena cava ☐

pulmonary artery ☐

aorta ☐

[1]

The arrows on **Figure 1** show the direction of blood flow through the **left side** of the heart.

1.2 Which of the following answers should be used to complete the sentence?
Write the correct letter, **A**, **B** or **C** in the box below.

A vena cava

B pulmonary artery

C aorta

The left ventricle pumps blood through the ☐ to cells all over the body.

[1]

1.3 Draw arrows on **Figure 1** to show the direction of blood flow through the **right side** of the heart.

[1]

[Total 3 marks]

2 The heart has a pacemaker. Grade 3-4

2.1 Which of these statements about the pacemaker is true?
Tick **one** box.

It is found in the left atrium. ☐   It keeps blood flowing in the right direction. ☐

It controls the resting heart rate. ☐   It supplies the heart muscle with blood. ☐

[1]

2.2 Suggest why someone might need to be given an artificial pacemaker.

....

[1]

[Total 2 marks]

3 Explain why the human circulatory system is described as a 'double circulatory system'. Grade 4-5

....

....

....

....

....

[Total 3 marks]

Circulatory System — Blood Vessels

1   **Figure 1** shows the three types of blood vessel.

Figure 1

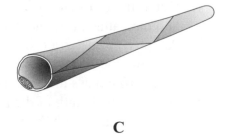

A	**B**	**C**

Which of these blood vessels, **A**, **B** or **C**, is an artery?

Write your answer in the box.   ☐

Give a reason for your answer.

....

....

[Total 2 marks]

2   Different types of blood vessel have different structures and functions.

2.1 Complete **Table 1** to show whether each feature is part of a capillary, an artery or a vein.
     Put a tick in each row.

Table 1

Feature	Capillary	Artery	Vein
Elastic fibres in blood vessel walls			
Large lumen			
Thin walls, with gaps between the cells			
Valves			

[3]

2.2 Describe the function of capillaries.

....

....

[2]

2.3 Explain why arteries have a different structure to veins.

....

....

....

[2]

[Total 7 marks]

Target AO3

3   An experiment was carried out to investigate how elastic arteries and veins are.

The experiment was set up as shown in **Figure 2**.
The method used was as follows:

1. Cut a ring of tissue from an artery, measure the width
   and then attach it to the hook.
2. Attach a mass carrier to the bottom of the ring.
3. Measure the length of the ring with the mass carrier attached.
4. Add a 10 g mass to the mass carrier.
5. Measure the length of the ring with the mass attached,
   and then again with the mass removed.
6. Repeat steps 4 and 5 with a 20 g mass, 30 g mass, etc.
7. Repeat the experiment using a ring of vein of the same width.

Figure 2

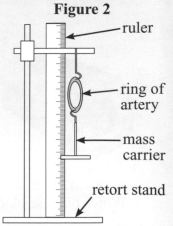

The percentage change between the original length of the ring with
just the mass carrier attached and its length after each mass was removed
was calculated for each mass. The results are plotted in **Figure 3**.

Figure 3

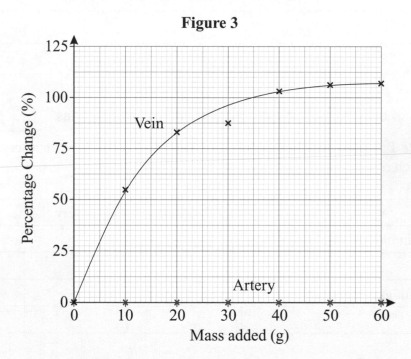

3.1 Based on the results in **Figure 3**, which of the following statements is correct?
Tick **one** box.

The greater the mass added to the vein, the less it stretched.   ☐

The artery returned to its original length when the mass was removed.   ☐

The ring of vein was shorter at the end of the experiment than it was at the start. ☐

[1]

3.2 There is an anomalous result in **Figure 3**.
Suggest **one** reason why this anomalous result may have occurred.

....

[1]

[Total 2 marks]

Topic B2 — Organisation

Circulatory System — Blood

1 The blood has several different parts. **Figure 1** shows a white blood cell.

Grade 1-3

Figure 1

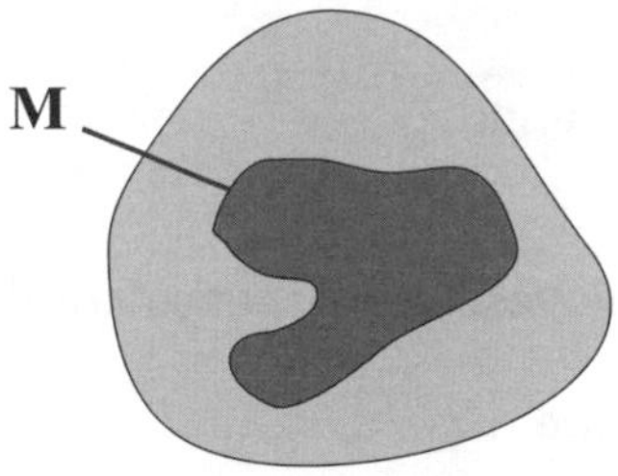

1.1 What is structure **M** on **Figure 1**?
Tick **one** box.

cytoplasm ☐

cell membrane ☐

nucleus ☐

[1]

1.2 The different parts of the blood are carried in a liquid. What is this liquid called?
Tick **one** box.

plasma ☐   cell sap ☐   urine ☐   bile ☐

[1]

1.3 Which of the following parts of the blood is responsible for clotting?
Tick **one** box.

white blood cells ☐   red blood cells ☐   platelets ☐   antibodies ☐

[1]

[Total 3 marks]

2 Red blood cells carry oxygen around the body. **Figure 2** shows the shape of a red blood cell.

Grade 3-4

Figure 2

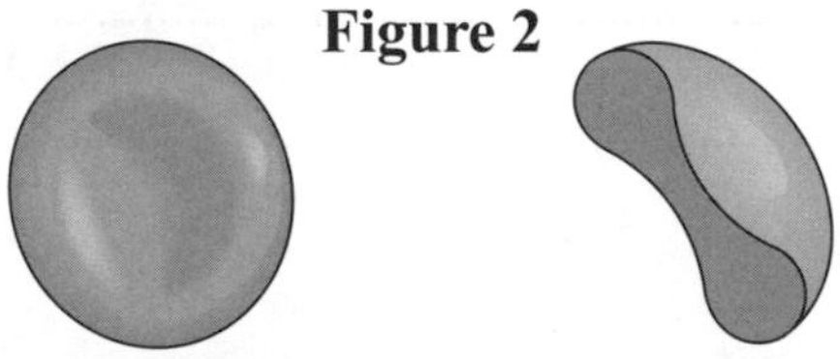

View from above   Cut through view

2.1 Describe how a red blood cell's shape helps it to carry out its function.

....

[1]

2.2 Red blood cells don't have a nucleus. How does this help them to carry out their function?

....

[1]

2.3 Give **one** more feature of red blood cells that help them to carry out their function.

....

[1]

[Total 3 marks]

Exam Tip

A lot of the easier marks in the exam come from just knowing your facts inside out — like in Question 1 on this page. Having that key knowledge under your belt will make all the difference on exam day. You'll also feel more confident tackling the harder questions in the exam if you know you've got the answers to some of the easier ones right already.

 ☐   ☐   ☐

Cardiovascular Disease

Fill in the gaps to complete the following sentence. Choose **two** of the words below.

lungs   blood vessels   heart   legs

Cardiovascular diseases are diseases of the ....

and the ....

---

1   Statins are drugs that can be used to prevent cardiovascular diseases.   (Grade 3-4)

1.1   What do statins do?
Tick **one** box.

They lower the blood cholesterol level.   ☐

They increase the blood cholesterol level.   ☐

They remove all cholesterol from the blood.   ☐

[1]

1.2   Give **one** disadvantage of using statins to prevent cardiovascular diseases.

....

....

[1]

[Total 2 marks]

---

2   Heart attacks happen when the heart muscle does not get enough oxygen.   (Grade 4-5)

2.1   Explain how **stents** prevent heart attacks from happening.

....

....

....

[2]

2.2   A doctor is advising a patient about having a stent fitted.
Give **one** risk that the doctor is likely to tell the patient about.

....

....

[1]

[Total 3 marks]

More on Cardiovascular Disease

1 A man has a leaky heart valve. (Grade 4-5)

1.1 Which statement about leaky heart valves is correct?
Tick **one** box.

Leaky heart valves increase blood flow through the heart. ☐

Leaky heart valves stop blood flowing through the heart. ☐

Leaky heart valves allow blood to flow in both directions through the heart. ☐

Leaky heart valves do not affect blood flow through the heart. ☐

[1]

1.2 Apart from being leaky, describe **one** other way that a valve might be faulty.

....

[1]

1.3 Suggest **one** way in which the man's surgeons could treat the leaky valve.

....

....

[1]

[Total 3 marks]

2 A patient is having a heart transplant. (Grade 4-5)

2.1 Why might a patient need a heart transplant?

....

[1]

A donor heart can be transplanted into a patient, or an artificial heart may be used instead.

Donor hearts come from a person who has recently died.
Artificial hearts are machines made from metal or plastic.

2.2 Suggest **one** advantage of using an artificial heart over a donor heart.

....

....

[1]

2.3 Suggest **one** disadvantage of using an artificial heart over a donor heart.

....

....

[1]

[Total 3 marks]

Exam Tip

There are quite a few different ways of treating cardiovascular disease that you need to know about for your exam.
As well as knowing what they are and how they work, make sure you can discuss their advantages and disadvantages.

 ☐   ☐   ☐

Topic B2 — Organisation

Health and Disease

1   Diseases can lead to poor health.   (Grade 3-4)

1.1 What is health?

....
[1]

1.2 List **two** factors other than disease that can cause poor health.

1. ....

2. ....
[2]

1.3 What is the difference between a communicable disease and a non-communicable disease?
Tick **one** box.

They are caused by different types of pathogens. ☐

Only communicable diseases can spread between people. ☐

Only non-communicable diseases can spread between people. ☐

[1]

[Total 4 marks]

2   AIDS is a disease caused by a virus.
People with AIDS have a weakened immune system.   (Grade 4-5)

2.1 Explain why a person with AIDS is likely to get other diseases.

....

....
[2]

2.2 Give **one** other example of how different diseases can interact.

....

....
[1]

2.3 The virus that causes AIDS can be passed between people during sexual intercourse.

Is AIDS a communicable or non-communicable disease?
Give a reason for your answer.

....

....
[1]

[Total 4 marks]

Risk Factors for Non-Communicable Diseases

1   Substances in a person's environment   (Grade 4-5)
     can be risk factors for certain diseases.

1.1 What is meant by a risk factor for a disease?

....

....
                                                                                                    [1]

1.2 Other than substances in the environment, state **two** types of risk factor.

1. ....

2. ....
                                                                                                    [2]

1.3 Obesity is a risk factor for many different diseases.
     Name **one** disease that obesity is a risk factor for.

....
                                                                                                    [1]
                                                                                          [Total 4 marks]

2   A patient has been diagnosed with cardiovascular disease.   (Grade 4-5)

2.1 Give **two** risk factors that might have contributed to the patient developing cardiovascular disease.

1. ....

2. ....
                                                                                                    [2]

2.2 Suggest **one** reason why non-communicable diseases can be expensive for an individual.

....

....
                                                                                                    [1]

2.3 Suggest **one** reason why non-communicable diseases can be expensive for a country.

....

....
                                                                                                    [1]
                                                                                          [Total 4 marks]

Exam Tip

Scientists find risk factors by looking for correlations (relationships) in data. Many risk factors don't directly cause a disease, but they do make it more likely. A person is even more likely to get a disease if they have several risk factors for it.

Target AO3

3   **Figure 1** shows the prevalence of adult obesity in England, between 2012 and 2018. **Figure 2** shows the number of people diagnosed with diabetes in England, between 2012 and 2018.

Figure 1

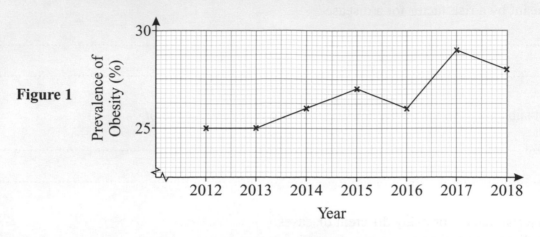

Figure 2

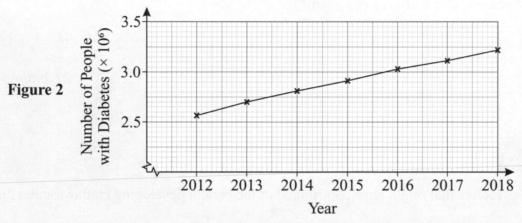

3.1 Give **one** similarity and **one** difference between the trends shown in **Figures 1** and **2**.

Similarity: ....

....

Difference: ....

....

[2]

3.2 A student says: "the increasing rate of obesity has caused the rate of diabetes to increase". Give **one** reason why this is not a valid conclusion based on the data in **Figures 1** and **2**.

....

....

[1]

[Total 3 marks]

Exam Tip

You've got to be really careful with the conclusions you make about data you're given — they need to match the data and not go beyond it. So have a close look at all the information you get and don't jump to conclusions too quickly.

Topic B2 — Organisation

Cancer

Warm-Up

Tumours can be benign or malignant. Draw lines to match the types of
tumour on the left with each characteristic on the right that applies to them.

Malignant Tumours

Benign Tumours

Are cancerous

Are not cancerous

Can spread to other parts of the body

1 There are many risk factors for cancer. **Grade 3-4**

1.1 Give **one** example of a **lifestyle factor** which increases the risk of getting cancer.

....

[1]

1.2 Apart from lifestyle factors, give **one** other type of risk factor for cancer.

....

[1]

[Total 2 marks]

2 A tumour is a mass of cells. **Grade 4-5**

2.1 What do tumours result from? Tick **one** box.

Rapid cell death ☐   No cell division ☐

Slow cell division ☐   Uncontrolled cell division ☐

[1]

Figure 1 shows two tumours in a person's body.
The secondary tumour was formed from the original tumour.

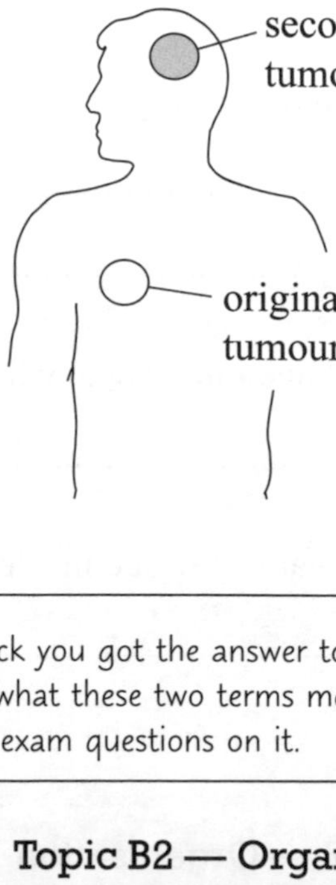

2.2 Explain how secondary tumours form in the body.

....

....

....

....

[2]

[Total 3 marks]

Figure 1

secondary
tumour

original
tumour

Exam Tip

The terms 'malignant tumour' and 'benign tumour' are really easy to get mixed up. Check you got the answer to
the Warm-Up question on this page right. If you didn't, take the time to go and learn what these two terms mean.
Cancer might not be the nicest topic in the world, but that doesn't mean there won't be exam questions on it.

Topic B2 — Organisation

Plant Cell Organisation

1 Leaves have many different types of tissue. (Grade 1-3)

1.1 Draw **one** line to match each tissue on the left with its function on the right.

Tissue

epidermal

meristem

xylem

Function

transports water into the leaf

covers the upper and lower surface of the leaf

absorbs water from the soil

causes growth at the tips of roots and shoots

[3]

1.2 Which of the following answers should be used to complete the sentence?
Write the correct letter, **A**, **B** or **C**, in the box below.

A   organ

B   organ system

C   tissue system

A leaf is an example of a plant ☐ .

[1]

[Total 4 marks]

2 **Figure 1** shows a diagram of a palisade cell. (Grade 4-5)

Figure 1

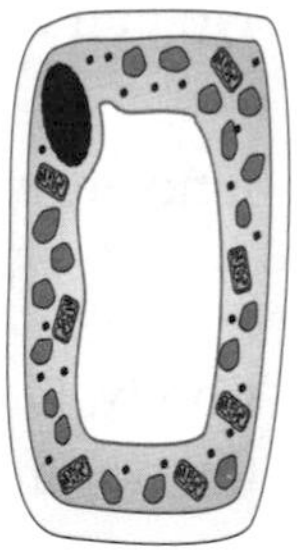

2.1 Explain why most palisade cells are found near the top of a leaf.

....

....

[2]

2.2 Give **one** way in which the structure of a palisade cell helps it to carry out its function.

....

[1]

2.3 Name a tissue inside the leaf that is specialised for gas exchange.

....

[1]

[Total 4 marks]

Transpiration and Translocation

Warm-Up

The diagrams show a phloem tube and a xylem tube.
In the spaces below, write down which one is the phloem tube and which one is the xylem tube.

elongated cells

end wall with pores

A: ....

hollow tube

cell wall strengthened with lignin

B: ....

1 Xylem and phloem transport substances through a plant. (Grade 1-3)

1.1 What does the xylem transport?
Tick **two** boxes.

mineral ions ☐   protein ☐   sugar ☐   water ☐   starch ☐

[2]

1.2 Which statement about transport in the phloem is correct?
Tick **one** box.

It only occurs in the leaves. ☐

It is called transpiration. ☐

It moves sugar around the plant. ☐

It only moves substances upwards from the roots. ☐

[1]

[Total 3 marks]

2 Complete the following passage by filling in the blanks. (Grade 3-4)

Use words from the box. Each word can only be used once.

| transpiration | translocation | condensation | evaporation |

The process by which water is lost from a plant is called ....

It is caused by the .... and diffusion of water from a plant's surface.

The transport of sugars around the plant is called ....

[Total 3 marks]

Exam Tip

It can be tricky to remember which is which when thinking of xylem and phloem. They're pretty similar and they've both got weird names. If you're struggling to remember, keep practising these questions. It will soon stick in your head.

Topic B2 — Organisation

Transpiration and Stomata

1   **Figure 1** shows what the surface of a leaf looks like under a microscope.

Figure 1

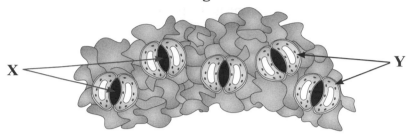

X   Y

1.1   Name the structures labelled **X** and **Y** in **Figure 1**.

X ....   Y ....

[2]

1.2   What is the function of the structures labelled **Y**?

....

....

[2]

[Total 4 marks]

2   Some students were investigating the effect of air flow on the rate of transpiration.
To do so, they measured the water uptake of a plant in still and moving air.
The rate of water uptake is assumed to be equal to the transpiration rate.

Table 1 shows the students' results.

Table 1

	Repeat	1	2	3	4	5	Mean
Water uptake in 30 minutes (cm³)	Still Air	1.2	1.2	1.0	0.8	1.1	1.1
	Moving Air	2.0	1.8	2.3	1.9	1.7	**X**

2.1   Calculate the value of **X** in **Table 1**.
Give your answer to 2 significant figures.

X = ... cm³
[2]

2.2   Describe the relationship between air flow around the plant and transpiration rate.

....
[1]

2.3   Explain the effect of air flow on the rate of transpiration.

....

....

....
[2]

[Total 5 marks]

Topic B2 — Organisation

Communicable Disease

Warm-Up

Circle the word below which is **not** a type of pathogen.

bacteria   viruses   insects   fungi   protists

---

1 What is a pathogen? Tick **one** box.   (Grade 1-3)

A type of disease. ☐

A microorganism that causes disease. ☐

Something used to prevent the spread of disease. ☐

Something used to treat a disease. ☐

[Total 1 mark]

---

2 There are different ways to prevent or reduce the spread of disease.   (Grade 3-4)

2.1 Vectors are organisms that spread disease.
Give **one** way that vectors can be stopped from passing on diseases.

....

....

[1]

2.2 Give **one** other way that humans can help prevent the spread of a disease.

....

[1]

[Total 2 marks]

---

3 Hassan has the common cold.
The common cold is a communicable disease.   (Grade 4-5)

3.1 What is meant by the term 'communicable disease'?

....

[1]

3.2 Hassan uses a tissue when he coughs and sneezes.
Suggest how this helps to prevent others from catching his cold.

....

....

[2]

[Total 3 marks]

Bacterial Diseases

1 *Salmonella* food poisoning in humans is caused by a type of bacterium. **Grade 4-5**

1.1 Symptoms of *Salmonella* food poisoning include fever and vomiting.
What substances are produced by *Salmonella* bacteria that cause these symptoms?

....

[1]

1.2 Give **two** ways that somebody could get *Salmonella* food poisoning.

1. ....

2. ....

[2]

1.3 In the UK, poultry are vaccinated against *Salmonella*. Why it is important to vaccinate poultry?

....

....

....

[2]

[Total 5 marks]

2 Gonorrhoea is a disease that can affect both men and women. **Grade 4-5**

2.1 How is gonorrhoea spread from person to person?

....

[1]

2.2 State **two** symptoms of the disease in women.

1. ....

2. ....

[2]

2.3 Name the antibiotic that was previously used to treat people infected with gonorrhoea.

....

[1]

2.4 Why is the antibiotic in **2.3** no longer able to effectively treat gonorrhoea?

....

[1]

2.5 Name **one** barrier method of contraception that prevents the spread of gonorrhoea.

....

[1]

[Total 6 marks]

Exam Tip

You'll often get questions that tell you how many things you need to include in your answer. Double-check that you've written the right number of things before you move on. There's no way you can get full marks if you don't write enough.

Topic B3 — Infection and Response

Viral Diseases

1 Measles is a highly infectious disease. (Grade 1-3)

1.1 What are the symptoms of measles?
Tick **two** boxes.

fever ☐   constipation ☐   yellow discharge ☐   red skin rash ☐   painful urination ☐

[2]

1.2 What can be given to prevent someone from developing measles?
Tick **one** box.

antibiotics ☐   antiretrovirals ☐   a vaccination ☐   aspirin ☐

[1]

[Total 3 marks]

2 The tobacco mosaic virus (TMV) affects many species of plants. (Grade 3-4)

2.1 Name **one** species of plant that can be attacked by the tobacco mosaic virus.

....

[1]

2.2 Which of the following plants, **A**, **B** or **C**, is infected with TMV?

A yellow leaves   **B** leaves lost   **C** green leaf — discoloured patches

Your answer = ...

[1]

[Total 2 marks]

3 A virus called HIV causes a disease known as AIDS. (Grade 4-5)

3.1 What type of drug can be used to control HIV?

....

[1]

3.2 What system in the body does HIV attack?

....

[1]

3.3 Describe how viruses such as HIV cause cell damage.

....

....

[2]

[Total 4 marks]

Topic B3 — Infection and Response

Fungal and Protist Diseases

Fill in the gaps in the passage about malaria. Use words on the left.
Not all of the words will be used.

protist

fungus

fever

vectors

Malaria is caused by a ....

Mosquitoes are the .... that carry the malaria pathogen to humans.

Malaria causes repeating episodes of ....

1   **Figure 1** shows a rose plant affected by a fungal disease.

Figure 1

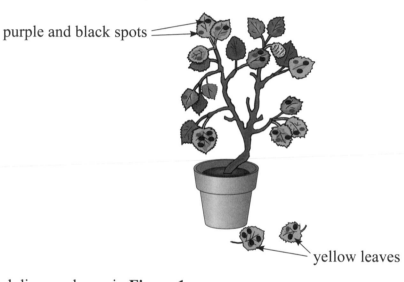

purple and black spots

yellow leaves

1.1 Name the fungal disease shown in **Figure 1**.

   ....

   [1]

A gardener notices that one of her rose plants has the disease shown in **Figure 1**.
She is worried that the rest of her rose plants may also become infected.

1.2 Give **one** way that the disease could spread to other rose plants in her garden.

   ....

   [1]

1.3 Describe how the gardener could treat the disease and stop it from spreading.

   ....

   ....

   ....

   [3]

   [Total 5 marks]

Topic B3 — Infection and Response

Fighting Disease

1   Different types of white blood cell have different roles in the immune system.

Complete the sentences below. Use words from the box.

phagocytosis	dissolve	antitoxins	antibodies	digest

Some white blood cells engulf and .... pathogens.

This is called ....

Other white blood cells produce proteins that lock onto invading pathogens.

These proteins are called ....

[Total 3 marks]

2*   The human body has several defences against the entry of pathogens.
Explain how these defences reduce the number of pathogens entering the body.

....

....

....

....

....

....

....

....

....

....

....

....

[Total 6 marks]

Topic B3 — Infection and Response

Fighting Disease — Vaccination

Why are people given vaccinations? Underline the correct answer.

To help them get better if they are already ill.

To stop them getting ill in the future.

To get rid of their symptoms.

1 Children are often vaccinated against measles.

1.1 What is usually injected into the body during a vaccination?
Tick **one** box.

antibiotics ☐

antibodies ☐

dead or inactive pathogens ☐

active pathogens ☐

[1]

1.2 How should a child's white blood cells respond to a vaccination?

....

[1]

[Total 2 marks]

2 Two children become infected with the measles pathogen.
One child has been vaccinated against measles and the other has not.

Figure 1 shows how the concentration of the measles antibody in each child's bloodstream changes after infection with the measles pathogen.

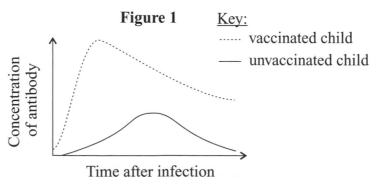

Using **Figure 1**, describe how antibody production differs between the vaccinated child and the unvaccinated child.

....

....

....

[Total 2 marks]

Topic B3 — Infection and Response

Fighting Disease — Drugs

Warm-Up

Complete each sentence below by ticking the correct box.

Digitalis is a drug used to treat ☐ heart conditions ☐ lung conditions

Digitalis was made from a chemical found in ☐ daisies ☐ foxgloves

1 A student has a sore throat. Her doctor says it is caused by a virus. *(Grade 3-4)*

1.1 The student says: "My sore throat cannot be treated with antibiotics."
Is the student correct? Give a reason for your answer.

....

....

[1]

1.2 Name a type of drug that the student could use to reduce her symptoms.

....

[1]

[Total 2 marks]

2 A hospital records the number of cases of infections that are caused by antibiotic-resistant bacteria each year. The figures for three years are shown in **Table 1**. *(Grade 4-5)*

Table 1

Year	2013	2014	2015
No. of infections	84	102	153

2.1 Describe the trend shown in **Table 1**.

....

[1]

2.2 Suggest why doctors in the hospital might be concerned about the trend shown in **Table 1**.

....

....

[2]

[Total 3 marks]

Exam Tip

If a question asks you to 'describe the trend', it just means 'look at the data and say what patterns you can see in it'.

Topic B3 — Infection and Response

Developing Drugs

1 New drugs have to undergo pre-clinical and clinical testing before they can be used. *(Grade 4-5)*

1.1 Which of the following is preclinical testing carried out on?
Tick **one** box.

healthy human volunteers ☐

cells, tissues and dead animals ☐

patients in a hospital ☐

cells, tissues and live animals ☐

[1]

1.2 During preclinical testing, scientists test a drug to find out whether it works.
Give **two** more things that the drug is tested for during preclinical testing.

1. ....

2. ....

[2]

During clinical testing, patients are split into two groups.
One group is given the drug. Another group is given a placebo.

1.3 What is a placebo?

....

[1]

1.4 Explain why some patients are given the drug and others are given a placebo.

....

....

[2]

1.5 Which of the following answers should be used to complete the sentence?
Write the correct letter, **A**, **B** or **C**, in the box below.

A only the patients

B only the doctors

C both the patients and the doctors

In a double blind trial, ☐ involved in the trial don't know who is receiving the placebo.

[1]

[Total 7 marks]

Exam Tip

There's a lot going on when it comes to drug development. The best way to learn it all is to write out each step of the process in order, in as much detail as you can. Keep going over the information till it sticks. Then, if you're asked a question about the development of a particular drug in the exam, it's just a case of applying what you know.

Topic B3 — Infection and Response

Photosynthesis

1 Plants produce glucose during photosynthesis. The glucose is then used to make other substances, which have their own uses.

1.1 The words on the left are all substances made using glucose.
Draw **one** line from each substance to its use.

Substance made using glucose   **Use**

starch   storage

fats and oils   making proteins

amino acids   making cell walls

cellulose   storage

                                            making DNA

[4]

1.2 What else is glucose used for in plant cells?

....

[1]

[Total 5 marks]

2 Photosynthesis takes place inside plant cells. *Grade 3-4*

2.1 Name the subcellular structures where photosynthesis takes place.

....

[1]

2.2 Complete the following word equation for photosynthesis.

.... + water → glucose + ...

[2]

2.3 Which of the following statements is correct?
Tick **one** box.

Energy is transferred from the environment during photosynthesis. ☐

Energy is transferred to the environment during photosynthesis. ☐

Energy is made during photosynthesis. ☐

Energy is broken down during photosynthesis. ☐

[1]

[Total 4 marks]

The Rate of Photosynthesis

Which of the following things limit the rate of photosynthesis?
Circle the **four** correct answers.

carbon dioxide
concentration

amount of soil

amount of glucose

light intensity

temperature

amount of
chlorophyll

1   An experiment was done to test the effect of increasing the carbon dioxide
concentration on the rate of photosynthesis. The results are shown in **Figure 1**.

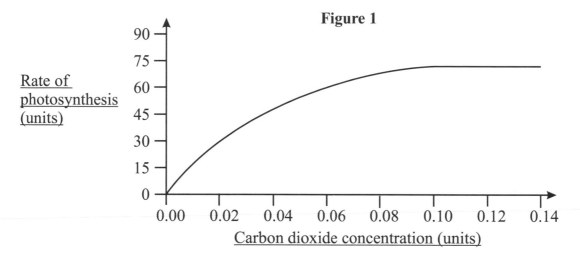

1.1   What conclusion can be drawn from the data in **Figure 1**?
Tick **one** box.

Carbon dioxide becomes a limiting factor at a concentration of 0.10 units. ☐

Carbon dioxide stops being a limiting factor at a concentration of 0.10 units. ☐

Carbon dioxide is a limiting factor at all concentrations. ☐

[1]

1.2   At a carbon dioxide concentration of **0.02 units**, the rate of photosynthesis was **30 units**.
At what carbon dioxide concentration had the rate of photosynthesis **doubled**?
Tick **one** box.

0.00 units ☐   0.04 units ☐   0.06 units ☐   0.08 units ☐

[1]

[Total 2 marks]

You might need to read a value off a graph in the exam. If so, you'll need to get your ruler out. For example, imagine
you were asked to use the graph above to find the rate of photosynthesis at a carbon dioxide concentration of 0.02 units.
You'd find 0.02 units on the bottom axis and use a ruler to draw a straight line up from there to the line of the graph.
Then you'd draw a straight line across to the 'rate of photosynthesis' axis and read off the value there (30 units).

 PRACTICAL

2 A student did an experiment to see how the rate of photosynthesis depends on light intensity.
   She measured the volume of oxygen produced by pondweed at different intensities of light.
   Table 1 shows her results. **Figure 2** shows some of her apparatus.

Table 1

Relative light intensity	1	2	3	4	5	6	7	8	9	10
Volume of oxygen produced in 10 minutes (cm^3)	8	12	18	25	31	13	42	48	56	61

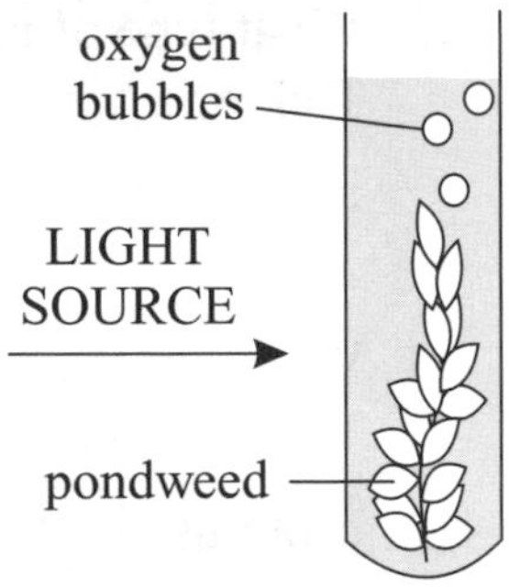

2.1 State the dependent variable and the independent variable in this experiment.

Figure 2

oxygen bubbles

LIGHT SOURCE →

pondweed

Dependent variable: ....

Independent variable: ....
[2]

2.2 State **two** factors that should be kept constant during this experiment.

1. ....

2. ....
[2]

2.3 **Figure 3** is a graph showing the student's results.
    Complete the graph using the results from **Table 1**.

Figure 3

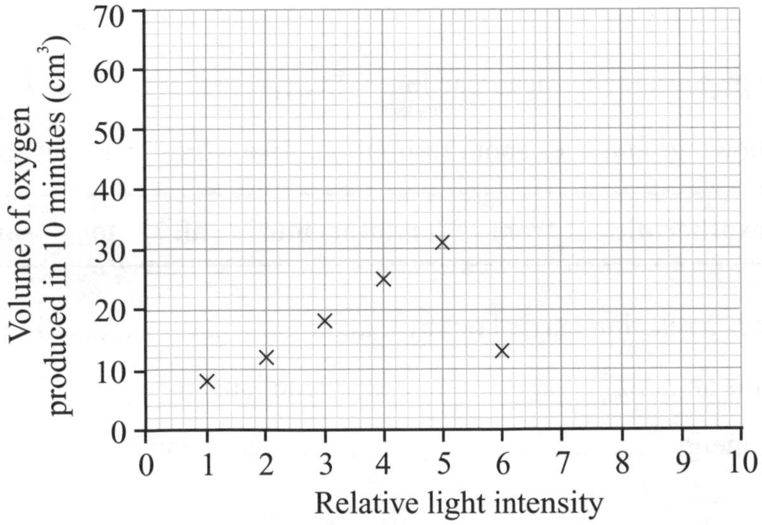

(graph: Volume of oxygen produced in 10 minutes (cm^3) vs Relative light intensity)

[2]

2.4 One of the student's results is anomalous.
    At which relative light intensity is the result anomalous?

Relative light intensity = ...
[1]

2.5 Describe what the student's results show about the relationship between light intensity and rate of photosynthesis.

....
[1]

[Total 8 marks]

    Topic B4 — Bioenergetics

Respiration and Metabolism

1 Metabolism is the sum of all of the reactions that happen in a cell or the body. Metabolism includes reactions that make molecules. *(Grade 1-3)*

1.1 Complete the sentence below. Use a word from the box.

| glycogen | glycerol | amino acids |

Lipids are made from fatty acids and ....

[1]

1.2 What type of ion is needed to make amino acids?
Tick **one** box.

magnesium ☐   phosphate ☐   potassium ☐   nitrate ☐

[1]

1.3 Which of these molecules is **not** made during metabolism in animals?
Tick **one** box.

proteins ☐   glycogen ☐   cellulose ☐   lipids ☐

[1]

1.4 Metabolism also involves breaking down molecules.
What is produced when excess protein is broken down?

....

[1]

[Total 4 marks]

2 Respiration is an important chemical reaction. *(Grade 3-4)*

2.1 Complete the following sentences about respiration. Use words from the box.

| exothermic | from | endothermic | all | to | some |

Respiration is a reaction carried out by .... living organisms.

Respiration is an .... reaction.

It transfers energy .... the environment.

[3]

Figure 1 shows a gull.

Figure 1

2.2 Give **one** example of how a gull uses the energy transferred by respiration.

....

[1]

[Total 4 marks]

Topic B4 — Bioenergetics

Target AO3

3   A student is investigating respiration in germinating peas. She predicts that germinating peas will respire, and so will release energy as heat.

The student sets up her experiment as shown in **Figure 2**.

Figure 2

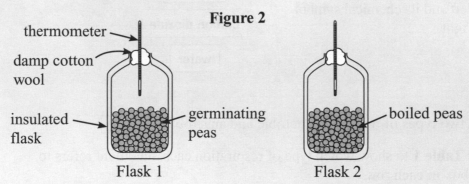

The student records the temperature of each flask at the beginning of the experiment (day 0), then every day for three days.

Table 1 shows her results.

Table 1

Day	Temperature (°C)	
	Flask 1	Flask 2
Day 0	20	20
Day 1	23	31
Day 2	25	21
Day 3	28	21

3.1 Give **one** variable that the student needed to control to make the experiment a fair test.

....

[1]

3.2 One of the student's readings was anomalous. Circle the anomalous reading in **Table 1**.

[1]

3.3 Explain why the student included Flask 2 in her experiment.

....

....

[1]

3.4 Which of these statements is a conclusion the student can make based on her results?
Tick **one** box.

The temperature in both flasks decreased over time.   ☐

The peas in Flask 1 released heat energy.   ☐

Boiling the peas did not affect the amount of heat energy released.   ☐

The peas in Flask 1 respired more on Day 3 than on Day 1.   ☐

[1]

[Total 4 marks]

Exam Tip

When you're designing an experiment, or looking at a method in an exam, it's really important that only one thing is changed at a time. That way you can be sure it's the thing that's been changed that has affected the results.

 ☐   ☐   ☐   Topic B4 — Bioenergetics

Aerobic and Anaerobic Respiration

1 There are two types of respiration, aerobic and anaerobic.

Complete **Table 1** to show which type of respiration each statement refers to.
Tick **one** box in each row.

Table 1

Statement	Aerobic respiration	Anaerobic respiration
It transfers more energy.		
It uses O_2.		
It can produce ethanol and CO_2 as products.		
It is the incomplete breakdown of glucose.		

[Total 3 marks]

2 An experiment was set up using a sealed beaker, with a carbon dioxide monitor attached. The set up is shown in **Figure 1**.

After two hours, the carbon dioxide concentration in the beaker in **Figure 1** had **increased**.

Figure 1

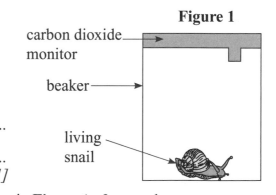

carbon dioxide monitor

beaker

living snail

2.1 Explain why the carbon dioxide concentration in the beaker increased.

....

....

[1]

2.2 Suggest what happened to the level of **oxygen** in the beaker in **Figure 1** after two hours. Explain your answer.

....

....

[2]

[Total 3 marks]

Exercise

1 Complete the sentences about exercise below. Use words from the box.

> lactic acid   muscles   brain   glucose   oxygen   ethanol

During exercise your .... may respire anaerobically.

This causes a build up of ....

It also leads to an .... debt.

[Total 3 marks]

2 A student was investigating the effect of exercise on his own breathing rate. The results are shown in **Table 1**.

Table 1

	Breathing rate (number of breaths per minute)			
	Before exercise	During exercise	One minute after exercise	Five minutes after exercise
Repeat 1	11	16	15	12
Repeat 2	12	15	14	11
Repeat 3	11	15	14	12
Mean	11	15	14	

2.1 Calculate the mean breathing rate five minutes after exercise.

Mean = ... breaths per minute

[1]

2.2 Explain why the student's breathing rate increased during exercise.

....

....

[2]

2.3 Explain why the student's breathing rate remained high one minute after exercise.

....

....

[1]

2.4 Suggest what would have happened to the student's heart rate during the period of exercise.

....

[1]

[Total 5 marks]

Topic B4 — Bioenergetics

Homeostasis

Warm-Up

The sentences below are about the control systems used in homeostasis.
Circle **one** underlined word or phrase in each sentence, so that the sentence is correct.

Control systems <u>are</u>/<u>are not</u> automatic.

If a control system detects the level of something is too high, it will <u>increase</u>/<u>decrease</u> the level.

If a control system detects the level of something is too low, it will <u>increase</u>/<u>decrease</u> the level.

1   Which of the following is **not** part of homeostasis? Tick **one** box.   (Grade 3-4)

    responding to changes outside the body   ☐

    keeping conditions inside the body at the right level   ☐

    allowing large changes in conditions inside the body   ☐

    responding to changes inside the body   ☐

[Total 1 mark]

2   Human body temperature is kept at about 37 °C.
A homeostatic control system is used to do this.   (Grade 4-5)

2.1   Suggest why it's important that body temperature is kept at around 37 °C.

....

[1]

2.2   A man is exercising. As he exercises, his body temperature increases.
The following sentences outline how the man's body temperature will be brought back to normal.
Complete the sentences. Use words from the box.

a coordination centre	a stimulus	effectors	receptors

The increase in body temperature is detected by ....

Information is then sent to ....

The information is processed and a signal is sent to .... ,

which produce a response. The man's body temperature decreases.

[3]

2.3   Shivering is a homeostatic response to a drop in body temperature. It is controlled by the
nervous system. Which other system controls homeostatic responses?

....

[1]

[Total 5 marks]

The Nervous System

1   Information is carried through the nervous system as electrical impulses. **(Grade 3-4)**
Effectors react to these electrical impulses to produce a response.

1.1   Which type of neurone carries electrical impulses to effectors?
Tick **one** box.

relay neurone ☐   motor neurone ☐   sensory neurone ☐

[1]

1.2   Muscles and glands are both types of effector. They respond differently to electrical impulses.
How do muscles and glands respond to electrical impulses?

Muscles: ....

Glands: ....

[2]

[Total 3 marks]

2   **Figure 1** shows part of the human nervous system. **(Grade 4-5)**

Figure 1

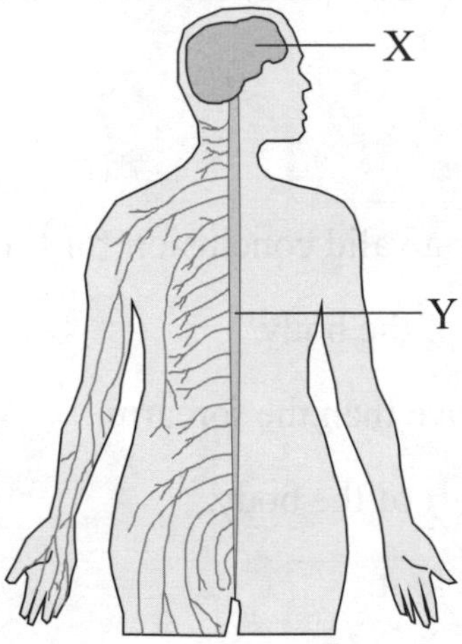

2.1   Name the structures labelled **X** and **Y** on **Figure 1**.

X   ....

Y   ....

[2]

2.2   Which part of the nervous system do structures **X** and **Y** form?

....

[1]

2.3   What is the role of the part of the nervous system formed by structures **X** and **Y**?

....

....

[1]

[Total 4 marks]

Topic B5 — Homeostasis and Response

Target AO3

3 Two students are investigating the sensitivity of the skin on different areas of the body using the method below.

1. Blindfold the person being tested.
2. Tape two toothpicks onto a ruler so that they are 50 mm apart.
3. Lightly press the two toothpicks onto the person's arm.
4. Ask whether the person can feel one or two toothpicks.
5. If they can feel two toothpicks, move the toothpicks 5 mm closer together and repeat steps 3 and 4. Keep doing this until they can only feel one toothpick.

The students did their experiment on different areas of the body and repeated it three times for each area. Each time, they recorded the distance between toothpicks at which the person could only feel one toothpick. Their results are shown in **Table 1**.

Table 1

Area of the body	Forearm			Palm			Back of hand		
Repeat	1	2	3	1	2	3	1	2	3
Distance between toothpicks (mm)	30	30	35	5	5	5	25	20	15

3.1 Calculate the mean distance between toothpicks for the back of the hand.

Mean = ... mm
[2]

3.2 Which of the following sentences is a valid conclusion for this experiment? Tick **one** box.

The palm is the most sensitive part of the body. ☐

The back of the hand is more sensitive than the forearm. ☐

The forearm is the least sensitive part of the body. ☐

The palm is more sensitive than the foot. ☐

[1]

3.3 The cheek is less sensitive than the palm, but more sensitive than the back of the hand. Predict a possible value for the mean distance between toothpicks if the students tested the person's cheek.

.... mm
[1]

3.4 Another student repeated the experiment but she forgot to blindfold the person being tested. Suggest why this might have been a source of error.

....

....

[1]

[Total 5 marks]

Exam Tip

If you're asked to draw a conclusion from an experiment, don't go beyond what the data tells you. For example, in the experiment above, the students didn't test the feet — so you can't conclude anything about foot sensitivity from their data.

Topic B5 — Homeostasis and Response

Synapses and Reflexes

Warm-Up

Which of these actions is a reflex? Circle the correct answer.

Dropping a hot plate.   Running to catch a bus.   Writing a letter.

1 Which of the following sentences is correct? Tick **one** box. *(Grade 3-4)*

Reflex reactions are slow and under conscious control. ☐

Reflex reactions are slow and automatic. ☐

Reflex reactions are rapid and automatic. ☐

Reflex reactions are rapid and under conscious control. ☐

[Total 1 mark]

2 **Figure 1** shows a reflex arc. *(Grade 4-5)*

Figure 1

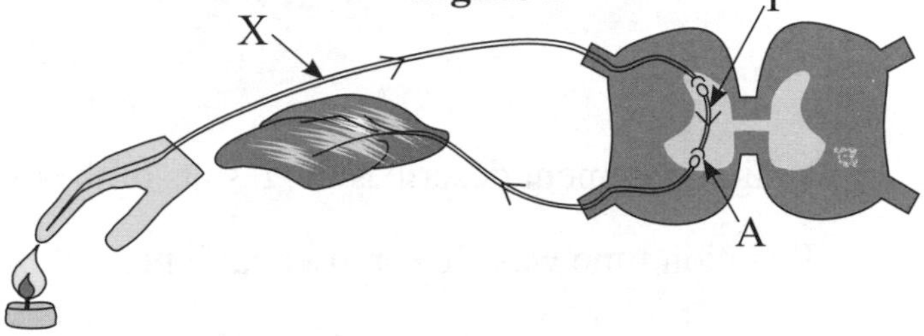

2.1 Name structures **X** and **Y**.

X ....

Y ....

[2]

2.2 What is the **stimulus** shown in **Figure 1**?

....

[1]

2.3 Structure **A** is the junction between two neurones. Name structure **A**.

....

[1]

2.4 Explain how structure **Y** receives a signal about the stimulus.
Your answer should include how the signal is transmitted across structure **A**.

....

....

....

....

[4]

[Total 8 marks]

Exam Tip

If an exam question asks you to 'name' something like a structure or process, don't start writing an essay. In fact, you can stay clear of explaining or describing anything at all. A little word or phrase is all the examiners are looking for.

PRACTICAL
Investigating Reaction Time

1 A scientist carried out an experiment to investigate the impact of caffeine on reaction time.

- The scientist measured a volunteer's reaction time using a simple test.
- He then gave the volunteer a drink containing caffeine.
- After ten minutes, he measured the volunteer's reaction time again.
- He repeated the test on four different days with the same volunteer.

The results are shown in **Table 1**.

Table 1

	Reaction time (s)				
	Repeat 1	Repeat 2	Repeat 3	Repeat 4	Mean
Before caffeine	0.16	0.15	0.18	0.17	
After caffeine	0.13	0.14	0.16	0.14	0.15

1.1 Calculate the mean reaction time before the volunteer had caffeine.
Give your answer to two significant figures.

Mean = ... s

[2]

1.2 Which statement describes the results of the experiment? Tick **one** box.

Reaction time was slower after caffeine. ☐

Reaction time was faster after caffeine. ☐

Reaction time was no different after caffeine. ☐

[1]

1.3 Each time the scientist repeated the test he got similar results.
What does this say about the scientist's results? Tick **one** box.

The results are repeatable. ☐

There are no errors in the method. ☐

The results prove there's a link between caffeine and reaction time. ☐

[1]

1.4 Give **two** variables that the scientist should have kept the same each time he repeated the experiment.

1. ....

2. ....

[2]

[Total 6 marks]

Exam Tip

You'll definitely get tested on your practical knowledge as part of your exams. Make sure you know what terms like 'repeatable' and 'variable' mean, so you understand what questions like the ones above are asking you.

Topic B5 — Homeostasis and Response   ☐   ☐   ☐

The Endocrine System

1 **Figure 1** shows the positions of some glands in the human body. *(Grade 1-3)*

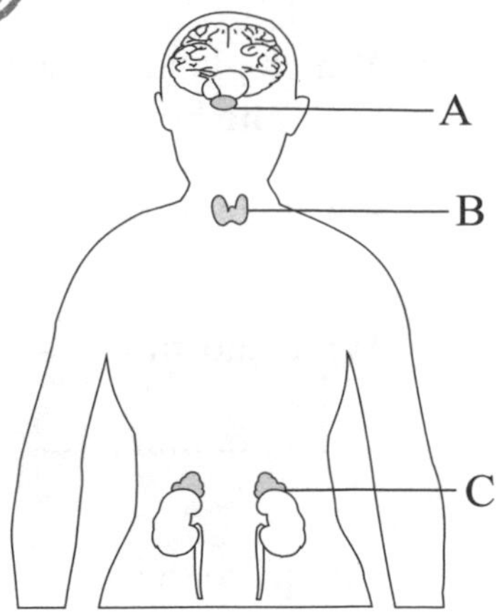

Which part of the diagram, **A**, **B** or **C**, represents the thyroid gland?

Your answer = ...

[Total 1 mark]

Figure 1

2 The endocrine system is a collection of glands in the body that secrete hormones. *(Grade 3-4)*

2.1 Which of the following statements about glands is correct?
Tick **one** box.

Glands secrete hormones directly into cells. ☐

Glands secrete hormones directly into the blood. ☐

Glands secrete hormones directly into organs. ☐

[1]

2.2 Which of the following statements best describes hormones?
Tick **one** box.

Hormones are cells. ☐   Hormones are chemicals. ☐   Hormones are enzymes. ☐

[1]

2.3 State **two** ways in which the effects of the endocrine system differ from the nervous system.

1. ....

2. ....

[2]

[Total 4 marks]

3 One of the glands in the body is known as the 'master gland'. This gland secretes several hormones in response to body conditions. *(Grade 4-5)*

3.1 What is the name of the 'master gland'?

....

[1]

3.2 What is the function of the hormones released by the 'master gland'?

....

....

[2]

[Total 3 marks]

Topic B5 — Homeostasis and Response

Controlling Blood Glucose

1 The concentration of glucose in the blood is controlled by hormones. (Grade 3-4)

1.1 Which gland in the human body monitors and controls blood glucose concentration?
Tick **one** box.

pancreas ☐   pituitary gland ☐   thyroid ☐   testis ☐

[1]

1.2 Which hormone is produced when blood glucose concentration becomes too high?

....

[1]

1.3 Complete the sentences to describe what happens when there is too much glucose in the blood.
Use words from the box.

pancreas	glycogen	insulin	liver

When there is too much glucose in the blood, some of it moves into the ....

The glucose is then changed into .... so it can be stored.

[2]

[Total 4 marks]

2 Diabetes exists in two different forms, Type 1 and Type 2. (Grade 4-5)

2.1 Which of the following statements describes **Type 1** diabetes?
Tick **one** box.

The body produces too little glucose. ☐

The body becomes resistant to its own insulin. ☐

The body produces too much insulin. ☐

The body produces little or no insulin. ☐

[1]

2.2 How is **Type 1** diabetes treated?

....

[1]

2.3 Give **two** treatments that a doctor would recommend for **Type 2** diabetes.

1. ....

2. ....

[2]

2.4 Give a risk factor for **Type 2** diabetes.

....

[1]

[Total 5 marks]

Topic B5 — Homeostasis and Response   ☹ ☐   😐 ☐   🙂 ☐

Puberty and the Menstrual Cycle

1 Males begin producing sex hormones during puberty. (Grade 1-3)

1.1 What is the main sex hormone in men? Tick **one** box.

insulin ☐   testosterone ☐   oestrogen ☐   adrenaline ☐
[1]

1.2 Where is the main sex hormone in men produced? Tick **one** box.

pancreas ☐   pituitary gland ☐   thyroid gland ☐   testes ☐
[1]

1.3 Which of the following is a role of the main sex hormone in men? Tick **one** box.

stimulating egg production ☐   control of water content in the body ☐

control of blood glucose levels ☐   stimulating sperm production ☐
[1]

[Total 3 marks]

2 Female sex hormones control the menstrual cycle. (Grade 3-4)

2.1 What is the name of the main female reproductive hormone produced in the ovary?

....
[1]

2.2 What is the name of the process by which eggs are released from the ovary?

....
[1]

2.3 How often is an egg released from an ovary? Tick **one** box.

Every 7 days. ☐   Every 14 days. ☐   Every 21 days. ☐   Every 28 days. ☐
[1]

2.4 Name the hormone that causes the release of an egg.

....
[1]

[Total 4 marks]

3 During the menstrual cycle, a change in the level of progesterone causes the woman to menstruate (bleed). (Grade 4-5)

Suggest how the progesterone level changes before a woman starts to bleed. Explain your answer.

....

....

....

....
[Total 3 marks]

Controlling Fertility

All of the methods below are forms of contraception. Circle the **two** hormonal methods.

avoiding sexual intercourse   condom   contraceptive injection   contraceptive patch   diaphragm

1   Some methods of contraception use hormones to control the fertility of a woman.   *(Grade 4-5)*

1.1   How is an oral contraceptive taken into the body?
Tick **one** box.

As an injection. ☐

As a tablet taken by mouth. ☐

Through the skin from a patch. ☐

[1]

1.2   How do oral contraceptives containing multiple hormones prevent pregnancy?
Tick **one** box.

The hormones stop oestrogen production. ☐

The hormones stop FSH production. ☐

The hormones stop LH production. ☐

[1]

1.3   The contraceptive implant is inserted under the skin of the arm.
Which hormone does it release?

....
[1]

1.4   How does the hormone released by the contraceptive implant prevent pregnancy?

....
[1]

1.5   An oral contraceptive has to be taken daily.
Suggest **one** advantage of the contraceptive implant over an oral contraceptive.
Explain your answer.

....

....
[2]

[Total 6 marks]

Exam Tip

Knowing the roles of the hormones that control the menstrual cycle can be very handy when it comes to understanding how those hormones are used in contraceptives. So make sure you've got them all sorted out in your head.

Topic B5 — Homeostasis and Response   ☺ ☐

More on Controlling Fertility

Warm-Up

Draw lines to match the barrier method of contraception on the left,
to the description of how it's worn on the right.

Method of contraception	Description
diaphragm	worn inside the vagina
male condom	worn over the entrance to the uterus
female condom	worn over the penis

1 There are several different non-hormonal methods of contraception. *(Grade 4-5)*
These include barrier methods of contraception.

1.1 How do barrier methods of contraception prevent a woman from becoming pregnant?
Tick **one** box.

They break down eggs once they have been fertilised by sperm. ☐

They prevent eggs from being released. ☐

They stop sperm from getting to an egg. ☐

They kill sperm. ☐

[1]

1.2 Name a barrier method of contraception that protects against sexually transmitted infections.

....
[1]

1.3 Some barrier methods need to be used with spermicides.
Explain how spermicides help to prevent pregnancy.

....

....

....
[2]

A couple not wishing to have children do not want to use any form of contraception.
1.4 Suggest how they could avoid pregnancy.

....

....
[1]

[Total 5 marks]

Exam Tip

Remember to read all the different options in multiple choice questions. Don't be tempted to dive right in and tick the first option that sounds right — sometimes there might only be slight differences in the wording of different options.

Topic B5 — Homeostasis and Response

Topic B6 — Inheritance, Variation and Evolution

DNA

1 DNA makes up the genetic material in animal and plant cells. (Grade 3-4)

1.1 Which of the following statements about DNA is correct? Tick **one** box.

DNA is found in the cytoplasm of animal and plant cells. ☐

DNA is found in the ribosomes in animal and plant cells. ☐

DNA is found in the nucleus of animal and plant cells. ☐

DNA is found in vacuoles in animal and plant cells. ☐

[1]

1.2 What are chromosomes? Tick **one** box.

Proteins coded for by DNA. ☐

The structures that contain DNA. ☐

The site of protein synthesis. ☐

The bases that make up DNA. ☐

[1]

[Total 2 marks]

Figure 1

2 **Figure 1** shows part of a DNA molecule. (Grade 4-5)

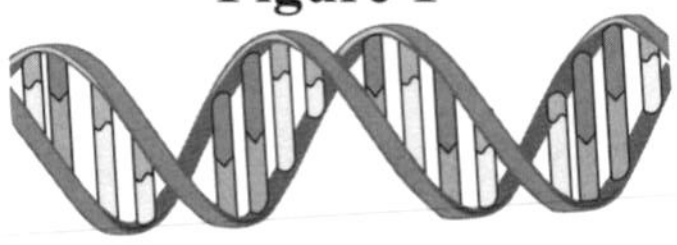

2.1 Describe the overall structure of a DNA molecule.

....

....

[2]

2.2 DNA contains lots of sections called genes. Describe the function of genes.

....

....

[2]

2.3 What is meant by the term genome?

....

....

[1]

2.4 Give **one** reason why it is important for scientists to understand the human genome.

....

....

[1]

[Total 6 marks]

Exam Tip
To properly understand this topic, you need to know how DNA, genes, chromosomes, proteins and amino acids relate to each other. Once you've got all of that sorted out, it'll make answering the questions a whole lot easier.

Topic B6 — Inheritance, Variation and Evolution

Reproduction

1 Sexual reproduction involves male and female gametes.

Draw **one** line from each type of gamete on the left to the correct description on the right.

Type of gamete

sperm

egg

pollen

Description

female gamete

male gamete in animals

male gamete in plants

[Total 2 marks]

2 There are different types of cell division in sexual and asexual reproduction.

2.1 Which type of cell division is involved in the production of gametes?

....

[1]

2.2 Name the type of cell division used in asexual reproduction.

....

[1]

2.3 Cells produced by asexual reproduction are called clones.
What does this mean?

....

[1]

[Total 3 marks]

3 There are several differences between asexual and sexual reproduction.

Complete **Table 1** to show if each statement applies to asexual or sexual reproduction.
Tick **one** box in each row.

Table 1

	Asexual reproduction	Sexual reproduction
There is only one parent.		
There is no mixing of genes.		
It results in genetic variation in the offspring.		
There is fusion of gametes.		

[Total 3 marks]

Topic B6 — Inheritance, Variation and Evolution

Meiosis

1   Sexual reproduction in humans involves meiosis.   (Grade 4-5)

1.1   Where in the body does meiosis take place? Tick **one** box.

all tissues ☐

growing tissues only ☐

the skin ☐

the reproductive organs ☐

[1]

1.2   Before a cell starts to divide by meiosis, what happens to its DNA?

....

[1]

1.3   How many cell divisions are there during the process of meiosis?

....

[1]

1.4   Briefly describe the results of meiosis.

....

....

....

....

[3]

[Total 6 marks]

2   After an egg cell has been fertilised, it divides many times.   (Grade 4-5)

2.1   What type of cell division does the fertilised egg cell undergo?

....

[1]

2.2   The dividing cells form an embryo.
       What happens to the cells in the embryo as it develops in order to form the whole organism?

....

....

[1]

[Total 2 marks]

Exam Tip

It's easy to get mixed up between meiosis and mitosis. Remember, meiosis is the one that makes eggs and sperm.
Mitosis makes twin (identical) cells. Even if you know the difference, it's still easy to accidentally write one when you
mean the other, just because the words are so similar. So always check your answer through after you've written it.

Topic B6 — Inheritance, Variation and Evolution   ☐   ☐   ☐

X and Y Chromosomes

1 Chromosomes help to determine the characteristics of individuals, including their sex. (Grade 1-3)

1.1 How many pairs of chromosomes are there in a normal human body cell?
Tick **one** box.

22 ☐   23 ☐   24 ☐   25 ☐

[1]

1.2 How many pairs of chromosomes decide what sex you are?
Tick **one** box.

1 ☐   2 ☐   4 ☐   8 ☐

[1]

[Total 2 marks]

2 **Figure 1** is an incomplete genetic diagram.
It shows how the sex chromosomes are inherited in humans. (Grade 4-5)

Figure 1

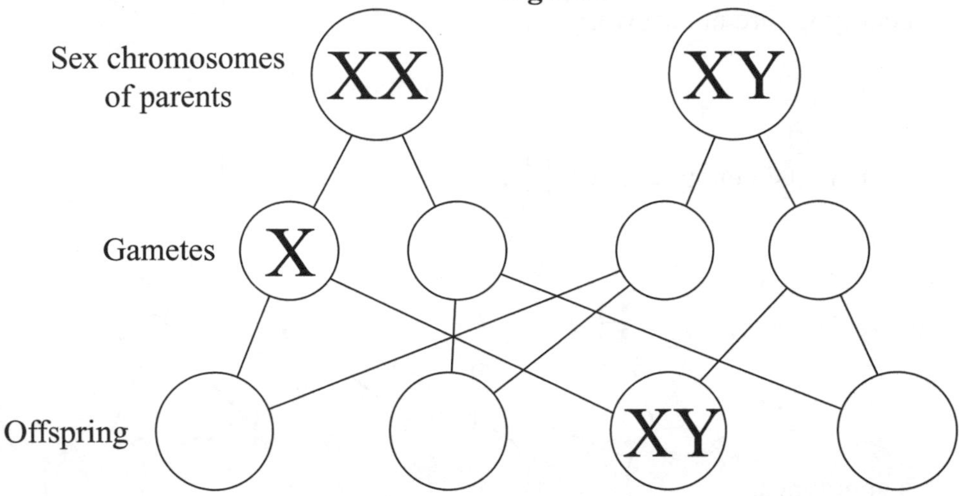

Sex chromosomes
of parents   XX   XY

Gametes   X   ○   ○   ○

Offspring   ○   ○   XY   ○

2.1 Circle the male parent in **Figure 1**.

[1]

2.2 Fill in the sex chromosomes of the gametes produced by each parent in **Figure 1**.

[1]

2.3 Complete **Figure 1** to show the combination of sex chromosomes in the offspring.

[1]

2.4 What is the ratio of male to female offspring in the cross in **Figure 1**?

....

[1]

[Total 4 marks]

Exam Tip

You could be asked to complete a genetic diagram in the exam. Most of the time they deal with how individual genes are passed on, but here you're dealing with whole chromosomes. Don't forget that genetic diagrams can be drawn in a few different ways — you might also see them drawn in the form of a Punnett square or a family tree.

 ☐   ☐   ☐   Topic B6 — Inheritance, Variation and Evolution

Genetic Diagrams

Warm-Up

Use the words and phrases to complete the passage below.
You don't have to use every one.

| homozygous | alleles | multiple genes | dominant |

Genes exist in different versions called ....

If the two versions are the same, the organism is .... for that gene.

Some characteristics are controlled by a single gene, but most are controlled by

....

1   Hair length in dogs is controlled by two alleles. Short hair is caused by
the dominant allele, 'H'. Long hair is caused by the recessive allele, 'h'.

Grade 3-4

Figure 1 shows a genetic diagram of a cross between a short-haired and a long-haired dog.
The offspring's genotypes are not shown.

Figure 1

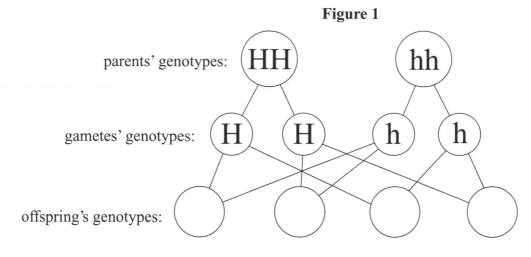

parents' genotypes: HH   hh

gametes' genotypes: H   H   h   h

offspring's genotypes:

1.1   Circle the long-haired parent in **Figure 1**.

[1]

1.2   All the offspring have the same genotype.
What is the offspring's genotype? Tick **one** box.

Hh ☐   HH ☐   h ☐   hh ☐

[1]

1.3   What phenotype do the offspring have?

....

[1]

[Total 3 marks]

Exam Tip

Watch out for those upper and lower case letters in genetic diagrams. It's very easy to write 'H' when you mean 'h'.
Getting just one letter wrong in the gametes could mess up the genotypes of the offspring, so be really careful.

Inherited Disorders

1   Polydactyly is an inherited disorder.   (Grade 1-3)

   1.1   What are the symptoms of polydactyly?
Tick **one** box.

     missing fingers or toes   ☐

     faulty cell membranes   ☐

     extra fingers or toes   ☐

[1]

   1.2   Which of the following statements about polydactyly is correct?
Tick **one** box.

     It is caused by a recessive allele.   ☐

     It is caused by a dominant allele.   ☐

     It is only inherited by boys.   ☐

     Two copies of the allele are needed for an individual to have polydactyly.   ☐

[1]

[Total 2 marks]

2   Cystic fibrosis is an inherited disorder.
The allele which causes cystic fibrosis is a recessive allele, 'f'.
'F' represents the dominant allele.   (Grade 4-5)

Figure 1 is an incomplete Punnett square.
It shows the possible inheritance of cystic fibrosis from one couple.

Figure 1

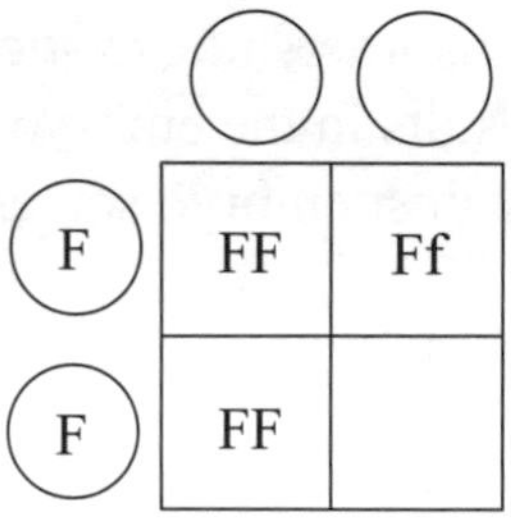

	◯	◯
F	FF	Ff
F	FF	

   2.1   Complete the Punnett square to show:
     • the missing gametes' genotypes,
     • the missing offspring's genotype.

[2]

   2.2   What proportion of the possible offspring are heterozygous?

....

[1]

   2.3   What proportion of the possible offspring have cystic fibrosis?

....

[1]

[Total 4 marks]

Topic B6 — Inheritance, Variation and Evolution

Family Trees and Embryo Screening

1   **Figure 1** shows a family tree. The family have a history of an inherited disorder.

Figure 1

Freddy   Zelda

Arthur   Akheira   Hilda   Buster

Key
☐ Male   ◯ Female
■ ⬤ Have the disorder
◧ ◖ Carrier of the disorder but unaffected
☐ ◯ Unaffected and not a carrier

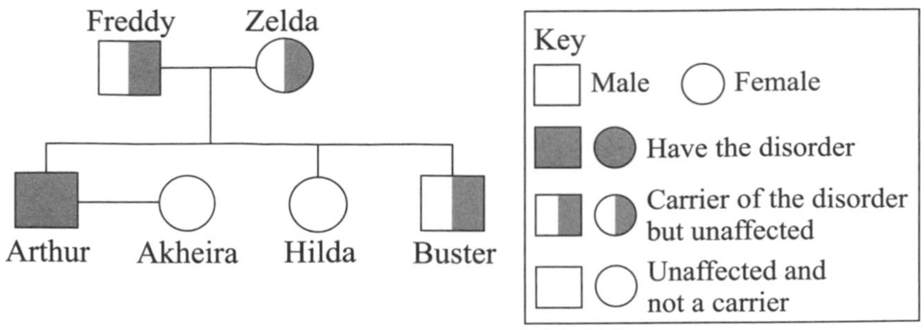

1.1   Which family member is **not** a carrier of the disorder? Tick **one** box.

Hilda ☐   Freddy ☐   Zelda ☐   Buster ☐

[1]

The disorder is caused by a recessive allele, 'd'. The dominant allele is 'D'.

1.2   What is **Arthur's** genotype? Tick **one** box.

DD ☐   Dd ☐   dd ☐   d ☐

[1]

1.3   What is **Zelda's** genotype?

....

[1]

[Total 3 marks]

2   Embryos can be screened for genetic disorders like cystic fibrosis. The results of screening sometimes results in the embryo being destroyed. There are lots of arguments for and against embryo screening. *(Grade 4-5)*

2.1   Give **one** argument **against** embryo screening.

....

....

[1]

2.2   Give **one** argument **for** embryo screening.

....

....

[1]

[Total 2 marks]

Exam Tip

Family trees can be confusing, but don't panic. Look at the key first, to make sure you understand what each symbol means. It can also be helpful to write the genotypes of the family members next to their symbols as you work them out. This will make it easier to keep track of whose genotypes you already know, and whose you still need to work out.

Topic B6 — Inheritance, Variation and Evolution

Variation

1 Mutations can lead to variation in an organism. Grade 1-3

1.1 What is a mutation?

....

[1]

1.2 Which of the following answers should be used to complete the sentence?
Write **A**, **B** or **C** in the box below.

A Most

B Very few

C All

☐ mutations have a large effect on the phenotype of an organism.

[1]

[Total 2 marks]

2 **Figure 1** shows two plants of different species, **A** and **B**.
Both plants were grown in the same controlled environmental conditions in a greenhouse. Grade 3-4

Figure 1

A   **B**

Give **one** example of a difference between plants **A** and **B** which is likely to be due to genetic variation.

....

[Total 1 mark]

3 Helen and Stephanie are identical twins. This means they have identical DNA. Grade 4-5

Helen weighs 7 kg more than Stephanie.
Explain whether this is due to genes, environmental factors or both.

....

....

[Total 2 marks]

Exam Tip

Remember, variation can be caused by genes, environmental factors, or a mixture of both. In the exam, you might get asked about an example of variation that you've never heard of before. Don't worry if you do — all the information that you need in order to answer the question will be there. Just read it all through carefully and then apply your knowledge.

Evolution

1 Complete the sentences about evolution below. Use words from the box. Grade 3-4

environmental	three	inherited	some	all	six

Evolution is the change in the .... characteristics of a population over time.
According to the theory of evolution by natural selection, ... organisms evolved from simple life forms that first started to develop over .... billion years ago.

[Total 3 marks]

2 Over time, many species have become extinct. Grade 3-4

2.1 What does it mean if a species becomes extinct?

....

[1]

2.2 Give **two** factors which might cause a species to become extinct.

1. ....

2. ....

[2]

[Total 3 marks]

3* **Figure 1** is a photograph of a hare species which lives in a warm climate. It has large ears which help to keep it cool. The size of ears in hares is partly controlled by genes. Grade 4-5

Figure 1

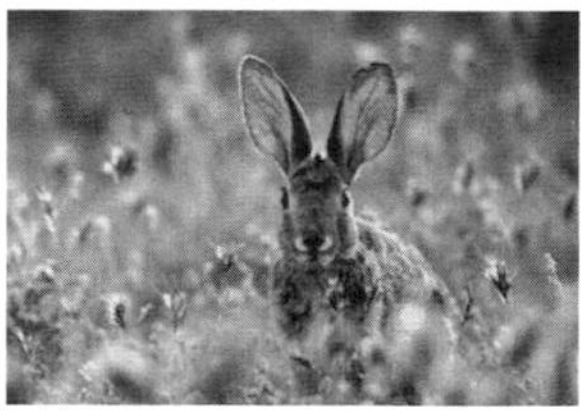

Describe how natural selection could have led to the evolution of hares with large ears, from a population of hares with smaller ears.

....

....

....

....

....

....

....

....

....

[Total 6 marks]

Antibiotic-Resistant Bacteria

Warm-Up

> Draw circles to show whether the statements below are **true** or **false**.
>
> Antibiotics are drugs that can kill all pathogens.   True / False
>
> Bacteria can evolve quickly because they divide very rapidly.   True / False
>
> Antibiotic-resistant bacteria don't spread easily.   True / False

1 Bacteria can evolve to become resistant to antibiotics.

Which of the following answers should be used to complete the sentence?
Write **A**, **B** or **C** in the box below.

A   normal variation

B   natural variation

C   natural selection

Bacteria can become resistant to antibiotics by ☐ .

[Total 1 mark]

2 *S. aureus* is a bacterium. It can cause serious illness in some people.
Some strains of *S. aureus* have developed resistance to the antibiotic
meticillin. These strains are known as MRSA.

2.1 **Table 1** shows the different stages that led to *S. aureus* becoming resistant to meticillin.
Put the stages in order by writing the correct number (**1**, **2**, **3** or **4**) in the space provided.

Table 1

Number of stage	Stage
....	The gene for meticillin resistance became more common in the population. Eventually most of the population of *S. aureus* had resistance.
....	Individual bacteria with the mutated genes were more likely to survive and reproduce in a host being treated with meticillin.
....	Random mutations in the DNA of *S. aureus* led to it not being killed by meticillin.
....	The gene for meticillin resistance was passed on to lots of offspring. These offspring survived and reproduced.

[2]

2.2 Explain why a person is more likely to become seriously ill if they are infected with MRSA than
with a non-resistant strain of *S. aureus*.

....

....

....

[2]

[Total 4 marks]

Topic B6 — Inheritance, Variation and Evolution

More on Antibiotic-Resistant Bacteria

1   How can farmers help to prevent the development of antibiotic-resistant bacteria? Tick **one** box.   *(Grade 1-3)*

By regularly treating their livestock with antibiotics to prevent disease.   ☐

By restricting the amount of antibiotics they give to their livestock.   ☐

By only using antibiotics to treat viral infections in their livestock.   ☐

[Total 1 mark]

2   New antibiotics are being developed against resistant strains of bacteria.   *(Grade 4-5)*

Give **two** reasons why the development of antibiotics is unlikely to keep up with the rate at which new antibiotic-resistant bacteria appear.

1. ....

2. ....

[Total 2 marks]

3   Antibiotic resistance in bacteria is becoming more common. This is partly due to the overuse of antibiotics in medicine.   *(Grade 4-5)*

3.1   Give **one** way in which doctors can help to prevent the overuse of antibiotics.

....

....

[1]

A patient has been prescribed antibiotics by his doctor. He needs to take them for two weeks.

After one week, the patient feels better. He wants to stop taking the antibiotics. His doctor tells him he should complete the course.

3.2   Explain why taking the full course of antibiotics reduces the chance of antibiotic-resistant strains developing.

....

....

....

[2]

[Total 3 marks]

> **Exam Tip**
> An exam question on antibiotic-resistant bacteria could ask you to link lots of ideas together. So, make sure you know the risks of antibiotic-resistant strains to human health, what's causing them to get more common, and what we can do to prevent them evolving. There's a lot to remember in this topic, but just go over it a few times and you'll be alright.

Topic B6 — Inheritance, Variation and Evolution

Target AO3

4   A scientist has samples of two strains of the same species of bacterium, strain A
     and strain B. This species of bacterium is usually killed by the antibiotic ampicillin,
     but the scientist believes that strain B may have become resistant to ampicillin.

Grade 4-5

The scientist has the following materials and equipment:

- nutrient broth solution (culture medium)
- ampicillin solution
- samples of bacterial strain A and strain B, growing in nutrient broth solution
- four small glass bottles, with lids
- pipettes of different sizes

The nutrient broth is clear, but turns cloudy when bacteria grow in it.

4.1   The scientist uses a pipette to add nutrient broth solution to all of the glass bottles.
      Then he uses another pipette to add ampicillin solution to two of the glass bottles.

      Give **one** variable that the scientist should keep the same during this part of the experiment.

      ....
      [1]

4.2* Describe what the scientist should do next in order to find out whether strain B
      is resistant to ampicillin.

      ....

      ....

      ....

      ....

      ....

      ....

      ....

      ....
      [4]

4.3   Give **one** reason why it is important that the scientist makes sure that all of the material
      from the experiment is disposed of safely when it is over.

      ....

      ....
      [1]

      [Total 6 marks]

Exam Tip

You could well be asked to write part of a method for an experiment in your exams. If you are, don't worry. Just think
carefully through what you'd need to do if you were actually doing the experiment, then write it all down in a sensible
order. Don't forget to use any clues you're given in the question about things like the equipment you might need too.

      Topic B6 — Inheritance, Variation and Evolution

Selective Breeding

1 Selective breeding is used in several different industries. *(Grade 3-4)*

1.1 What is selective breeding?

....

[1]

1.2 Which of these is another name for the process of selective breeding? Tick **one** box.

evolution ☐   natural selection ☐   inheritance ☐   artificial selection ☐

[1]

Figure 1 shows four wheat plants (**A-D**). Each plant has different characteristics.

Figure 1

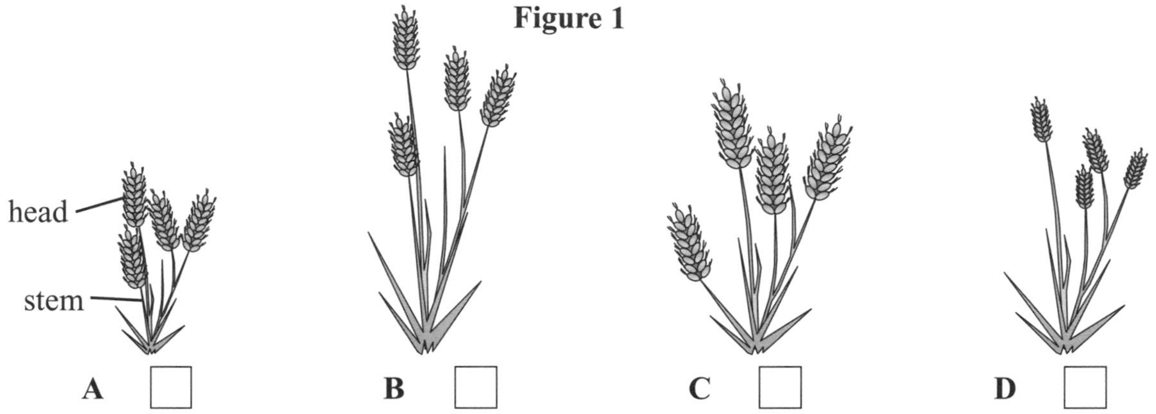

head ⟵

stem ⟵

A ☐   **B** ☐   **C** ☐   **D** ☐

1.3 Which two plants should be bred together to get a wheat plant with a tall stem and a large head? Tick **two** boxes.

[1]

1.4 Suggest why dairy farmers might use selective breeding.

....

[1]

[Total 4 marks]

2 Selectively breeding organisms can lead to inbreeding. *(Grade 4-5)*

2.1 Inbreeding can make a population more likely to get a disease. Explain why.

....

....

[2]

2.2 Describe **one** other problem which may be caused by inbreeding.

....

[1]

[Total 3 marks]

Exam Tip

Selective breeding is another one of those processes that examiners like to get you to apply your knowledge to. Whatever feature you're asked about, the key thing to remember is this: you select the offspring with the best of that feature and breed them together. It doesn't matter what the feature in the question is — it's always the same process.

Topic B6 — Inheritance, Variation and Evolution

Genetic Engineering

1 Genetic engineering has many uses. (Grade 1-3)

1.1 What is genetic engineering? Tick **one** box.

Choosing organisms with particular characteristics to produce the next generation. ☐

The transfer of a gene from one organism's DNA into another organism's DNA. ☐

Creating the right conditions for the growth of organisms. ☐

[1]

1.2 How can bacteria be genetically engineered to help someone with diabetes? Tick **one** box.

They can be made to produce antibiotics. ☐

They can be made to produce antibodies. ☐

They can be made to produce insulin. ☐

[1]

[Total 2 marks]

2 Crop plants can be genetically engineered to be resistant to herbicides. (Grade 3-4)

2.1 What is the benefit of genetically engineering crop plants to be resistant to herbicides?
Tick **one** box.

It makes the crop healthier. ☐   It can increase crop yield. ☐

It makes the crop cheaper to grow. ☐   It reduces damage to the crop from pests. ☐

[1]

2.2 Give **two** other ways in which crop plants are genetically engineered.

1. ....

2. ....

[2]

[Total 3 marks]

3 A team of scientists is investigating the number of wildflowers in two meadows.
One meadow is next to a field containing a GM crop. The other meadow is next to a field
containing a non-GM crop. The scientists compare their results for the two meadows. (Grade 4-5)

3.1 Suggest why the scientists are carrying out this investigation.

....

....

[1]

3.2 Suggest **one** thing the scientists could do to make their results more valid.

....

[1]

[Total 2 marks]

Topic B6 — Inheritance, Variation and Evolution

Fossils

Draw circles to show whether the statements below are **true** or **false**.

Fossils are all between 100 and 1000 years old.   True / False

Fossils are the remains of organisms.   True / False

Fossils are often found in rocks.   True / False

1 Scientists are not sure how life on Earth began.

Which of the following answers should be used to complete the sentence?
Write the correct letter, **A**, **B** or **C**, in the box below.

A   there weren't the right conditions for decay

B   they were hard-bodied

C   they were soft-bodied

Many early forms of life didn't form fossils because ☐ .

[Total 1 mark]

2 **Figure 1** shows a fossilised insect preserved in amber (fossilised tree sap).

Figure 1

2.1 The fossilised insect in **Figure 1** has been protected from moisture and oxygen.
Explain why this has stopped the insect from decaying.

....

....

[2]

2.2 Traces of organisms can also be considered fossils.
Give **two** examples of a trace which may be left behind by an organism.

1. ....

2. ....

[2]

2.3 Apart from preserved organisms or traces left behind by organisms, give **one** other way in which
fossils may be formed.

....

....

[1]

[Total 5 marks]

Topic B6 — Inheritance, Variation and Evolution

Classification

Use the words to complete the Linnaean classification system.
Put the words in the correct order, going from left to right.

species   phylum   order

kingdom, ..., class, ..., family, genus, ...

---

1 Organisms used to be classified into groups using the Linnaean system. *(Grade 1-3)*

1.1 Which of the following is the largest group in the Linnaean classification system?
Tick **one** box.

phylum ☐   kingdom ☐   species ☐   genus ☐

[1]

1.2 What does the Linnaean classification system use to classify organisms?
Tick **one** box.

physical characteristics ☐

DNA ☐

the binomial system ☐

[1]

[Total 2 marks]

---

2 The three-domain classification system was proposed in 1990. *(Grade 3-4)*

2.1 What is the name of the scientist who proposed the three-domain system?
Tick **one** box.

Charles Darwin ☐

Carl Woese ☐

Niels Bohr ☐

James Watson ☐

[1]

2.2 Which of the domains includes primitive bacteria often found in extreme environments?

....

[1]

2.3 Give **two** groups of organisms which are in the Eukaryota domain.

1. ....

2. ....

[2]

[Total 4 marks]

Topic B6 — Inheritance, Variation and Evolution

74

3 The black-crested coquette is a species of hummingbird. Its scientific name is *Lophornis helenae*.

What is the genus of the black-crested coquette?

....

[Total 1 mark]

4 Improvements in our understanding of organisms led to the development of new classification systems, like the three-domain system.

Give **two** of these improvements.

1. ....

....

2. ....

....

[Total 2 marks]

5 Evolutionary trees show how scientists think that organisms are related to each other. **Figure 1** shows the evolutionary tree for species **A-K**.

Figure 1

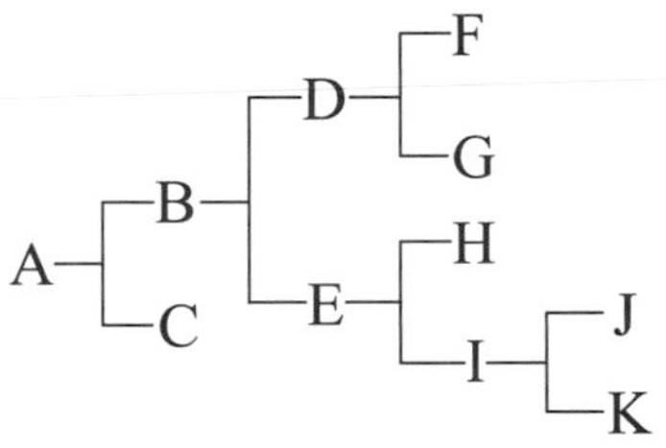

5.1 Give **two** types of data that can be used to make evolutionary trees.

1. ....

2. ....

[2]

5.2 Which species is the most recent common ancestor of species **G** and species **J**?

....

[1]

5.3 Which pair of species, **G** and **H**, or **J** and **K**, are more distantly related?

....

[1]

[Total 4 marks]

Exam Tip

Evolutionary trees are very handy for figuring out how species are related to each other. If you get given an evolutionary tree in the exam, you could be asked to interpret it. But don't worry — just keep practising with questions like these.

Topic B6 — Inheritance, Variation and Evolution

Competition

1 There are different levels of organisation within an ecosystem. *(Grade 1-3)*

1.1 Which of the following levels of organisation contains the smallest number of organisms?
Tick **one** box.

community ☐

population ☐

ecosystem ☐

[1]

1.2 Which of the following answers should be used to complete the sentence?
Write the correct letter, **A**, **B** or **C**, in the box below.

A one species

B different species

C one population

A community is all the organisms of ☐ living in a habitat.

[1]

[Total 2 marks]

2 **Figure 1** shows a woodland food web. *(Grade 3-4)*

Figure 1

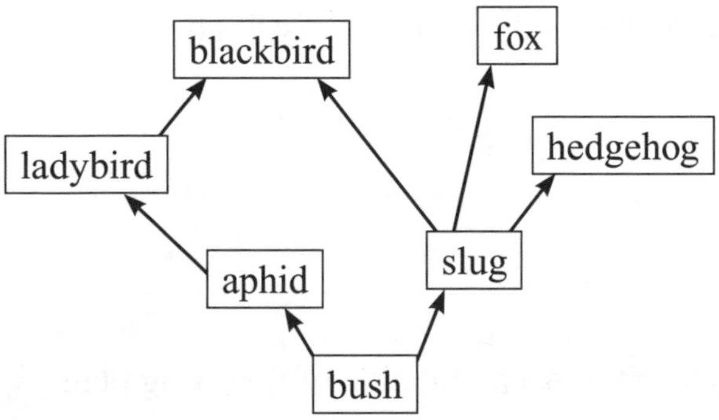

2.1 Which of the following statements is correct?
Tick **one** box.

All the organisms in **Figure 1** are independent. ☐

All the organisms in **Figure 1** are interdependent. ☐

The organisms in **Figure 1** only interact with individuals of the same species. ☐

[1]

2.2 Slugs rely on the bushes for food.
Suggest **one** other factor that slugs may rely on bushes for.

....

[1]

2.3 Apart from food, suggest **two** factors that the **blackbirds** in the ecosystem are likely to compete for.

1. .... 2. ....

[2]

[Total 4 marks]

☐ ☐ ☐   Topic B7 — Ecology

Abiotic and Biotic Factors

Biotic factors are the living factors in an environment. Circle **three** biotic factors below.

moisture level   competition   temperature

wind direction   pathogens   predators

1   Abiotic factors can affect the distribution of organisms. (Grade 3-4)

1.1   Which of the following statements is correct? Tick **one** box.

Light intensity and temperature are examples of biotic factors. ☐

Availability of food and carbon dioxide level are examples of abiotic factors. ☐

Light intensity and carbon dioxide level are examples of abiotic factors. ☐

Availability of food and light intensity are examples of biotic factors. ☐

[1]

1.2   Suggest **one** abiotic factor that could affect the distribution of animals living in water.

....

[1]

1.3   Suggest **two** abiotic factors that could affect the distribution of plants growing in soil.

1. ....

2. ....

[2]

[Total 4 marks]

2   A new pathogen is introduced into a population of flowering plants. (Grade 4-5)

2.1   Describe how the introduction of the new pathogen is likely to affect the plant population.

....

....

[1]

2.2   Bees in the ecosystem rely on the flowering plants for a source of food.
Explain how the introduction of the pathogen is likely to affect the bee population.

....

....

[2]

[Total 3 marks]

Ecology questions in the exam will often ask you about specific organisms — slugs, bees, dandelions, camels, herons, bladderwrack, rat-tailed maggots... Don't worry though — you're not expected to know anything about any particular organism before the exam. These questions are just getting you to apply your knowledge of ecology to real-life examples.

Target AO3

3 The sizes of a population of herons and a population of perch in a lake ecosystem were monitored over ten years. The pH of the lake was also monitored over the same time period. The results are shown in **Figures 1** and **2**.

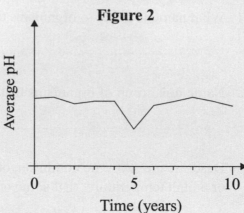

3.1 Describe the trend shown by the heron population in **Figure 1**.

....

.... *[1]*

A scientist says: 'A fall in the pH level causes perch to die'.

3.2 Suggest how the data in **Figures 1** and **2** supports the scientist's claim.

....

....

.... *[2]*

3.3 Give **one** reason why the data provided cannot be used to confirm whether the scientist is correct.

....

.... *[1]*

3.4 A new disease has emerged that is predicted to kill most of the perch in the lake. Using **Figure 1**, suggest and explain what effect the disease is likely to have on the heron population.

....

....

....
[2]

[Total 6 marks]

Exam Tip

If a question in the exam asks you to use some data, make sure you do use it. It's sitting there in a nice little graph or a lovely table, just to help you out, so make the most of it. If you don't use it, you'll miss out on some handy marks.

Topic B7 — Ecology

Adaptations

1 Some organisms live in environments that are very extreme, such as environments with a high salt concentration. *(Grade 3-4)*

1.1 What name is given to organisms that live in extreme environments?

....

[1]

1.2 Name **one** group of organisms that can live in deep sea vents where temperatures are very high.

....

[1]

1.3 Describe **one** extreme condition, other than a high salt concentration or a high temperature, that some organisms can tolerate.

....

[1]

[Total 3 marks]

2 Camels live in hot, dry desert conditions.
Table 1 shows some of the adaptations of camels to these conditions. *(Grade 4-5)*

Table 1

Adaptation	Reason for adaptation
Long eyelashes	Prevent sand from entering eyes
Very concentrated urine	?
Large surface area to volume ratio	Helps to lose heat
Drinks large quantities of water when available	Helps to replace water lost in hot conditions

2.1 Using **Table 1**, give **one** structural adaptation and **one** behavioural adaptation of the camel.

structural adaptation: ....

behavioural adaptation: ....

[2]

The production of very concentrated urine is a functional adaptation.

2.2 Explain what is meant by a functional adaptation.

....

....

[2]

2.3 Suggest how the production of concentrated urine helps the camel to survive in desert conditions.

....

....

[1]

[Total 5 marks]

Food Chains

Warm-Up

On the food chain below, circle the **producer**.

seaweed → fish → shark → whale

1 **Figure 1** shows an example of a woodland food chain. Grade 3-4

Figure 1

green plants → greenflies → blue tits → sparrowhawk

1.1 Green plants make their own food. What process do they use to do this?

....

[1]

1.2 What term would be used to describe the greenflies' position in **Figure 1**? Tick **one** box.

primary consumer ☐

secondary consumer ☐

tertiary consumer ☐

producer ☐

[1]

1.3 Name **one** organism from **Figure 1** which is a predator.

....

[1]

[Total 3 marks]

2 Foxes are predators. Rabbits are their prey. Grade 4-5

2.1 The number of foxes in an ecosystem increases.
Suggest what will happen to the number of rabbits in the ecosystem. Explain your answer.

....

....

[2]

2.2 A new disease appears in a rabbit population.
Suggest how this could lead to a decrease in the fox population in the same ecosystem.

....

....

....

[2]

[Total 4 marks]

Exam Tip

The arrows in a food chain show the direction of biomass transfer — in other words, they tell you what's eaten by what. For example, greenflies —are eaten by→ blue tits. It might help you remember this to think 'you —are eaten by→ the lion'.

Using Quadrats

1   A group of students used 1 m² quadrats to compare the population sizes of buttercups in two areas of a field. They collected data from three randomly placed quadrats in each area. Their results are shown in **Table 1**.

Table 1

	Quadrat 1	Quadrat 2	Quadrat 3	Mean
Area 1	15	14	13	14
Area 2	26	23	18	X

1.1 Calculate the value of **X** in **Table 1**.
    Give your answer to 2 significant figures.

X = ...
                                                                    [2]

1.2 A student says: "The **median** number of buttercups in **Area 1** is 14."
    Is she correct? Explain your answer.

    ....

    ....
                                                                    [1]

The students notice that the buttercups in **Area 1** were growing in the shade.
The buttercups in **Area 2** were growing in full sun.

1.3 Another student says:
    "The lower light intensity has affected the growth of the buttercups in **Area 1**."
    Do you agree with the student? Give a reason for your answer.

    ....

    ....
                                                                    [1]

1.4 **Area 1** has an area of 1750 m².
    Estimate the total number of buttercups in **Area 1**.

                                            .... buttercups
                                                                    [1]
                                                        [Total 5 marks]

Exam Tip

Make sure you use the right numbers from the data when you're carrying out calculations like the ones above — you don't want to lose marks just for writing down a number wrong. And remember, the first significant figure of a number is the first digit that's not a zero. The second and third significant figures come straight after (even if they are zeros).

Using Transects

1   **Figure 1** shows a transect line. It is being used to record the distribution of four types of plant in a field.

Figure 1

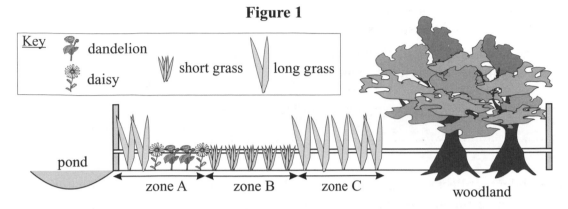

The field is split up into three zones — **A**, **B** and **C**.

1.1 In **Figure 1**, which zones contain only **one** species of plant?

....

[1]

1.2 Dandelions grow best in soils which have a high level of moisture.
Which zone, **A**, **B** or **C**, is most likely to have a high level of moisture?

....

[1]

1.3 Name **one** piece of equipment that may have been used to help collect the information in **Figure 1**.

....

[1]

[Total 3 marks]

2   A student is measuring how much of a habitat is covered by a grass species.
Figure 2 shows the area of a single quadrat covered by the grass.
The quadrat is divided into 100 squares.

Figure 2

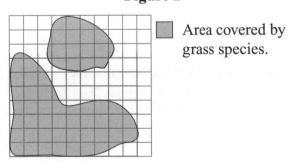

Area covered by grass species.

Estimate the percentage area of the quadrat covered by the grass species in **Figure 2**.

Area covered: .... %

[Total 2 marks]

Topic B7 — Ecology

82

3   A group of students are using a transect to investigate the distribution of organisms across a rocky shore.

Grade 4-5

PRACTICAL

Figure 3 shows a diagram of the shoreline as seen from above. The students plan to place a quadrat at set intervals along the transect and record the species in the quadrat at each point.

Figure 3

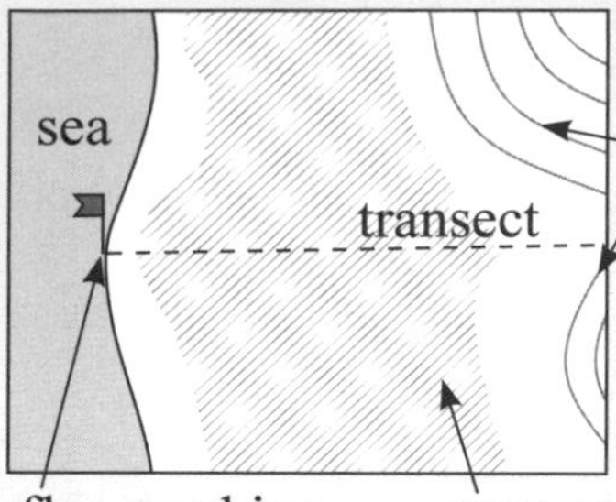

sea · transect · sand dunes

flag marking low tide point · area covered by rock pools

3.1   Suggest one hazard that the students should be aware of while carrying out their investigation.

....

.... [1]

3.2   The students collect their data by placing a 1 m² quadrat at 2 m intervals along the transect and estimating the percentage cover of each organism within the quadrat.

Why might this be a better method than placing the quadrat every metre, with no gap between the intervals? Tick **one** box.

It will make the results more accurate.   ☐

It will allow more species to be recorded.   ☐

It will take less time to collect the data.   ☐

[1]

Table 1 shows the data that the students collected about a seaweed called bladderwrack.

Table 1

Distance from low tide point (m)	2	4	6	8	10	12	14	16	18	20
Percentage cover of bladderwrack in quadrat (%)	0	0	10	10	20	30	40	70	80	60

3.3   Describe the trend in the percentage cover of bladderwrack shown by the data in **Table 1**.

....

....

.... [2]

3.4   Suggest **one** way that the students could make sure that their results are repeatable.

.... [1]

[Total 5 marks]

Exam Tip

If you have time at the end of the exam, it's always a good idea to have a look back at your answers to make sure that everything you've written is clear and that you've fully answered each question. For example, if a question asked you to describe a trend in some data, make sure you've looked at the right data and that you've actually described the trend.

Topic B7 — Ecology

The Water Cycle

Warm-Up

Find the **three** types of precipitation in the wordsearch below and circle them.

g	h	a	v	o	u	p	s	d
r	a	i	n	z	x	q	n	k
f	d	e	g	t	h	y	o	r
s	f	j	h	l	p	e	w	e
p	h	a	i	l	w	e	a	a

1   **Figure 1** represents the stages in the water cycle.   Grade 4-5

Figure 1

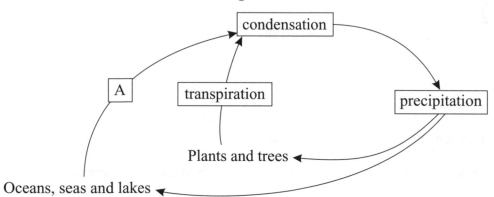

1.1 Name the process represented by **A** in the diagram.

....

[1]

1.2 What is meant by the term 'precipitation'?

....

[1]

1.3 Explain why precipitation is an important stage in the water cycle.

....

....

[1]

1.4 Suggest how the water in plants can be passed on to animals.

....

[1]

[Total 4 marks]

Topic B7 — Ecology

The Carbon Cycle

1   **Figure 1** shows a simplified version of the carbon cycle.

Figure 1

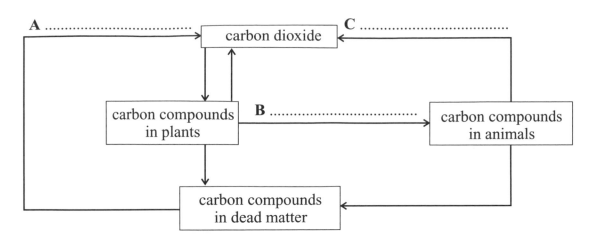

Complete **Figure 1**.
Fill in the labels **A**, **B** and **C** using words from the box.

decay	respiration	eating	photosynthesis

[Total 3 marks]

2   The carbon cycle describes how carbon moves between organisms and their environment.

2.1   Explain how microorganisms in the soil release carbon from dead matter.

....

....

[2]

2.2   Describe how carbon from the air can become a part of the carbon compounds in a plant.

....

....

....

....

[3]

[Total 5 marks]

Exam Tip

Make sure you know all of the carbon cycle, not just bits of it. Sketching it out might help you to remember it. First, write down all of the different places that the carbon can be, e.g. in the air, in plants. Then add the processes that move the carbon between these places, e.g. respiration. Add arrows to show which way the carbon in each process is moving.

Biodiversity and Waste Management

1   Many scientists are interested in the biodiversity of ecosystems.

Complete the sentences below about biodiversity.
Use answers from the box.

species	more	less	habitats	plants

Biodiversity is the variety of different .... in an ecosystem.

An ecosystem with a high biodiversity is .... stable than

an ecosystem with a low biodiversity.

[Total 2 marks]

2   The global population is using an increasing amount of resources.

2.1   State **two** reasons why humans are using more resources.

1. ....

2. ....

[2]

People are also creating more waste and more pollution.
Table 1 shows three different parts of the environment that can become polluted.

Table 1

	Types of pollutant
Air	1. smoke 2. ....
Land	1. pesticides 2. ....
Water	1. .... 2. ....

2.2   Complete **Table 1** to show examples of the different types of pollutant that can affect air, land and water.

[4]

2.3   Explain how pollution affects biodiversity.

....

....

[2]

[Total 8 marks]

Topic B7 — Ecology

Target AO3

3   The presence of indicator species in an area can provide evidence for the level of pollution in the ecosystem. A student is surveying the numbers of three indicator species in two small rivers as a measure of water pollution.

This is the method that the student used:

1. Place a long-handled net with a fine mesh on the bottom of the river. It should be positioned so that water is flowing into the net.
2. Stand upstream of the net and gently disturb the bottom of the river by moving your feet for 30 seconds.
3. Empty the contents of the net into a large tray filled with a 3 cm depth of water.
4. Identify and count the individuals of the indicator species in your sample.
5. Empty the contents of the tray back into the river.

Table 2 shows the results. **Table 3** gives details of the indicator species.

Table 2

Individuals counted in survey	River 1	River 2
freshwater shrimp	29	0
water louse	60	10
rat-tailed maggot	4	88

Table 3

Indicator species	Presence of species indicates:
freshwater shrimp	low level of pollution
water louse	medium level of pollution
rat-tailed maggot	high level of pollution

3.1 State an appropriate way to display the results in **Table 2**.

   ....
   [1]

3.2 Use the results to decide which of the statements below is correct. Tick **one** box.

   River 2 is more polluted than River 1 because there are more freshwater shrimp. ☐

   Water lice are found in both rivers, so the rivers are equally polluted. ☐

   River 1 is less polluted than River 2 because there are fewer rat-tailed maggots. ☐

   All three indicator species are present in River 1, so it isn't polluted. ☐

   [1]

3.3 A factory discharges waste water into another small river, River 3.
   A local newspaper claims that the waste water is causing an increase in pollution in the river.
   The student plans to use the method outlined above to investigate the claim.

   State **two** locations that the student would need to survey in her investigation.

   1. ....

   2. ....
   [2]

   [Total 4 marks]

Exam Tip

In your exams, you could be given the method for an experiment and asked how you could adapt it to test a different hypothesis. You'll need to have a think about what the original method was testing. Then have a good read of the new hypothesis you've been given, and work out what things you'd need to change in order to test that instead.

Topic B7 — Ecology

Global Warming

Warm-Up

The sentences below are to do with global warming.
Circle **one** underlined phrase in each sentence, so that the sentence is correct.

<u>Carbon dioxide</u> / <u>Sulfur dioxide</u> is a greenhouse gas.

<u>Oxygen</u> / <u>Methane</u> is also a greenhouse gas.

The levels of these greenhouse gases are <u>decreasing</u> / <u>increasing</u>.

This is <u>cooling down</u> / <u>heating up</u> the Earth.

1   **Figure 1** shows the distribution of a butterfly species in Britain in 1986 and in 2016.

Figure 1

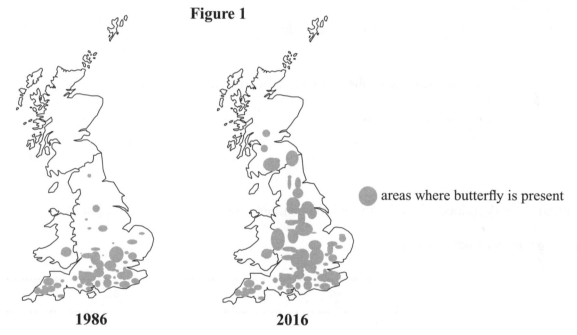

areas where butterfly is present

1986   **2016**

1.1 Give **two** ways in which the distribution of the butterfly species changed between 1986 and 2016.

   1. ....

   2. ....

[2]

A scientist thinks that the change in the distribution of the butterfly is due to global warming.

1.2 Suggest **one** other piece of data the scientist might need to find out if she is correct.

   ....

[1]

[Total 3 marks]

Exam Tip

Greenhouse gases cause the 'greenhouse effect'. Without greenhouse gases trapping energy in the Earth's atmosphere, it'd be too cold for us to survive. But as we do things that increase the amounts of these gases in the atmosphere, the amount of energy that they trap is increasing too. That's why we're getting all hot and bothered about them...

                                                             Topic B7 — Ecology

Deforestation and Land Use

1 The destruction of peat bogs can lead to problems. *(Grade 1-3)*

1.1 How can peat be used by humans?
Tick **one** box.

as a cleaning product ☐

as an animal feed ☐

as a pesticide ☐

as a compost ☐

[1]

When harvesting peat, peat bogs are drained before the peat is removed.
Because the bogs are drained, any peat left behind will begin to decay.

1.2 What gas is released when peat decays?
Tick **one** box.

carbon monoxide ☐   carbon dioxide ☐   nitrogen ☐   oxygen ☐

[1]

1.3 What problem does the release of the gas you named in **1.2** contribute to?

....

[1]

[Total 3 marks]

2 Human activity reduces the amount of land available for other animals and plants. *(Grade 4-5)*

2.1 Give **two** uses of land by humans.

1. ....

2. ....

[2]

Areas of land are often deforested so that they can be used by humans.

2.2 Give **one** reason why an area of land in the tropics may be deforested.

....

....

[1]

2.3 What effect does deforestation have on biodiversity in an area? Give a reason for your answer.

Effect: ....

Reason: ....

....

[2]

[Total 5 marks]

Topic B7 — Ecology

Maintaining Ecosystems and Biodiversity

1   A farmer grows a single type of crop.
     As a result, her fields have a low biodiversity.   **Grade 3-4**

What could the farmer do to increase the biodiversity of her fields?
Tick **two** boxes.

Replace the fences around her fields with hedgerows.   ☐

Cut down trees around the edges of her fields.   ☐

Increase her use of chemical pesticides.   ☐

Allow wild flowers and grasses to grow around the edges of her fields.   ☐

Reduce her use of chemical fertilisers.   ☐

[Total 2 marks]

2   In some areas, programmes have been put in place to reduce the
     negative effects of human activity on ecosystems and biodiversity.   **Grade 4-5**

2.1   Which of the following could reduce carbon dioxide emissions into the atmosphere?
      Tick **one** box.

Setting up more breeding programmes for endangered species.   ☐

Using more land for landfill sites.   ☐

Increasing the number of power stations.   ☐

Reducing deforestation.   ☐

[1]

2.2   The government encourages people to recycle as much of their waste as possible.
      Suggest how this could help to protect ecosystems.

      ....

      ....

[2]

2.3   Breeding programmes are carried out in zoos in many countries.
      Suggest how breeding programmes in zoos could increase biodiversity in the wild.

      ....

      ....

[2]

[Total 5 marks]

Exam Tip

Humans do a lot to reduce biodiversity (boo, hiss). But remember — there are also lots of ways that we can have a positive effect on it. Make sure that you can describe a few different methods for protecting or increasing biodiversity. You should be able to explain how the different methods that you've described work, too.

 ☐   ☐   ☐

Topic B7 — Ecology

Atoms

Choose from the words below to fill in the blanks in the passage.

protons   neutrons

electrons   compounds

heavy   light

......Protons......... and ......Neutrons.... are found in the nucleus of an atom.

.....electrons...... move around the nucleus in shells.

Compared to electrons, protons and neutrons are ....heavy......... .

1 This question is about the particles inside an atom. (Grade 1-3)

1.1 Complete **Table 1**.

Table 1

Particle	Relative Charge
Proton	+1
Neutron	0
Electron	-1

[3]

1.2 What is the overall charge of an atom? Tick **one** box.

Positive ☐   Negative ☐   Neutral ☑

[1]

[Total 4 marks]

2 A potassium atom can be represented by the nuclear symbol $^{39}_{19}K$. (Grade 4-5)

2.1 What is the mass number of a potassium atom?

39

[1]

2.2 What is the atomic number of a potassium atom?

19

[1]

2.3 How many protons, neutrons and electrons does an atom of potassium have?

protons: ....19.......   neutrons: .....20.....   electrons: .....19......

[3]

[Total 5 marks]

It's pretty likely that you will be asked an exam question about the relative charges of the three subatomic particles. All you need to remember is that **p**rotons are **p**ositive, **neut**rons are **neut**ral and that electrons are... the other one.

Elements

1 Which of the following statements about elements is true? (Grade 3-4)

Tick **one** box.

Atoms of the same element can contain different numbers of protons. ☐

There are about 200 different elements. ☐

Elements contain more than one type of atom. ☐

Atoms are the smallest part of an element that can exist. ☑

[Total 1 mark]

2 Bromine has two stable isotopes, A and B. **Table 1** shows some information about them. (Grade 4-5)

2.1 Complete **Table 1** by calculating the number of neutrons for each isotope of bromine.

Table 1

isotope	mass number	number of protons	number of neutrons	abundance (%)
A	79	35	44	51
B	81	35	46	49

[2]

2.2 Using the information in **Table 1**, state the number of electrons in isotope A.

........44..

[1]

2.3 Using the information in **Table 1**, calculate the following values:

abundance of isotope A × mass number of isotope A: ....4029...

....

abundance of isotope B × mass number of isotope B: ....3969...

....

[2]

2.4 Calculate the relative atomic mass of bromine. Give your answer to 1 decimal place.
Use the equation:

$$\text{Relative atomic mass} = \frac{\text{sum of (isotope abundance} \times \text{isotope mass number)}}{\text{sum of abundances of all the isotopes}}$$

$$\frac{4029 + 3969}{51 + 49} = \frac{7998}{100} = 79.98 = 80.0$$

Relative atomic mass = ...79.98 = 80.0

[2]

[Total 7 marks]

Topic C1 — Atomic Structure and the Periodic Table

Compounds

1 Ammonia is a compound with the formula NH_3. Grade 4-5

1.1 Why is ammonia classified as a compound? Tick **one** box.

It contains only one type of atom. ☐

It contains two different elements held together by chemical bonds. ☑

It cannot be broken down into elements using chemical methods. ☐

It contains more than one atom. ☐

[1]

1.2 How many atoms are there in a single molecule of ammonia?

........4..

[1]

[Total 2 marks]

2 The following list shows the chemical formulas of some different substances. Grade 4-5

   A. O_2 **B.** $NaCl$ **C.** C_2H_4 **D.** H_2 **E.** SO_2Cl_2

2.1 Name substance **B**.

...........Sodium......chloride...

[1]

2.2 Identify **two** substances from the list that are compounds.

.......NaCl....and......SO_2Cl_2..

[2]

2.3 How many elements are there in a molecule of substance **A**?

.............1...

[1]

2.4 State how many atoms of each element there are in one molecule of substance **E**.

   S: ....1.............

   O: ....2.............

   Cl: ....2.............

[2]

[Total 6 marks]

Exam Tip

Make sure you know the difference between atoms, elements and compounds — here's a quick round up. Everything is made of atoms (which contain protons, neutrons and electrons). Elements only contain one type of atom (all the atoms have the same number of protons). A compound is made up of atoms of different elements all bonded together. Got it?

Topic C1 — Atomic Structure and the Periodic Table

Chemical Equations

The word equation for a reaction is shown below:

magnesium + hydrochloric acid → magnesium chloride + hydrogen

For each of the following statements circle whether the statement is **true** or **false**.

1) Hydrogen is a product in the reaction — <u>True</u>   Or   False

2) The equation shows the reaction between chlorine and hydrogen — True   Or   <u>False</u>

3) Hydrochloric acid is a reactant — <u>True</u>   Or   False

4) The equation shows the reaction between magnesium and hydrochloric acid — <u>True</u>   Or   False

---

1   Look at the following word equation: calcium + water → calcium hydroxide + hydrogen   Grade 1-3

1.1   Name the **two** reactants in this reaction.

............Calcium + water..

[1]

1.2   Name the **two** products of this reaction.

............Calcium Hydroxide + Hydrogen...

[1]

[Total 2 marks]

---

2   Sodium (Na) reacts with chlorine gas (Cl_2) to form sodium chloride (NaCl) only.   Grade 4-5

2.1   Write a word equation for this reaction.

............Sodium + chlorine → Sodium chloride...

[1]

2.2   Which of the following equations correctly represents this reaction?
Tick **one** box.

$Na + Cl \rightarrow NaCl$ ☐ $Na_2 + 2Cl \rightarrow 2NaCl$ ☐

$Na_2 + Cl_2 \rightarrow 2NaCl$ ☐ $2Na + Cl_2 \rightarrow 2NaCl$ ☑

[1]

2.3   Sodium also reacts with oxygen (O_2) to form sodium oxide (Na_2O).
Balance the equation for this reaction.

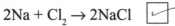

..............4 $Na + O_2 \rightarrow$ ....2 Na_2O

[2]

[Total 4 marks]

 ☐   ☐   ☺ ☐   Topic C1 — Atomic Structure and the Periodic Table

Mixtures

1 Which of the following substances is a mixture? (Grade 3-4)

Tick **one** box.

copper ☐   calcium chloride ☐

crude oil ☑   ammonia ☐

[Total 1 mark]

2 Mixtures contain different substances. (Grade 3-4)

2.1 State the smallest number of substances a mixture must contain.

.....2..

[1]

2.2 Complete the sentence that describes the different parts in a mixture.
Use words from the box.

| change | don't change | electrical | physical | chemical |

The chemical properties of the different parts in a mixture ....don't......change............. when

they're added together. The different parts can be separated from the mixture using

..................physical.............. methods.

[2]

[Total 3 marks]

3 Air contains many gases. These gases include nitrogen, oxygen and argon. (Grade 4-5)

3.1 Is air an element, a compound or a mixture? Give a reason for your answer.

Type of substance: .....Mixture...2 or more.................

Reason: .....mixture......of.........different.......gases.........and........contains ^ elements.............

.....Nitrogen, oxygen, Argon.......and.......Compound......CO2.— aren't.......chemically...bonded...

[3]

3.2 Argon can be separated out from air. Will the chemical properties of argon as a separate gas be
different from the properties of argon in air? Explain your answer.

.....No..

....

[2]

[Total 5 marks]

Topic C1 — Atomic Structure and the Periodic Table

Chromatography

1   The first three steps for carrying out paper chromatography of an ink are shown below.   (Grade 3-4)

     1. Draw a pencil line near the bottom of a sheet of filter paper.
     2. Add a spot of ink to the line.
     3. Pour a small amount of solvent into a beaker.

1.1   Which of the following steps should be done next?
Tick **one** box.

Place a lid on the beaker. ☐

Place the sheet in the solvent so that the solvent is just below the pencil line. ☑

Leave the paper to dry. ☐

Let the solvent seep up the paper until it's almost reached the top. ☐

[1]

1.2   Why is pencil used to make the line on the filter paper?

........pencil....marks.......are......insoluble..
[1]
[Total 2 marks]

2   **Figure 1** shows the result of a paper chromatography experiment to separate the dyes in an ink.   (Grade 4-5)

Figure 1

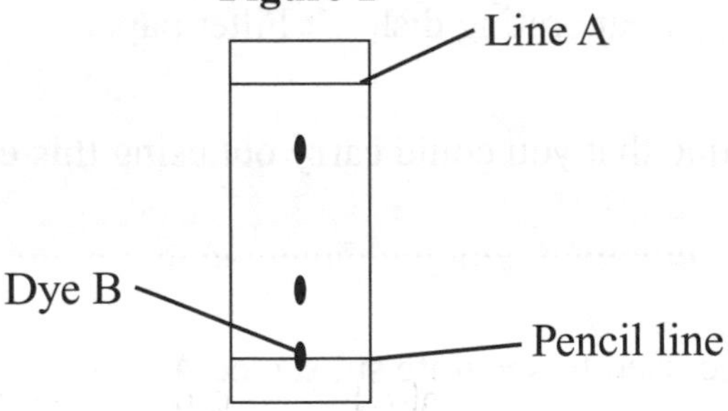

Line A

Dye B

Pencil line

2.1   In **Figure 1** line A represents the point reached by the solvent. What is the name of this point?

........solvent.....front...
[1]

2.2   Why does the ink separate into different spots of dye?

....diff.....dyes.......in......the........ink.......move.......at.......diff......speeds...................
[1]

2.3   Dye B has stayed on the pencil line.
Predict whether Dye B is soluble or insoluble in the solvent used in the experiment.

.......Insoluble...
[1]
[Total 3 marks]

Topic C1 — Atomic Structure and the Periodic Table

More Separation Techniques

1 Filtration is a way of separating substances. (Grade 1-3)

1.1 Complete the sentence below that describes filtration.
Use the words from the box.

| soluble | insoluble | solids | liquids | solutions |

Filtration is used to separate ....insoluble........ solids from ....liquids........... .

[2]

1.2 Which two pieces of equipment would you use in a filtration experiment?
Tick **two** boxes.

Filter paper ☑   Evaporating dish ☐

Bunsen burner ☐   Funnel ☑

[2]

[Total 4 marks]

2 A mixture is made by dissolving substance **A** (a solid) in warm water.
Substance **A** breaks down at high temperatures.
Figure 1 shows the equipment that could be used to separate substance **A** from the solution. (Grade 4-5)

Figure 1

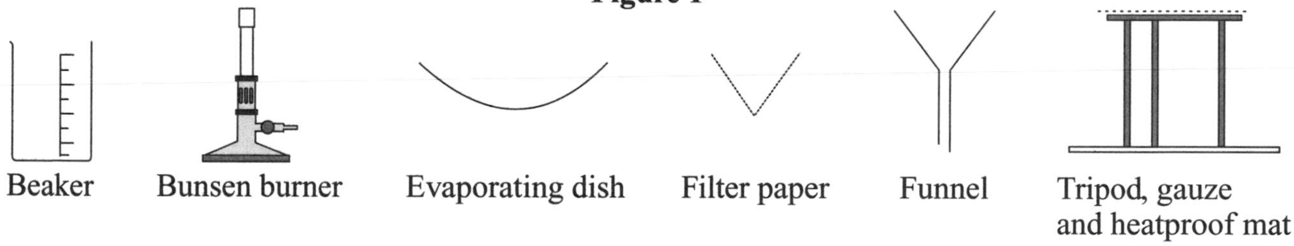

Beaker   Bunsen burner   Evaporating dish   Filter paper   Funnel   Tripod, gauze and heatproof mat

2.1 Name the separation technique that you could carry out using this equipment.

..........Crystallisation..........

[1]

2.2* Write a method that could be used to separate substance **A** from the water using this equipment.

..........Gently.......heat.......the.......solution.......in.......the.......evaporating.......dish.,.stop........
.....heating.......once.......some.......of.......the.......solvent.......has.......evaporated......or......
.....when.......crystals.......start.......to.......form.-.......leave.......solution.......to.......cool.......until.
.....crystals.......are.......formed.,.......put.......filter.......paper.......in.......Funnel.-.place.......in......
.....Beaker.-.pour.......mixture.......into.......filter.......paper.-.......liquid.......passes.-.......crystals....
.....remain.-.......leave.......crystals.......to.......dry.......out.:

[6]

[Total 7 marks]

Exam Tip

Q2.2 is an example of a question with multiple levels of response in the mark scheme. To ensure you get full marks for these questions, make sure that your points are clear, well-structured and contain all the relevant information.

Topic C1 — Atomic Structure and the Periodic Table

Distillation

1 A mixture contains two liquids. The liquids have similar boiling points. *(Grade 3-4)*

Which of the following techniques would be best for separating the two liquids?
Tick **one** box.

☐ Evaporation ☐ Condensation ☐ Simple distillation ☑ Fractional distillation

[Total 1 mark]

PRACTICAL

2 A sample of butanol, which has a boiling point of 118 °C, was prepared. The sample contained an impurity with a boiling point of 187 °C. The distillation apparatus shown in **Figure 1** was set up to separate butanol from the impurity. *(Grade 4-5)*

Figure 1

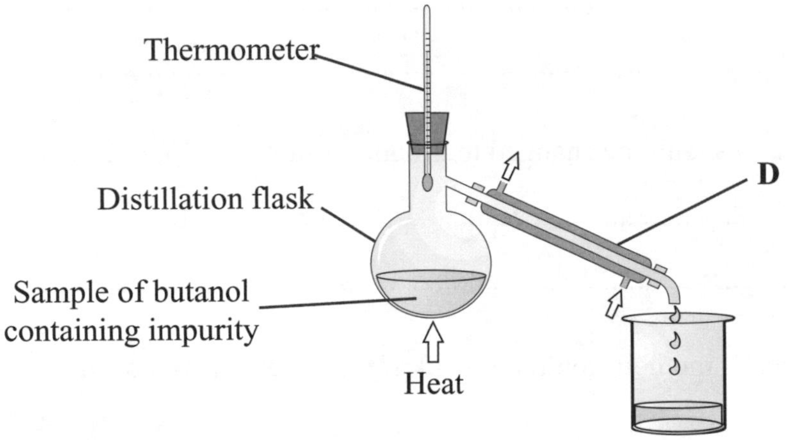

Thermometer

Distillation flask

Sample of butanol containing impurity

Heat

D

2.1 Name the piece of apparatus labelled **D**.

..........Condenser..

[1]

2.2 What happens to the vapour that enters the piece of apparatus labelled **D**?

........changes gas to liquid - condenses...

[1]

2.3 Describe how you could use the thermometer to identify when butanol is being distilled from the mixture.

.....Thermometer will read 118°c..

[1]

2.4 Suggest why butanol can't be distilled by heating the flask with a water bath.

.....Butanol has a boiling point greater than 100°c - greater.....
.....than the boiling point of water - It wouldn't evaporate when
heated by a water bath.

[2]

[Total 5 marks]

Exam Tip

Distillation is an important technique that examiners love to ask questions on. Make sure that you are familiar with the equipment used, how the experiment works and how changing certain conditions might affect the experiment.

Topic C1 — Atomic Structure and the Periodic Table

Target AO3

3   A student was given a solution containing water, ethanol and bismuth iodide.
Bismuth iodide is soluble in ethanol but is not very soluble in water.
The boiling point of ethanol is 78 °C and bismuth iodide has a melting point of 408 °C.

Here is the method the student uses to separate each component of the mixture:

> 1. Using distillation apparatus, heat the mixture to 120 °C
>   to separate the ethanol from the solution.
> 2. Pour the remaining mixture through a filter to remove the solid bismuth iodide.
> 3. Leave the crystals to dry.

3.1 The student's method will not produce samples of ethanol and water.
Identify why the ethanol will not be separated from the water. Explain your answer.

In the first step, Temperature that the student heated the
solution to was too high, heating the mixture to 120°c will
cause both the Ethanol and the water to evaporate.

[2]

3.2 Explain how the method should be changed to produce a sample of pure ethanol.

he should heat the mixture to a temperature 78°c - causing
Ethanol and water evaporate.

[1]

3.3 Explain why the student's method would not work if the water was removed from the mixture
instead of the ethanol.

Bismuth iodine is insoluble in Ethanol but not in water -
if student removed water instead of Ethanol, The iodine would
still be disolved in solution and couldn't be removed by
filteration

[2]

3.4 Potassium hydrogencarbonate is an example of a water-soluble salt. The student plans to use the
following method to produce a pure sample of dry potassium hydrogencarbonate crystals:

> 1. Gently heat potassium hydrogencarbonate solution in an evaporating dish.
> 2. The solvent will start to evaporate and crystals will start to form.
> 3. Keep heating the solution until only dry crystals remain.

Potassium hydrogencarbonate decomposes on heating. Suggest how the student should change
their method from step 2 onwards to successfully produce a sample of the salt.

student should stop heating the solution when crystals
start to form - They should then filter the crystals out of
the solution and leave them in a warm place to dry.

[2]

[Total 7 marks]

Topic C1 — Atomic Structure and the Periodic Table

The History of The Atom

Use the words to label the different parts of the atom shown below.

shell

electron

nucleus

....electron...... .....shell...........

.....Nucleus.....

1   Models of the atom have changed over time.   Grade 3-4

1.1   Which of the following is the best description of what scientists thought an atom was like before the electron was discovered?
Tick **one** box.

Tiny solid spheres ✓   Formless 'clouds' ☐   Flat shapes ☐   Packets of energy ☐

[1]

1.2   Number the models of the atom below in the order they were created. Put a 1 next to the first model created, a 2 next to the second model created and a 3 next to the most recent model.

Nuclear model [2]   Bohr's nuclear model [3]   Plum pudding model [1]

[2]

[Total 3 marks]

2   Scientist's understanding of the atom has changed as different particles have been discovered.   Grade 4-5

2.1   Draw **one** line from each atomic model to the correct description of that model.

Atomic Model

Plum pudding model

Bohr's nuclear model

Nuclear model

Description

A positively charged 'ball' with negatively charged electrons in it.

A small positively charged nucleus surrounded by a 'cloud' of negative electrons.

Electrons in fixed orbits surrounding a small positively charged nucleus.

Solid spheres with a different sphere for each element.

[3]

2.2   James Chadwick discovered a neutral particle inside the nucleus. Give the name of this particle.

.................Neutrons...

[1]

[Total 4 marks]

Topic C1 — Atomic Structure and the Periodic Table

Electronic Structure

1 Complete **Table 1** to show how many electrons go in each of the first three electron shells.

Table 1

Electron shell	Number of electrons it can hold
1st	........2........
2nd	........8........
3rd	........8........

[Total 3 marks]

2 Calcium has an atomic number of 20.

2.1 What is the electron configuration of a calcium atom? Tick **one** box.

☐ 2, 18   ☐ 2, 16, 2   ☑ 2, 8, 8, 2   ☐ 2, 2, 8, 8

[1]

2.2 Calcium has two electrons in the shell closest to the nucleus. Explain why this is.

......Because......it's......in......group......2..

[1]

[Total 2 marks]

3 Electronic structures can be represented in different ways.

3.1 **Figure 1** shows the electronic structures of an
atom of chlorine (Cl), and an atom of boron (B).
Give the electronic structures of chlorine and boron in number form.

Chlorine: ......2,8,,7........

Boron: ....2,3..........

Figure 1

Chlorine   Boron

[2]

3.2 Sulfur has an atomic number of 16.
Complete the diagram to show the electronic structure of sulfur.

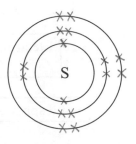

[2]

[Total 4 marks]

Exam Tip

Electronic structures are a key idea in chemistry, so it's really important that you understand them. Definitely make sure you know, or can work out (by remembering how many electrons can fit into each electron shell), the electronic structures for the first 20 elements in the periodic table. Doing this will be really helpful for your exams.

Topic C1 — Atomic Structure and the Periodic Table

Development of The Periodic Table

1 In early periodic tables, scientists ordered elements by their atomic weights. The modern periodic table is ordered by atomic number. *(Grade 3-4)*

1.1 Why were early periodic tables ordered by atomic weight and not atomic number?

...... Protons (neutrons and electrons) hadn't been discovered , Atomic numbers weren't known

[1]

1.2 State **two** problems with early periodic tables.

1. ...... not complete

2. ...... elements were put in the wrong place - columns - groups

[2]

[Total 3 marks]

2 When Mendeleev arranged his periodic table, he left some gaps and also swapped the order of some elements. This meant the elements weren't ordered strictly by atomic weight. *(Grade 4-5)*

2.1 Give **one** reason why Mendeleev arranged his table in this way.

...... so that elements with similar properties were in the same group.

[1]

2.2 How did the discovery of new elements help to show that the arrangement of Mendeleev's table was correct?

...... properties of elements that were found after Mendeleev made his table fitted with the gaps that he'd left in table

[1]

2.3 The discovery of which of the following things also helped to show that the arrangement of Mendeleev's table was correct? Tick **one** box.

Neutrons ☐

Isotopes ☑

Atomic weight ☐

Molecules ☐

[1]

[Total 3 marks]

Exam Tip

Mendeleev's table of the elements is a great example of Working Scientifically. Mendeleev came up with an idea, and later discoveries showed that he was right. Make sure you can explain what he did and why it was accepted by scientists.

Topic C1 — Atomic Structure and the Periodic Table

The Modern Periodic Table

1 **Figure 1** shows the periodic table. *Grade 3-4*

Figure 1

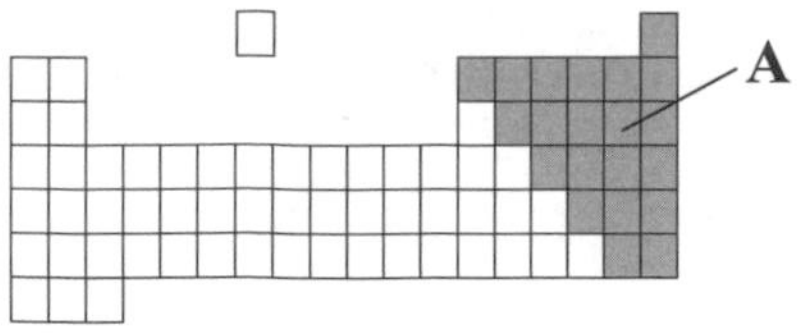

1.1 How are the elements ordered in the periodic table?

......according........to......atomic.......number...

[1]

1.2 What are the vertical columns in the periodic table called?

......Groups...

[1]

1.3 What type of elements are found in the shaded area labelled **A**?

......Non-metals...

[1]

[Total 3 marks]

2 **Figure 2** shows the electronic configuration for atoms of three elements, **A**, **X** and **Z**. *Grade 4-5*

Figure 2

2.1 What group in the periodic table is element **X** in? Give a reason for your answer.

Group: ......2...

Reason: ....2.....outer.....electron...

[2]

2.2 Which period is element **X** in? Give a reason for your answer.

Period: .....3...

Reason: ...it......has......12....electrons - 3...shells....of.....electron..

[2]

2.3 Which **two** elements are in the same period?

......x and z..

[1]

2.4 Which element, **A** or **Z**, will react in a similar way to element **X**? Give a reason for your answer.

Element: ....A..

Reason: ..same......number.....of.^outer.electrons - element...A......same........group...as............
                                                                                          element x
[2]

[Total 7 marks]

Topic C1 — Atomic Structure and the Periodic Table

Metals and Non-Metals

1 About 80% of all the elements in the periodic table are metals. (Grade 3-4)

1.1 Describe where metals can be found in the periodic table.

..........Group....1..2..3..4..... All..... the...... left..... side....... and....... bottom..........................

[1]

1.2 Which **two** of the following properties are typical properties of metals?
Tick **two** boxes.

Conductors of electricity ☐

Liquids at room temperature ☐

Can be bent or hammered into different shapes ☑

Low density ☑

[1]

[Total 2 marks]

2 Some metals will react with particular non-metals to form compounds made of ions. (Grade 4-5)

2.1 Two elements, with the chemical symbols A and X, react together to form a compound made of A^{2+} ions and X^{2-} ions. One of the elements is a metal and one is a non-metal. State which element is the metal and which is the non-metal.

A^{2+} .....Metal..................... X^{2-} .....Non-metal..........

[1]

2.2 Fill in the gaps to complete the passage about how metals react. Use the words in the box.

gain	lose	share	half-full	full

When metals react, they ....lose.......... electrons.

When this happens they end up with a ....full.......... outer shell of electrons.

[2]

2.3 State **three** physical properties that non-metals are likely to have.

1. ....dull...

2. ....not.....ductile...

3. ....not.....malleable.......low.....density...........................

[3]

[Total 6 marks]

Exam Tip

Something you can do to help you remember the different properties of metals and non-metals is to think of examples of these materials in everyday life and then consider how their properties help them to do their job.

          Topic C1 — Atomic Structure and the Periodic Table

104

Group 1 Elements

1 The Group 1 elements show trends in their properties. *(Grade 3-4)*

1.1 The density of the Group 1 elements **increases** down the group. Put the elements lithium (Li), sodium (Na) and potassium (K) in order from least dense to most dense.

................Lithium................ Least dense

................Sodium................ ↕

................Potassium............ Most dense

[1]

1.2 Draw **one** line from each property to show how it changes as you go down Group 1.

Property   **Trend down Group 1**

Increases

Melting point   →

Decreases

Boiling point   →

Doesn't change

[2]

[Total 3 marks]

2 Lithium can react with chlorine. *(Grade 4-5)*

2.1 What is the charge on the lithium ions that form in this reaction?

......+1......

[1]

2.2 What type of compound is the product of this reaction?

......ionic......

[1]

[Total 2 marks]

3 This question is about the reactions of Group 1 elements with water. *(Grade 4-5)*

3.1 Complete the word equation for the reaction of sodium with water:

sodium + water → ....Sodim Hydroxi-.... + ...Hydrogen..........
                          de

[2]

3.2 Potassium reacts more strongly than sodium with water. Explain why.

Potassium has more electron shells than sodium So the oter electron of Potassim is further away from the Nucleus than the outer electron of sodium - means outer electron of Potassium is less attracted to the Nucleus and easily lost.

[3]

[Total 5 marks]

Group 7 Elements

1 Complete the passage about the Group 7 elements. Use the words in the box. **Grade 1-3**

| one | 1+ | seven | halogens | halides | 1– | eight |

The Group 7 elements all have ....Seven.......... electrons in their outer shell.

They can react to form ions with a ....1-.............. charge.

These ions are called ....Halides......... .

[Total 3 marks]

2 The elements in Group 7 of the periodic table are known as the halogens. **Grade 3-4**

2.1 Which of the following statements about the halogens is true? Tick **one** box.

They are non-metals that exist as single atoms. ☐

They are metals that exist as single atoms. ☐

They are non-metals that exist as molecules of two atoms. ☑

They are metals that exist as molecules of two atoms. ☐

[1]

2.2 Which halogen has the lowest boiling point?

......Flourine..

[1]

[Total 2 marks]

3 This question is about the reactivity of the halogens. **Grade 4-5**

3.1 Compare the chemical reactivity of chlorine and bromine. Explain your answer.

...chlorine....is....more....reactive....than....Bromine.....-....Because.........chlorine....has....
...fewer....electrons....shells....than....Bromine....so....it's....outer....shell....
...is....closer....to....Nucleus.....-....easier....for....chlorine....to.....gain.....an....electron
....when....it....reacts *[3]*

3.2 Halogens can react with other elements to form molecular compounds. Of the following elements, suggest which one might form a molecular compound with a halogen. Tick **one** box.

Na ☐   K ☐   H ☑   Cu ☐

[1]

Give a reason for your answer.

......Hydrogen....is....a....non-metal..../....Halogens.......form.......molecular.......compounds....
........with....non-metals.
[1]

[Total 5 marks]

Topic C1 — Atomic Structure and the Periodic Table

Group 0 Elements

1 The Group 0 elements have similar properties. (Grade 3-4)

1.1 Describe the state of the Group 0 elements at room temperature.

...... Gases ....

[1]

1.2 Which of the following best describes the structure of the Group 0 elements?
Tick **one** box.

molecules containing two atoms ☐

single atoms ☑

ions ☐

metallic ☐

[1]

1.3 The Group 0 elements are unreactive. Explain why.

...... Because they have a full - outer shell ....

[1]

[Total 3 marks]

2 The noble gases can be found in Group 0 of the periodic table. (Grade 4-5)

2.1 Using the information in **Table 1**, complete the table by predicting the boiling point of radon (Rn).

Table 1

Element	Boiling Point / °C
Ar	−186
Kr	−152
Xe	−108
Rn	any value between -108 and 25

[1]

2.2 Explain the trend in boiling points as you go down Group 0.

...As you go down, elements have more electrons., forces between...

...atoms get stronger - more energy needed to break the...

...bonds...

[3]

[Total 4 marks]

Exam Tip

You need to know why elements in Groups 1 and 7 are reactive and know what they react with. You also need to know why Group O elements don't react. Remember it's all about the number of electrons in the outer shell of the elements.

Topic C1 — Atomic Structure and the Periodic Table

Formation of Ions

1   This question is about ions. Grade 1-3

1.1 Complete the sentence below.
Use a word from the box.

| atoms | electrons | charges |

Ions are formed when ....atoms................ gain or lose electrons.

[1]

1.2 An ion has a charge of +1.
How many electrons were lost in the formation of this ion?

............1..

[1]

[Total 2 marks]

2   This question is about ions and their formation. Grade 4-5

2.1 Which statement about the atoms of metallic elements is correct?
Tick **one** box.

Metal atoms usually lose electrons to become negative ions. ☐

Metal atoms usually gain electrons to become negative ions. ☐

Metal atoms usually gain electrons to become positive ions. ☐

Metal atoms usually lose electrons to become positive ions. ☑

[1]

2.2 There are four different ions shown below. Each one is of a different element.
Draw **one** line between each ion and its description.

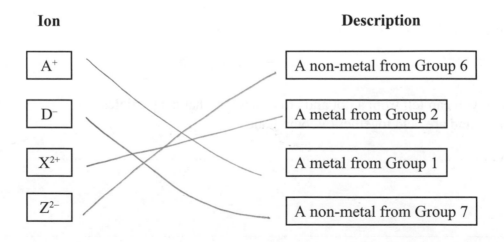

| Ion | Description |

[2]

[Total 3 marks]

Ionic Bonding

1 This question is about ionic bonding. *Grade 3-4*

1.1 Ionic bonding involves metal and non-metal atoms bonding together.
Complete the sentences. Use words from the box.

negatively	opposite	similar	neutrally	positively

Metal atoms lose electrons to form .... positively .... charged ions.

The non-metal atoms gain electrons and form .... negatively .... charged ions.

These ions have .... opposite .... charges so they are attracted to each other.

[3]

1.2 Magnesium and oxygen bond together to form the ionic compound magnesium oxide (MgO).
To form MgO a magnesium atom **loses** two electrons and an oxygen atom **gains** two electrons.

State the formulas of the magnesium and oxygen ions in MgO.

Magnesium ion ..... Mg^{2+} ....

Oxygen ion ..... O^{2-} ....

[2]

[Total 5 marks]

2 The dot and cross diagram below shows the formation of lithium fluoride from its elements. *Grade 4-5*

2.1 Complete the diagram by:
- adding an **arrow** to show the transfer of electron(s)
- adding the charges of the ions
- completing the outer shell electronic structure of the fluoride ion

[3]

2.2 Name the force that holds the ions together in an ionic bond.

...... electrostatic ...... force ....

[1]

2.3 State how you can tell from a dot and cross diagram that the particles
in a compound are held together by ionic bonds.

.. particles ...... in ...... Compound .... are .... oppositely .... charged ..... ions ....

[1]

[Total 5 marks]

Exam Tip

Understanding how ionic compounds are formed can be a bit tricky. Just remember that no electrons disappear, they just move. Make sure you practise drawing some compounds with arrows to show how the electrons move and form the ions.

Topic C2 — Bonding, Structure and Properties of Matter

Ionic Compounds

Warm-Up

Circle the correct words or phrases in the passage below.

In an ionic compound, the particles are held together by <u>weak</u>/(strong) forces of attraction.

These forces are called ionic bonds and act (in all directions)/<u>in one direction</u>.

---

1 Potassium bromide is an ionic compound made of potassium ions and bromide ions.

1.1 Complete the diagram below to show the position of the ions in potassium bromide.
Write a symbol in each circle to show whether it is a potassium ion (K^+) or a bromide ion (Br^-).

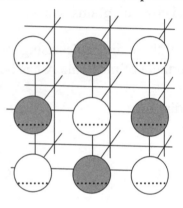

[1]

1.2 Give **one** disadvantage of using the type of diagram above
to show the structure of an ionic compound.

......doesn't....correctly......represent........the........sizes......of......ions.....−....shows......gaps...
......between......ions...

[1]

[Total 2 marks]

---

2 This question is about ionic compounds. (Grade 4-5)

2.1 Which of the following properties is **not** typical for an ionic compound?
Tick **one** box.

☐ high melting points   ☐ high boiling points

☐ conduct electricity in the liquid state   ☑ conduct electricity in the solid state

[1]

2.2 Name the type of structure that ionic compounds have.

..........stable,..regular..............giant.......ionic......lattice..

[1]

[Total 2 marks]

            Topic C2 — Bonding, Structure and Properties of Matter

Covalent Bonding

1 This question is about covalent bonding.

Complete the sentences. Use words from the box.

metal	share	non-metal	covalent	electrons	swap

Covalent bonds form between two ....non-metal............ atoms. These bonds form

because the atoms ....share............... a pair of ....electrons.............. .

[Total 3 marks]

2 The diagrams below show dot and cross diagrams of some covalent molecules.

2.1 Draw out the displayed formulas of these molecules using straight lines to represent covalent bonds. The displayed formula of molecule **A** has been done as an example.

Dot and cross diagram   **Displayed formula**

A   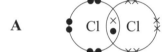   Cl — Cl

B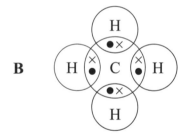

C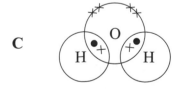

[2]

2.2 Write out the molecular formula for molecules **A**, **B** and **C**.

Molecule **A** ....Cl_2..

Molecule **B** ....CH_4..

Molecule **C** ....H_2O..

[3]

[Total 5 marks]

Topic C2 — Bonding, Structure and Properties of Matter

Simple Molecular Substances

1 **Figure 1** shows dot and cross diagrams of hydrogen and oxygen atoms. Grade 1-3

Figure 1

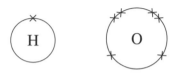

1.1 Complete the diagram below to show the shared electrons in a molecule of hydrogen (H_2).

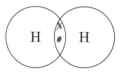

[1]

1.2 Complete the diagram below to show the shared electrons in a molecule of oxygen (O_2).

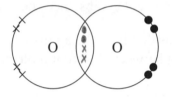

[1]

[Total 2 marks]

2 This question is about simple molecular substances. Grade 3-4

2.1 Which of the molecules in **Table 1** is a simple molecular substance?

Table 1

Molecule	Molecular formula	Type of bonding
A	HCl	covalent
B	NaCl	ionic

Write your answer in the box. A

[1]

2.2 Explain your answer to question 2.1.

It has covalent bonding and all simple molecular substances contain covalent bonds.

[1]

[Total 2 marks]

3   Methane (CH₄) is a simple molecular compound.

3.1   Draw a dot and cross diagram to show a molecule of methane.
You should only show the outer shells of electrons.

[2]

3.2   Give **one** disadvantage of this type of diagram.

.....don't.......show.......how........atoms.........are.........arranged..

[1]

[Total 3 marks]

4   The bonds and forces in simple molecular substances have different strengths. (Grade 4-5)

4.1   Compare the strength of the bonds that hold the atoms in a molecule
together with the forces that exist between different molecules.

....

....

[2]

4.2   When a simple molecular substance melts, is it the bonds between atoms
or the forces between molecules that are broken?

....

[1]

4.3   **Figure 2** shows two different simple molecular substances.

Figure 2

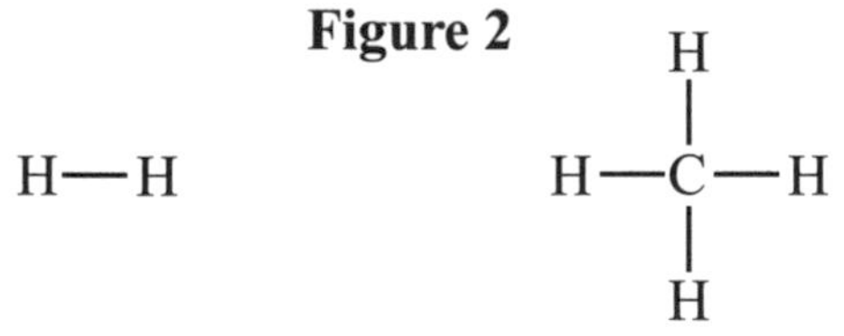

H—H

$$H—\overset{\displaystyle H}{\underset{\displaystyle H}{\overset{|}{\underset{|}{C}}}}—H$$

hydrogen   methane

Methane has a higher boiling point than hydrogen. Explain why.

....

....

....

[3]

[Total 6 marks]

Exam Tip

> It's a good idea to learn some examples of simple molecular substances — it'll help you remember what they are.
> Keep in mind that they're small and have covalent bonds between atoms. Don't forget to learn their properties too.

Topic C2 — Bonding, Structure and Properties of Matter

Polymers and Giant Covalent Structures

Complete the sentence below using words from the box.

long	small	heavy	dense

In a polymer lots of .... units are joined together

to form a ....*long*................ molecule.

---

1 Substances that contain covalent bonds can have very different structures. (Grade 1-3)

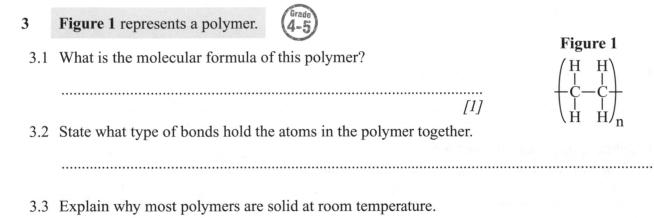

A   **B**   **C**   **D**

Which diagram, **A**, **B**, **C** or **D**, represents a giant covalent structure? ......*C*............................

[Total 1 mark]

---

2 This question is about giant covalent structures. (Grade 3-4)

2.1 Which of the following compounds is **not** an example of a giant covalent structure?
Tick **one** box.

✓ Ammonia   ☐ Diamond   ☐ Graphite   ☐ Silicon dioxide

[1]

2.2 Explain why most giant covalent compounds do not conduct electricity.

.....*Because*.............*there's*.........*a*.........*strong*.........*Covalent*.........*bonds*...........................

[1]

[Total 2 marks]

---

3 **Figure 1** represents a polymer. (Grade 4-5)

3.1 What is the molecular formula of this polymer?

....

[1]

Figure 1

$$\left(\begin{array}{cc} H & H \\ | & | \\ -C-C- \\ | & | \\ H & H \end{array} \right)_n$$

3.2 State what type of bonds hold the atoms in the polymer together.

....

[1]

3.3 Explain why most polymers are solid at room temperature.

....

[1]

[Total 3 marks]

Structures of Carbon

1 Several different carbon structures are shown in **Figure 1**. (Grade 3-4)

Look at the structures labelled **A**, **B**, **C**.

Figure 1

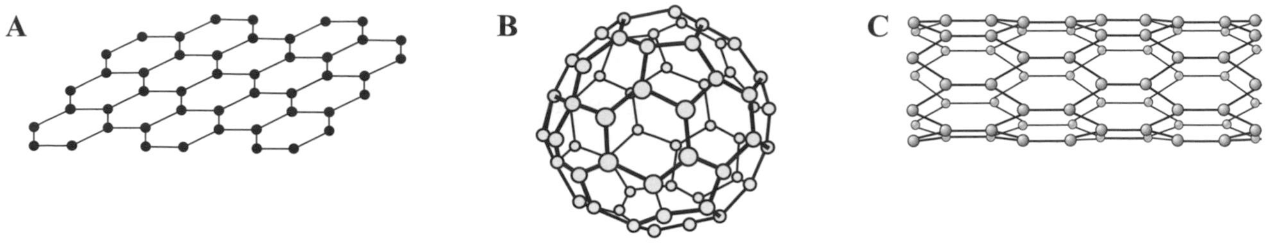

A   B   C

Which diagram above represents each of the following carbon structures?
Write a letter in each box.

Buckminsterfullerene [ ]   Nanotube [ ]   Graphene [ ]

[Total 3 marks]

2 Carbon can form different structures. These include diamond and graphite. (Grade 4-5)

2.1 In diamond, how many bonds does each carbon atom form?

    4 bonds

[1]

2.2 Draw **one** line between each of the properties of diamond and its explanation.

Property

Does not conduct electricity

High melting point

Hard (doesn't scratch easily)

Explanation

Electrons in covalent bonds cannot move.

Each carbon atom makes multiple strong covalent bonds.

[2]

2.3 Describe how carbon atoms are arranged in graphite.

    in hexagons layers.

[1]

2.4 Graphite is often used in electronics.
Explain why the structure of graphite makes it suitable for use in electronics.

    carbon has 3 bonds, one delocalized electron flows in the
    gap and moves around.

[2]

[Total 6 marks]

Topic C2 — Bonding, Structure and Properties of Matter

Metallic Bonding

Warm-Up

Circle the elements shown below that are metals.

Copper   Nitrogen   Chlorine   Tin   Oxygen   Magnesium   Aluminium

1 **Figure 1** shows two different metals. *(Grade 1-3)*

Which metal shown in **Figure 1** is an alloy?
Give a reason for your answer.

Metal ......𝑌..

Reason ....

....

[Total 2 marks]

Figure 1

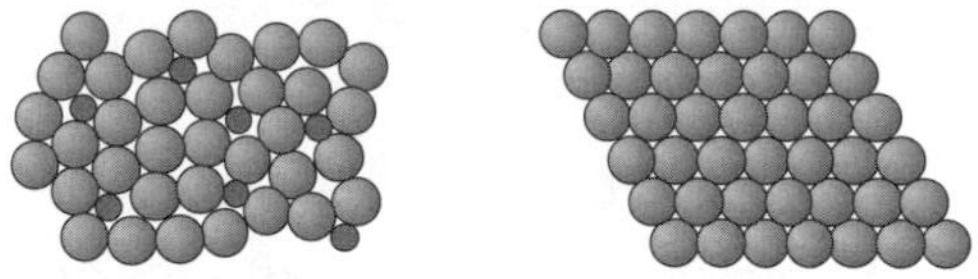

Metal X   Metal Y

2 **Figure 2** shows the structure of a pure metal. *(Grade 4-5)*

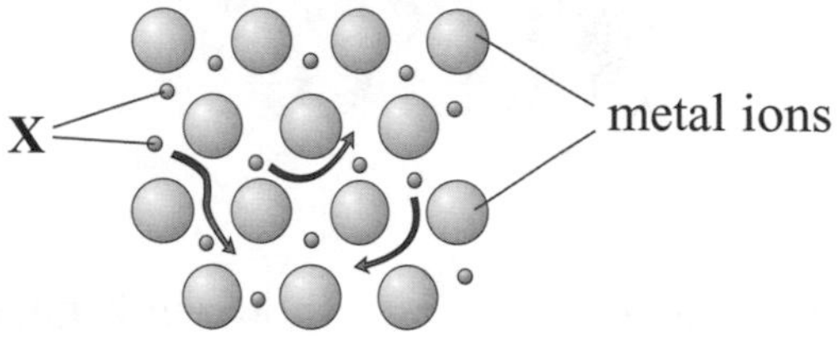

2.1 In **Figure 2** some particles are labelled with an **X**.
Name these particles.

....

[1]

Figure 2

X ←   → metal ions

2.2 Metal atoms form ions that are positively charged.
Explain how they are held together in the structure seen in **Figure 2**.

....

....

[2]

2.3 Metals have high melting and boiling points. Explain why.

......strong......electrostatic......force.,.....strong......bonds..............

....

[2]

2.4 A scientist has samples of two different metals, **A** and **B**.
Metal A is pure iron. Metal B contains iron and other elements.
Which metal would you expect to be **easier** to bend? Explain your answer.

....

....

....

[3]

[Total 8 marks]

Exam Tip

The unique properties of metals are quite different to those of other materials. If you're asked to explain a specific property (I'm looking at you, Q2.3), have a think about the metal structure — that should set you on the right path.

Topic C2 — Bonding, Structure and Properties of Matter

States of Matter

1 Look at the substances **A**, **B** and **C**, below. (Grade 1-3)

A: $NaCl_{(s)}$ **B**: $O_{2(g)}$ **C**: $Hg_{(l)}$

1.1 Which substance is a solid? ☐

1.2 Which substance is a liquid? ☐

1.3 Which substance is a gas? ☐

[Total 3 marks]

2 Substances exist in one of the three states of matter. These are solids, liquids and gases. **Figure 1** shows how particles are arranged in each of the three states. (Grade 1-3)

Figure 1

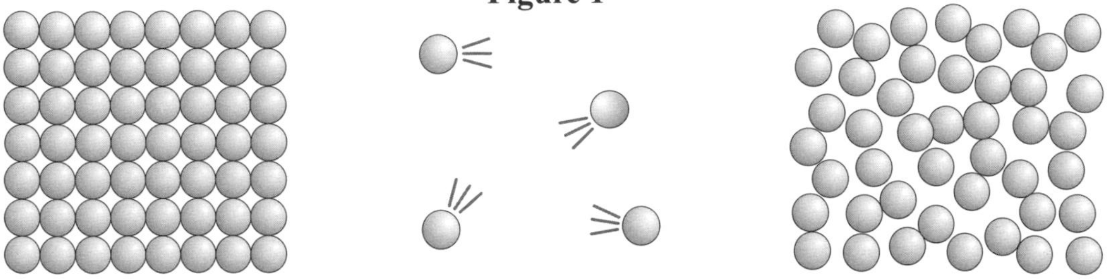

    A   **B**   **C**

2.1 Which of the states shown in **Figure 1** represents a liquid? Give your answer as A, B or C.

....
[1]

2.2 In **Figure 1**, what does each ball represent?

....
[1]

[Total 2 marks]

3 The strength of attraction between particles in each state of matter is different. (Grade 3-4)

3.1 Place solids, liquids and gases in order of the strength of attraction between their particles.

Strongest attraction   ....Solid..............

↕   ....liquid..............

Weakest attraction   ....caas..............

[1]

3.2 When gases and liquids are placed inside a container they change shape. Why does this **not** happen when a solid is put inside a container?

....
[1]

[Total 2 marks]

Changing State

1 This question is about changing state. (Grade 1-3)

In **Figure 1** the arrows represent processes that cause a change in state to happen.

Figure 1

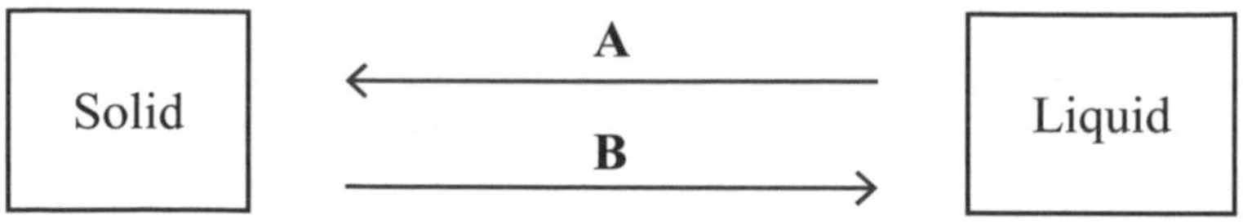

Solid ←——— A ——— Liquid
——— B ———→

1.1 Process **A** causes a liquid to turn into a solid. Name this process.

.............Freezing..

[1]

1.2 Process **B** causes a solid to turn into a liquid. Name this process.

.............Melting..

[1]

[Total 2 marks]

2 This question is about the processes by which a material changes state. (Grade 4-5)

2.1 What is the name of the process when a liquid turns into a gas?

.............Evapporation..

[1]

2.2 Liquid X turns into a gas at a very high temperature.
What does this suggest about the strength of the bonds between the particles in liquid X?

.............weaker..

[1]

[Total 2 marks]

3 Use the data in **Table 1** to help you answer the questions that follow: (Grade 4-5)

Table 1

Substance	Sodium Chloride	Water	Copper
Melting Point (°C)	801	0	1083
Boiling Point (°C)	1413	100	2567

3.1 Which substance in **Table 1** would be a liquid at 900 °C?

....

[1]

3.2 Which two substances in **Table 1** would be gases at 1500 °C?

....

[2]

[Total 3 marks]

Exam Tip

Q3 is a good example of an exam question where you're given melting and boiling points for compounds and asked to interpret the data. Just remember — solid below the melting point, gas above the boiling point, and liquid in between.

Topic C2 — Bonding, Structure and Properties of Matter

Relative Formula Mass

1 The relative atomic mass of chlorine is 35.5. The relative atomic mass of hydrogen is 1. *(Grade 3-4)*

1.1 Calculate the relative formula mass of hydrochloric acid (HCl).

Relative formula mass = ...
[1]

1.2 Calculate the relative formula mass of chlorine gas (Cl_2).

Relative formula mass = ...
[1]

[Total 2 marks]

2 Match up the following formulas with the correct relative formula mass of the substance. *(Grade 4-5)*

F_2		38
C_2H_6		40
CaO		30
NaOH		56

[Total 2 marks]

3 Magnesium oxide is a salt with the molecular formula MgO. Relative atomic masses (A_r): O = 16, Mg = 24 *(Grade 4-5)*

3.1 Calculate the relative formula mass (M_r) of magnesium oxide.

Relative formula mass = ...
[1]

3.2 Calculate the percentage mass of magnesium in magnesium oxide. Use the equation:

$$\text{Percentage mass of element in a compound} = \frac{A_r \text{ of element} \times \text{number of atoms of element}}{M_r \text{ of compound}} \times 100$$

Percentage mass of magnesium = ... %
[2]

[Total 3 marks]

Conservation of Mass

The word equation for a reaction is shown below.

magnesium $_{(s)}$ + hydrochloric acid $_{(aq)}$ → magnesium chloride $_{(aq)}$ + hydrogen $_{(g)}$

1) Draw circles around the reactants in the equation above.

2) Draw boxes around the products in the equation above.

3) Which of the substances in the reaction is a gas? ....

4) Which of the substances is most likely to escape from the reaction container? ....

---

1 Iron and sulfur react together to produce iron sulfide. *(Grade 1-3)*

1.1 Which statement is correct? Tick **one** box.

Some mass will be lost in the reaction. ☐

The mass of the substances will increase during the reaction. ☑

The mass of the reactants will be the same as the mass of the products. ☐

[1]

1.2 28 g of iron reacts with 16 g of sulfur.
How much iron sulfide is made? Tick **one** box.

28 g of iron sulfide. ☐   16 g of iron sulfide. ☐   44 g of iron sulfide. ☑ *[1]*

[Total 2 marks]

---

2 Sodium hydroxide reacts with hydrochloric acid to produce sodium chloride and water. *(Grade 3-4)*
The equation is: sodium hydroxide + hydrochloric acid → sodium chloride + water

2.1 In an experiment, 80.0 g of sodium hydroxide reacted with 73.0 g of hydrochloric acid.
36.0 g of water was produced. Calculate the mass of sodium chloride produced.

Mass = ... g
[1]

2.2 The experiment was repeated using 109.5 g of hydrochloric acid. 175.5 g of sodium chloride and 54.0 g of water were produced. Calculate the mass of sodium hydroxide that reacted.

Mass = ... g
[1]
[Total 2 marks]

120

3 A student burned 12 g of magnesium in oxygen to produce magnesium oxide. (Grade 4-5)

3.1 Which of the following is the correctly balanced equation for the reaction between magnesium and oxygen? Tick **one** box.

$Mg + O \rightarrow MgO$ ☐ $2Mg + O_2 \rightarrow 2MgO$ ☐

$Mg + O_2 \rightarrow 2MgO$ ☐ $Mg + O_2 \rightarrow MgO$ ☐

[1]

3.2 The student measured the mass of magnesium oxide produced. The mass was 20 g. Calculate the mass of oxygen that reacted with the magnesium.

Mass of oxygen = ... g

[1]

[Total 2 marks]

4 A student heated some sodium carbonate powder, as shown in **Figure 1**. When heated, sodium carbonate breaks down to produce sodium oxide and carbon dioxide. (Grade 4-5)

The student measured the mass of the reaction container at the start and at the end of the reaction. The measurements the student took are shown in **Figure 2**.

Figure 1

Figure 2

mass at the start of the reaction   25.4

mass at the end of the reaction   23.2

4.1 Calculate the change in mass of the reaction container during the reaction.

Change in mass = ... g

[1]

4.2 The student thinks that the measurements must be wrong, because no mass is lost or gained in a chemical reaction. Is the student correct? Explain your answer.

....

....

....

....

....

[4]

[Total 5 marks]

Topic C3 — Quantitative Chemistry

Target AO3

5 Two students carried out experiments to measure the change in mass when a compound, X, is heated. **Table 1** and **Table 2** show the results of each student's experiment.

Table 1

Repeat	Initial mass (g)	Final mass (g)	Decrease in mass (g)
1	4.00	2.62	1.38
2	4.00	2.58	1.42
3	4.00	2.69	1.31
4	4.00	2.95	1.05
		Mean:	1.37
		Uncertainty:	± 0.055

Table 2

Repeat	Initial mass (g)	Final mass (g)	Decrease in mass (g)
1	7.50	4.81	2.69
2	7.50	4.76	2.74
3	7.50	4.75	2.75
4	7.50	4.84	2.66
		Mean:	2.71
		Uncertainty:	± 0.045

5.1 The first student did not include one of her results when she calculated the mean decrease in mass in her experiment. Which repeat contained the anomalous result?

....

[1]

5.2 Which student's data is more precise? Explain your answer.

....

....

[2]

5.3 Calculate the percentage uncertainty in the mean decrease in mass for each set of results.
Percentage uncertainty = (uncertainty ÷ mean) × 100

Percentage uncertainty of the mean for Table 1 = ± .... %

Percentage uncertainty of the mean for Table 2 = ± .... %

[2]

5.4 Suggest how the students should change the initial mass of Compound X in their experiments to reduce the percentage uncertainty in their data.

....

[1]

[Total 6 marks]

Exam Tip

Somewhere in your exam, you might well get a question on an experiment — either one you know, or one that you haven't seen before — where you have to think about things like uncertainty, precision and accuracy. You don't just need to know what these words mean, but also how making tweaks to the design of the experiment can change these factors.

Topic C3 — Quantitative Chemistry

Concentrations of Solutions

Some units are listed in the table on the right.

Put a tick in the correct column to show whether each unit is a unit of mass or a unit of volume.

Unit	Mass	Volume
g		
cm^3		
dm^3		
kg		

1 This question is about solutions. Grade 1-3

Complete the sentences. Use words from the box.

more	dissolved	less	crystallised	filtered

When a solid is ....dissolved.......... in a liquid, a solution is formed.

The greater the mass of the solid, the ....more............... concentrated the solution.

The larger the volume of liquid, the ....less.............. concentrated the solution.

[Total 3 marks]

2 28 g of calcium chloride was dissolved in 0.4 dm^3 of water. Grade 4-5

2.1 Calculate the concentration of the solution and give the units.

Concentration = ...70......... Units = ...g/dm^3.......
[2]

2.2 Explain the term 'concentration of a solution'.

....

....
[1]

2.3 A student needs another solution of calcium chloride, this time with a concentration of 50 g/dm^3. What mass of calcium chloride do they need to add to 0.2 dm^3 of water to make this solution?

Mass = ... g
[2]

[Total 5 marks]

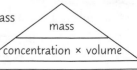

Topic C3 — Quantitative Chemistry

Acids and Bases

Warm-Up

Fill in the gaps in the following statements.

acids

bases

neutral

Substances with a pH of less than 7 are ....*acids*....... .
Substances with a pH of more than 7 are .....*Bases*....... .
Substances with a pH of 7 are .....*Neutral*..... .

1 This question is about acids and bases. **Table 1** shows some everyday substances. *Grade 3-4*

Table 1

Substance	Beer	Bicarbonate of Soda	Milk
pH	4	9	7

1.1 Write the name of the substance in **Table 1** that is an acid.

..........*beer*..

[1]

1.2 What colour would you expect universal indicator to turn in bicarbonate of soda solution?

...........*dark blue*..

[1]

[Total 2 marks]

2 The pH of a solution tells you how acidic or alkaline it is. *Grade 4-5*

2.1 Which ion is produced by an acid in aqueous solution? Tick **one** box.

Cl^- ☐ H^+ ☐ OH^- ☐ OH^+ ☑

[1]

2.2 State the range of the pH scale.

....

[2]

[Total 3 marks]

3 Acids and alkalis react together in neutralisation reactions. *Grade 4-5*

3.1 Write the word equation for a neutralisation reaction between an acid and an alkali.

.... + ... → .... + ...

[1]

3.2 Write an equation that shows how hydrogen (H^+) and hydroxide (OH^-) ions react together in a neutralisation reaction.

.... + ... → ....

[1]

3.3 State the pH of the products that form when an acid reacts with an alkali.

....

[1]

[Total 3 marks]

124

Reactions of Acids

1   Draw **one** line from each acid to the type of salt it forms when it reacts with a base. (Grade 1-3)

Acid

Hydrochloric acid

Nitric acid

Sulfuric acid

Salt

Nitrate

Sulfate

Chloride

[Total 2 marks]

2   Acids react with metal carbonates. (Grade 3-4)

2.1   Which of the following substances is **not** produced when a metal carbonate reacts with an acid?
Tick **one** box.

Salt ☐   Carbon dioxide ☐   Hydrogen ☐   Water ☐

[1]

2.2   A student adds 2 spatulas of zinc carbonate into a beaker of dilute hydrochloric acid.
The student sees that the reaction fizzes. What product causes the reaction to fizz?

....

[1]

[Total 2 marks]

3   Sulfuric acid reacts with lithium hydroxide to produce lithium sulfate and one other product. (Grade 4-5)

3.1   Name the product, other than lithium sulfate, that is produced in this reaction.

....

[1]

3.2   Which of the equations below is the balanced symbol equation for the reaction between lithium hydroxide and sulfuric acid?
Tick **one** box.

$2LiOH + H_2SO_4 \rightarrow Li_2SO_4 + 2H_2O$ ☐

$Li_2O + H_2SO_4 \rightarrow Li_2SO_4 + H_2O$ ☐

$Li_2O + H_2SO_4 \rightarrow Li_2SO_4 + H_2$ ☐

$2LiOH + H_2SO_4 \rightarrow Li_2SO_4 + H_2$ ☐

[1]

[Total 2 marks]

Exam Tip

There will almost certainly be an exam question about acid reactions. Luckily for you, they're really easy to memorise, as they always produce the same products. Learn how an acid reacts with each type of base and you'll be ready to go.

Topic C4 — Chemical Changes

4 The salt produced when an acid reacts with a metal hydroxide depends on the reactants. **Grade 4-5**

4.1 Complete **Table 1** to show the salts that are formed when the acids and hydroxides react together.

Table 1

		Acid	
		Hydrochloric acid	Sulfuric acid
Metal hydroxide	Calcium hydroxide	Calcium chloride	....
	Copper hydroxide	....	....
	Magnesium hydroxide	....	....

[2]

4.2 Write a word equation for the reaction between hydrochloric acid and calcium hydroxide.

.... + ... → .... + ...

[1]

4.3 Complete and balance the symbol equation for the reaction
between hydrochloric acid and calcium hydroxide.

$Ca(OH)_2$ + ... HCl → .... + 2 ....

[2]

[Total 5 marks]

5 Soluble metal salts can be made from the reactions of acids and metal oxides. **Grade 4-5** **PRACTICAL**

5.1 A student makes a soluble salt by reacting zinc oxide with hydrochloric acid.
Name the salt that is produced.

....

[1]

5.2 Write a method that could be used to produce pure crystals of the salt using this reaction.

• Describe how you would make the salt from the reactants.
• Describe how you would purify the salt from the reaction mixture.

....

....

....

....

....

....

....

....

[4]

[Total 5 marks]

Topic C4 — Chemical Changes

The Reactivity Series and Extracting Metals

1   **Figure 1** shows part of the reactivity series of metals. Carbon has also been included in this reactivity series.

Figure 1

Potassium	K
Magnesium	Mg
Carbon	C
Copper	Cu

1.1   Name **one** metal from **Figure 1** that is more reactive than magnesium.

......Potassium..

[1]

1.2   Name **one** metal from **Figure 1** which could be extracted from its ore by reduction with carbon.

....

[1]

1.3   Which metal in **Figure 1** forms positive ions most easily?

.........Group...1......Hydrogen..

[1]

[Total 3 marks]

2   Iron can be extracted from its ore by reduction with carbon. The equation for this reaction is shown below.

$$2Fe_2O_3 + 3C \rightarrow 4Fe + 3CO_2$$

2.1   What is reduction?

.........oxygen.........is.....reduced...

[1]

2.2   Which element is oxidised in this reaction? Give a reason for your answer.

Element: ....

Reason: ....

[2]

2.3   Explain why magnesium **cannot** be extracted from its ore by reduction with carbon.

....

....

[1]

[Total 4 marks]

Exam Tip

Learning the order of the reactivity series could be really useful when it comes to answering questions in the exams. Try learning this mnemonic to help you remember... <u>P</u>apa <u>S</u>murf <u>L</u>ikes <u>C</u>alling <u>M</u>y <u>C</u>larinet <u>Z</u>any — <u>I</u>sn't <u>H</u>e <u>C</u>ute. (You don't have to use my Booker prize winning version, though. You could also make up your own.)

Topic C4 — Chemical Changes

Reactions of Metals

1   What is the word equation for the reaction of a metal and an acid?   **Grade 1-3**
 Tick **one** box.

metal + acid → salt + water   ☐

metal + acid → salt + hydrogen   ☐

metal + acid → metal hydroxide + hydrogen   ☐

metal + acid → salt + water + hydrogen   ☐

[Total 1 mark]

2   A student reacts different metals with water.   **Grade 4-5**
 The results of this experiment are shown in **Table 1**.

Table 1

Reaction	Observation
Copper + water	No reaction
Calcium + water	Fizzing, calcium disappears
Lithium + water	Very vigorous reaction with fizzing, lithium disappears
Magnesium + water	No fizzing, a few bubbles on the magnesium

2.1   Write the word equation for the reaction of calcium and water.

.... + ... → .... + ...

[1]

2.2   Use **Table 1** to put the metals copper, calcium, lithium and magnesium in order of reactivity.

Most reactive ....Lithium - ....Calcium ..- ....Magnesium - ......Copper.............................. Least reactive

[2]

2.3   State one thing the student should do to make sure the experiment is fair.

....

[1]

2.4   The student then adds a piece of magnesium to a solution of copper chloride.
 A displacement reaction takes place. Predict the products of this reaction.

....

[2]

2.5   State how you can predict whether a displacement reaction will take place between a metal and a metal compound.

....

[1]

[Total 7 marks]

Topic C4 — Chemical Changes

Electrolysis

Warm-Up

Place the labels on the correct label lines to identify the parts of an electrochemical cell.

Electrode   Electrolyte

D.C. power supply

1   Electrochemical cells contain electrodes in an electrolyte. The electrolyte can be a liquid or a solution.   *Grade 3-4*

1.1   Why does the electrolyte need to be a liquid or a solution? Tick **one** box.

So the ions can move to the electrodes   ☐

So the electrons can be conducted through the substance   ☐

So the electrodes don't corrode   ☐

So there is enough heat for the reaction to occur   ☐

[1]

1.2   Complete the passage below about electrodes. Use the words in the box.
You can use words more than once.

| positive | anode | cathode | gain | negative | lose | neutral |

In electrolysis, the anode is the .... electrode.

.... ions move towards the anode and .... electrons.

The cathode is the .... electrode .

.... ions move towards the cathode and .... electrons.

[6]

[Total 7 marks]

2   Lead bromide can be electrolysed. The electrolyte is molten lead bromide.   *Grade 4-5*

2.1   What is an electrolyte?

....

[1]

2.2   Write the word equation for the electrolysis of lead bromide.

.... $\rightarrow$ .... + ...

[1]

[Total 2 marks]

Topic C4 — Chemical Changes

3   **Figure 1** shows the extraction of aluminium. Aluminium oxide is mixed with cryolite.
This mixture is then melted and electrolysed. Metallic aluminium is made at the cathode.

Figure 1

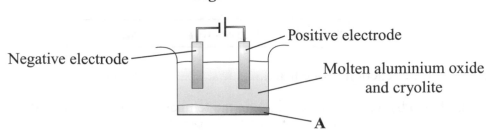

3.1   What is the liquid labelled **A**?

....

[1]

3.2   What is the purpose of mixing the aluminium oxide with cryolite?

....

[1]

3.3   The positive electrode is made of graphite. Why does it need to be replaced regularly?

....

....

[2]

[Total 4 marks]

4   Aqueous iron chloride solution can be electrolysed using inert electrodes.   Grade 4-5

4.1   Which of the following ions are **not** present in iron chloride solution? Tick **one** box.

☐ Cl^- ☐ Fe^{2+} ☐ OH^- ☐ O^{2-}

[1]

4.2   Explain why hydrogen, not iron, is formed at the cathode.

....

[1]

4.3   State what element is formed at the anode.

....

[1]

[Total 3 marks]

Exam Tip
Remember, when you electrolyse a salt solution, different substances form at the electrodes depending on how reactive
they are. If the metal's more reactive than hydrogen, hydrogen will form. If the metal's less reactive than hydrogen,
the metal will form. At the anode, water and oxygen form unless there are halide ions (e.g. Cl^-, Br^-) in the solution.

Topic C4 — Chemical Changes

Exothermic and Endothermic Reactions

1 Complete the following definition of an exothermic reaction. Use the words in the box. (Grade 1-3)

takes in	gives out	rise	fall

An exothermic reaction is one that .... *gives out* .... energy.

This is shown by a .... *fall* .... in the temperature of the surroundings.

[Total 2 marks]

2 Chemical reactions result in a transfer of energy. (Grade 3-4)

2.1 Compare the amount of energy stored in the products and reactants in an exothermic reaction.

....

[1]

2.2 Which of the following types of reaction is an example of an endothermic reaction?
Tick **one** box.

Combustion ☐   Oxidation ☐   Neutralisation ☐   Thermal decomposition ☑

[1]

[Total 2 marks]

3 During a reaction between solutions of citric acid and sodium hydrogencarbonate, the temperature of the surroundings went down. (Grade 3-4)

3.1 How can you tell the reaction is endothermic?

.... *Increase in temperature* ....

[1]

3.2 Where is energy transferred from in an endothermic reaction?

.... *gets absorbed* ....

[1]

3.3 What happens to the amount of energy in the universe after the reaction?

....

[1]

3.4 Give a practical use of this reaction.

....

[1]

[Total 4 marks]

Exam Tip

The 'en' in 'endothermic' sounds like 'in', and the 'do' is the start of 'down'. So endothermic reactions take energy in from the surroundings, and make the temperature of the surroundings go down. Exothermic reactions do the opposite.

Target AO3

4   **Figure 1** shows the temperature change of an endothermic reaction over time.

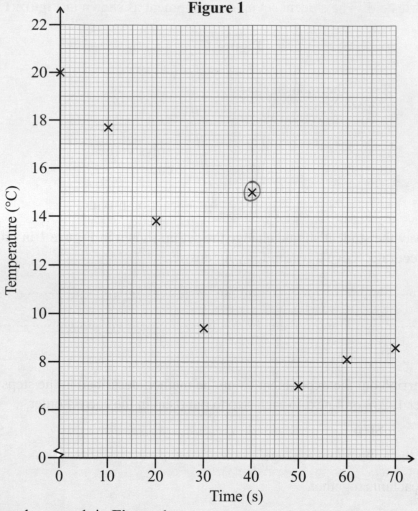

Figure 1

4.1 Circle the anomalous result in **Figure 1**.

[1]

4.2 Draw **two** straight lines of best fit on the graph in **Figure 1**.

[2]

4.3 Use the intersection of your lines to estimate the minimum temperature reached by the reaction.

minimum temperature = ... °C

[1]

4.4 Use your answer to part 4.3 and the starting temperature to estimate
the maximum temperature change.

maximum temperature change = ... °C

[1]

[Total 5 marks]

Exam Tip

If you're asked to draw a straight line of best fit, make sure you use a sharp pencil and a ruler so it's clear, crisp and perfectly straight. You should also make sure that you ignore any anomalies when you're drawing lines of best fit.

Topic C5 — Energy Changes

Measuring Energy Changes

1 A student investigated the temperature change of the reaction between sodium hydroxide and hydrochloric acid. The student set up the equipment as shown in **Figure 1**.

Figure 1

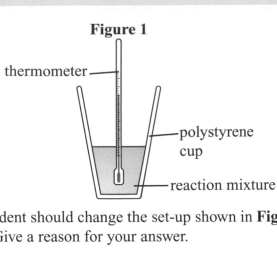

thermometer

polystyrene cup

reaction mixture

1.1 Suggest **one** way the student should change the set-up shown in **Figure 1** in order to make the results more accurate. Give a reason for your answer.

Change: ....

Reason: ....

[2]

1.2 The student carried out the experiment using the method described in the steps below. Write a number 1, 2, 3 or 4 next to each step to put them in the correct order.

Step	**Step number**
Calculate the temperature change.	....
Mix the reactants together.	....
Measure the temperature of the reactants.	....
Measure the maximum temperature reached by the reaction mixture.	....

[2]

1.3 The results of the experiment are shown in **Table 1**.

Table 1

Initial Temperature (°C)	Final Temperature (°C)
18	31

Calculate the temperature change of the reaction.

Temperature change = ... °C

[1]

1.4 The student repeated the experiment a number of times using a different concentration of acid each time. State the independent and dependent variables in this experiment.

Independent: ....

Dependent: ....

[2]

[Total 7 marks]

Reaction Profiles

1   For a reaction to happen, particles need to collide with enough energy.   (Grade 3-4)

1.1   What is the name given to the minimum amount of energy needed for a reaction to take place?

...........Activation......energy...

[1]

1.2   **Figure 1** shows the reaction profile of a reaction.

Figure 1

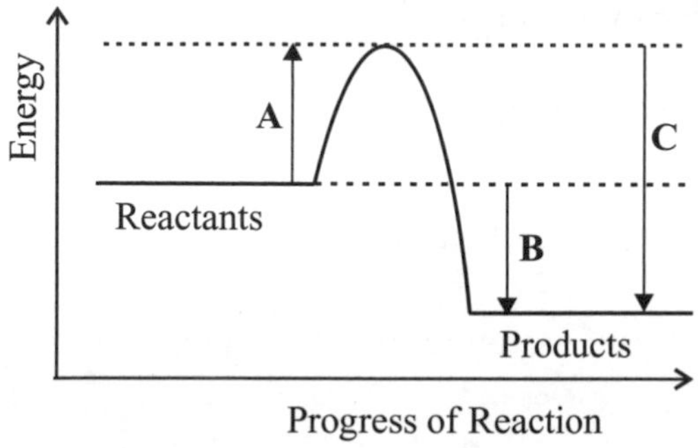

Which letter, **A**, **B**, or **C** shows the amount of energy needed for the reaction to take place?

...............A...

[1]

[Total 2 marks]

2   A reaction profile shows the overall energy change of a reaction.   (Grade 4-5)

2.1   **Figure 2** shows the reaction profile for a reaction. Mark the overall energy change on **Figure 2**.

Figure 2

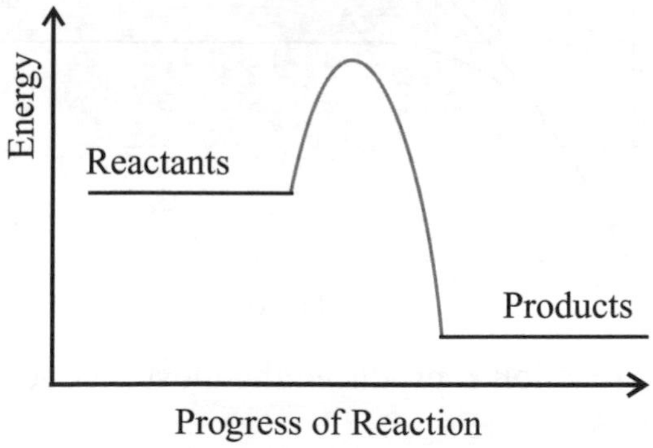

[1]

2.2   What type of reaction is represented by **Figure 2**? Give a reason for your answer.

Type of reaction: ......Exothermic...

Reason: ....Products.......level.......decreased...

[2]

[Total 3 marks]

Exam Tip

If you're struggling to memorise the key features of a reaction profile, try sketching and labelling a few for yourself and then checking if you got them right. Remember to practise drawing both exothermic and endothermic examples.

 ☐   ☐   ☐   **Topic C5 — Energy Changes**

Rates of Reaction

1   Collision theory can be used to explain the rate of a reaction.

1.1   According to collision theory, what **two** things will cause the rate of a reaction to increase?
Tick **two** boxes.

The particles colliding more often.   ☐

The particles colliding less often.   ☐

The particles colliding with more energy.   ☐

The particles colliding with less energy.   ☐

[2]

1.2   At what point in a reaction is the rate fastest?

....

[1]

[Total 3 marks]

2   **Figure 1** shows how the volume of gas produced in a reaction changes
over time, for the same reaction under different conditions, **A** and **B**.

Figure 1

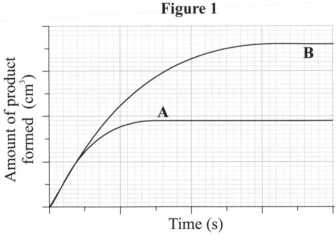

2.1   State whether reaction **A** or reaction **B** produced the most product.

....

[1]

2.2   What does it mean when the graph goes flat?

....

[1]

[Total 2 marks]

Exam Tip

Graph questions are notoriously tricky. The key thing to remember is not to rush straight into answering the question.
Take some time to look at the graph and make sure that you fully understand what is shown by the axes and the curves.

Topic C6 — The Rate and Extent of Chemical Change

Factors Affecting Rates of Reaction

Warm-Up

A student reacts nitric acid with three different forms of calcium carbonate. All other variables are kept the same. Circle the condition that will result in the slowest rate of reaction.

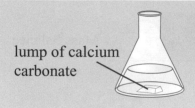

lump of calcium carbonate   calcium carbonate chips   powdered calcium carbonate

1   A scientist carries out a reaction between two gases. Grade 3-4

The scientist repeats the experiment but decreases the pressure. All other reaction conditions are kept the same. Complete the paragraph by filling in the gaps. Use the words in the box below.

decrease	more	increase	larger	less	smaller

Decreasing the pressure of the reaction will cause the rate of reaction to ....

This is because the same number of particles are in a .... space, so they will

collide .... frequently.

[Total 3 marks]

2   This question is about the rate of a chemical reaction between two reactants, one of which is in solution, and one of which is a solid. Grade 4-5

2.1   Which of the following changes would **not** cause the rate of the chemical reaction to increase? Tick **one** box.

Increasing the concentration of the solution. ☐

Heating the reaction mixture to a higher temperature. ☐

Using a larger volume of the solution, but keeping the concentration the same. ☐

Grinding the solid reactant so that it forms a fine powder. ☐

[1]

2.2   A catalyst is added to the reaction mixture and all other conditions are kept the same. The reaction rate increases. Explain why.

....

....
[1]

[Total 2 marks]

       Topic C6 — The Rate and Extent of Chemical Change

1   A certain reaction produces a gas product. Which **two** pieces of equipment below could be used to monitor the rate at which the gas is produced? Tick **two** boxes.

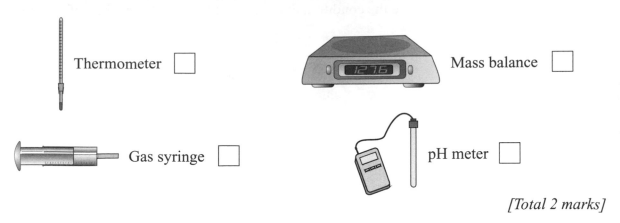

Thermometer ☐   Mass balance ☐

Gas syringe ☐   pH meter ☐

[Total 2 marks]

2   A student measures the volume of gas produced by the reaction between sulfuric acid and marble chips. He repeats the experiment with two different concentrations of acid, **A** and **B**. **Table 1** shows his results.

Table 1

		Time (s)					
		0	10	20	30	40	50
Volume of gas produced (cm³)	Concentration A	3	8	10	12	16	19
	Concentration B	9	19	25	29	32	35

2.1   State the concentration, **A** or **B**, which resulted in the fastest reaction. Give a reason for your answer.

Concentration: ....

Reason: ....

....

[2]

2.2   What are the dependent and independent variables in this experiment?

Dependent variable: ....

Independent variable: ....

[2]

2.3   Suggest **one** variable that would have to be controlled in this experiment to make it a fair test.

....

[1]

[Total 5 marks]

Exam Tip

As you can see from the questions, it's important to learn the different types of variable in an experiment and how changing them will affect the reaction. For example, a control variable is kept the same throughout to ensure a fair test.

More on Measuring Rates

PRACTICAL

1 A student carries out a reaction in a conical flask. She measures the time it takes for a black cross placed under the flask to disappear as a precipitate is formed. Under different conditions, the rate of the reaction changes.

Grade 3-4

Complete the sentences below. Use words from the box.

| more quickly | more slowly | in the same time |

If the rate is higher than the rate of the original reaction,

the cross will disappear ....

If the rate is lower than the rate of the original reaction,

the cross will disappear ....

[Total 2 marks]

2 A student investigates how the concentration of acid affects the rate of reaction between hydrochloric acid and sodium thiosulfate. The reaction forms a yellow precipitate. Her experimental set up is shown in **Figure 1**.

Grade 4-5

Figure 1

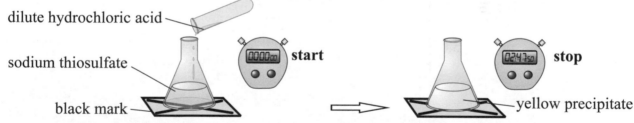

She uses five different acid concentrations and records how long it takes for the mark to disappear. All other variables are kept the same. Some of her results are shown in **Table 1**.

Table 1

Concentration of hydrochloric acid (g/dm³)	15	30	45	....	75
Time taken for mark to disappear (s)	....	187	....	174	168

2.1 Use the answers from the box below to complete **Table 1**.

| 90 | 181 | 165 | 60 | 194 |

[3]

2.2 Another student was observing these reactions but got different results to the first student. Suggest **one** reason why they may have different results.

....

[1]

[Total 4 marks]

Topic C6 — The Rate and Extent of Chemical Change

Graphs of Reaction Rate Experiments

1   The rate of a reaction was investigated by measuring the volume of gas produced at regular intervals. The results are shown in **Table 1**.

Table 1

Time (s)	0	50	100	150	200	250	300
Volume of gas (cm³)	0.0	9.5	14.5	16.0	16.5	16.5	16.5

1.1 Plot the data in **Table 1** on the axes below. Draw a curved line of best fit onto the graph.

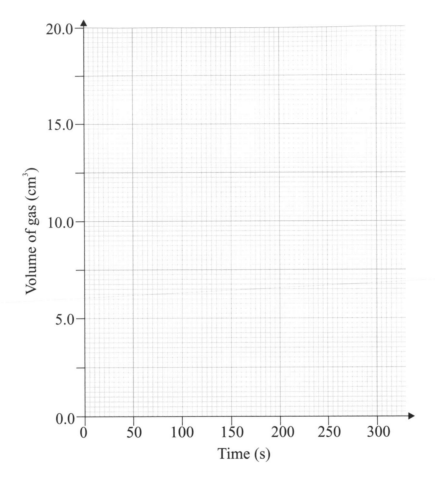

[3]

1.2 Draw tangents to the graph at 75 seconds and at 175 seconds.

[2]

1.3 Using the tangents drawn in part 1.2, state whether the reaction is fastest at 75 s or at 175 s. Give a reason for your answer.

Time: ....

Reason: ....

[2]

[Total 7 marks]

Topic C6 — The Rate and Extent of Chemical Change

Working Out Reaction Rates

1   In a reaction that lasted 125 seconds, 40 cm³ of gas was produced.   Grade 3-4

1.1   Calculate the mean rate of the reaction. Use the equation:

$$\text{mean rate of reaction} = \frac{\text{amount of product formed}}{\text{time}}$$

.... units

[2]

1.2   What will the units of the rate be? Tick **one** box.

s/cm³ ☐   cm³/s ☐   s³/cm ☐   cm/s³ ☐

[1]

[Total 3 marks]

2   **Figure 1** shows the volume of hydrogen gas produced during a reaction between magnesium and hydrochloric acid.   Grade 4-5

Figure 1

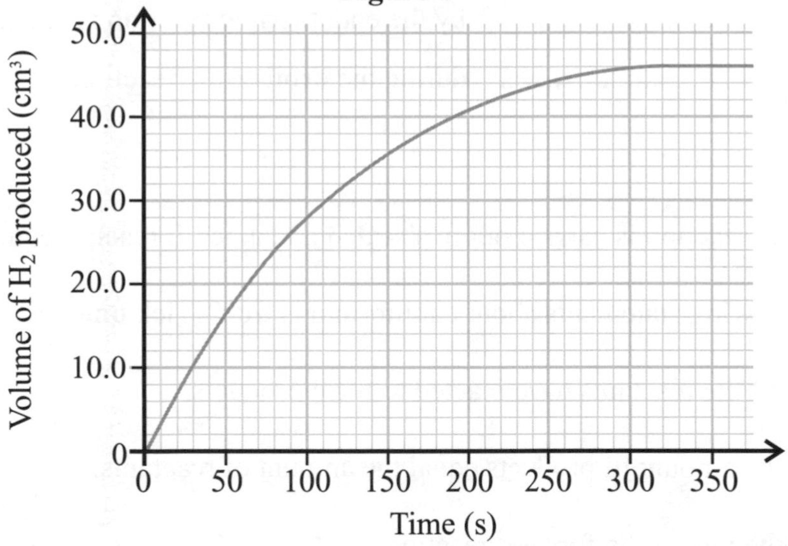

Volume of H₂ produced (cm³) vs Time (s)

2.1   Calculate the mean rate for the whole reaction. Give your answer to 3 significant figures.
Use **Figure 1** and the equation:

$$\text{mean rate of reaction} = \frac{\text{amount of product formed}}{\text{time}}$$

.... cm³/s

[2]

2.2   Calculate the mean rate of reaction between 100 seconds and 250 seconds.
Give your answer to 3 significant figures.

.... cm³/s

[4]

[Total 6 marks]

 ☐   ☐   ☐   **Topic C6 — The Rate and Extent of Chemical Change**

Reversible Reactions

1 Choose the symbol below that is used in a reaction equation to show that the reaction is reversible. Tick **one** box. `Grade 1-3`

⇌ ☐   ⇄ ☐   ⇔ ☐   ↔ ☐

[Total 1 mark]

2 The two sentences below describe a reversible reaction. The forward reaction is endothermic and the backward reaction is exothermic. Complete the two sentences. `Grade 3-4`

Use answers from the box.

taken in	products	given out	the same as	reactants	different to

1 When the reaction is heated, it moves in the forward direction

and the amount of .... increases.

2 The energy .... by the endothermic reaction is ....

the amount .... during the exothermic reaction.

[Total 4 marks]

3 When a reversible reaction is carried out in a sealed container, it reaches equilibrium. `Grade 4-5`

3.1 Which of the following statements about equilibrium is true? Tick **one** box.

At equilibrium, all the reactants have reacted to form products. ☐

At equilibrium, the amount of products equal the amount of reactants. ☐

At equilibrium, the rate of the forward reaction is equal to the rate of the backwards reaction. ☐

At equilibrium, both the forwards and the backwards reactions stop. ☐

[1]

3.2 The sealed container is an example of a 'closed system'. Explain what this term means.

....

....

[1]

[Total 2 marks]

Exam Tip

When a reaction's at equilibrium, if there are more products than reactants, the reaction is going in the forwards direction. If there are more reactants than products at equilibrium, it's going in the backwards direction. But remember, the forward and backward reactions are going at the same rate and the amounts of products and reactants don't change.

Topic C6 — The Rate and Extent of Chemical Change

Target AO3

4 A scientist investigated the reaction between carbon monoxide and hydrogen.
The equation for this reversible reaction is: $CO_{(g)} + 2H_{2(g)} \rightleftharpoons CH_3OH_{(g)}$.
Figure 1 shows how the concentration of carbon monoxide and methanol change with time.

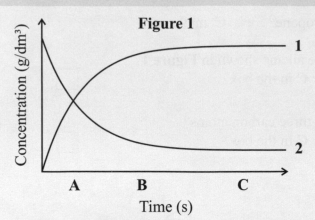

4.1 Suggest which line in **Figure 1** represents the concentration of methanol. Explain your answer.

....

....
[2]

4.2 State whether the reaction reached equilibrium at time **A**, **B** or **C**. Explain your answer.

....

....
[2]

4.3 Heating the reaction mixture causes the reaction to go in the backwards direction.
Suggest how the scientist could change the reaction conditions to produce more methanol.

....
[1]

4.4 Sketch a graph of the concentrations of both carbon monoxide and methanol versus time for
the **reverse** reaction, $CH_3OH_{(g)} \rightleftharpoons CO_{(g)} + 2H_{2(g)}$.

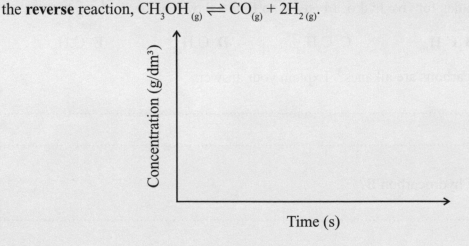

[2]
[Total 7 marks]

Exam Tip

As well as asking you to draw graphs, the examiner may ask you to interpret and explain what a graph tells you about a reaction. Make sure you understand the key details of the graph and how it relates to the reaction in the question.

Topic C6 — The Rate and Extent of Chemical Change

Hydrocarbons

1   The names of three alkanes (labelled **A**, **B** and **C**) are given below. **Figure 1** shows an alkane.

Grade 1-3

Figure 1

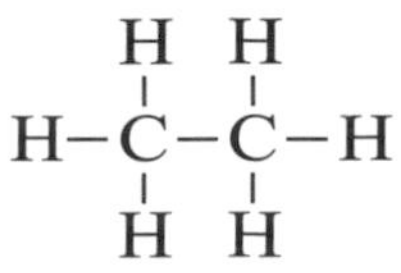

$$H-\overset{\displaystyle H}{\underset{\displaystyle H}{\overset{|}{\underset{|}{C}}}}-\overset{\displaystyle H}{\underset{\displaystyle H}{\overset{|}{\underset{|}{C}}}}-H$$

    A ethane   **B** propane   **C** methane

1.1 What is the name of the alkane shown in **Figure 1**?
Write the letter **A**, **B** or **C** in the box.

[1]

1.2 Which alkane contains three carbon atoms?
Write the letter **A**, **B** or **C** in the box.

[1]

[Total 2 marks]

2   Alkanes are a family of hydrocarbons.

Grade 3-4

2.1 What is a hydrocarbon?

....

[2]

2.2 Complete the word equation for the complete combustion of an alkane.

    alkane + oxygen → .... + ...

[1]

2.3 During a combustion reaction, the atoms in the alkane gain oxygen.
What is the name of this process?

....

[1]

[Total 4 marks]

3   The molecular formulas for five hydrocarbons, **A** to **E**, are shown below.

Grade 4-5

    A C_4H_8 **B** C_4H_{10} **C** C_5H_{10} **D** C_5H_{12} **E** C_3H_8

3.1 Which of the hydrocarbons are alkanes? Explain your answer.

....

....

[2]

3.2 What is the name of hydrocarbon **B**?

....

[1]

3.3 Hydrocarbon **D** can be burned in air. Balance the equation for this reaction.

$$C_5H_{12} + \text{.........} O_2 \rightarrow \text{.........} CO_2 + \text{.........} H_2O$$

[3]

[Total 6 marks]

Crude Oil

Warm-Up

Crude oil is used to make fuels for transport.
Circle the **four** substances below that are fuels made from crude oil.

diesel oil   petrol   kerosene   plastic

plankton   liquefied petroleum gas   oxygen

metal ores

1   This question is about crude oil.   (Grade 3-4)

1.1   Complete the sentences below. Use words from the box.

| mud   finite   organic   renewable   plankton |

Crude oil is formed from .... and the remains of other plants and animals

that were buried in .... millions of years ago. Crude oil is being used up

much more quickly than it's being made, so it's a .... resource.

[3]

1.2   Substances made from crude oil are useful as fuels.
Give **two other** useful products that can be made from crude oil.

1   ....

2   ....

[2]

[Total 5 marks]

2   Crude oil is a resource that contains hydrocarbons.   (Grade 4-5)

2.1   What property of hydrocarbons means that a large number of
different products can be made from crude oil? Tick **one** box.

Carbon can bond to all of the elements in the periodic table.   ☐

Hydrogen atoms can bond with each other to form chains and rings.   ☐

Carbon atoms bond together to form different groups of compounds.   ☐

[1]

2.2   Different hydrocarbons have carbon chains of different lengths.
How does the boiling point of hydrocarbons change as the length of their carbon chains increases?

....

[1]

2.3   State **one** property of hydrocarbons, other than boiling point,
that changes as the length of the carbon chain increases.

....

[1]

[Total 3 marks]

Topic C7 — Organic Chemistry

Fractional Distillation

1 **Figure 1** shows a fractionating column.
They are used in the fractional distillation of crude oil. (Grade 1-3)

Figure 1

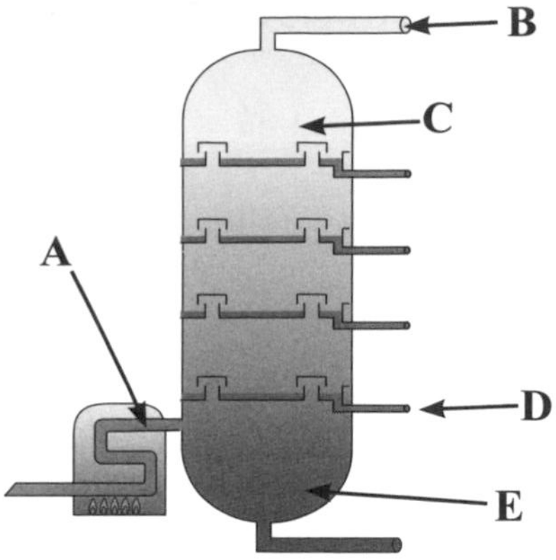

1.1 Where does crude oil enter the fractionating column?
Tick **one** box.

A ☐   B ☐   C ☐   D ☐   E ☐
[1]

1.2 Which is the hottest part of the fractionating column?
Tick **one** box.

A ☐   B ☐   C ☐   D ☐   E ☐
[1]

1.3 Where do the shortest hydrocarbons leave the fractionating column?
Tick **one** box.

A ☐   B ☐   C ☐   D ☐   E ☐
[1]

[Total 3 marks]

2 Before it enters the fractionating column, crude oil is heated until most of it evaporates. (Grade 4-5)

2.1 What change of state happens to the evaporated crude oil within the fractionating column?
Explain why this happens.

Change of state: ....

Explanation: ....

....
[2]

2.2* In fractional distillation of crude oil, the hydrocarbons are separated out
depending on the length of their carbon chains. Explain how this happens.

....

....

....

....

....

....

....
[6]

[Total 8 marks]

Topic C7 — Organic Chemistry

Cracking

1   Crude oil is processed to make a variety of different products.   (Grade 3-4)

1.1   Long-chain hydrocarbons can be processed to produce short-chain hydrocarbons.
What is the name of this process?

....

[1]

1.2   Name **two** types of hydrocarbons that are produced as a result of this process.

1 ....   2 ....

[2]

1.3   Why are long-chain hydrocarbons broken into shorter chain hydrocarbons?

....

[1]

[Total 4 marks]

2   Catalytic cracking and steam cracking can both be used to crack hydrocarbons.   (Grade 4-5)

2.1   Describe the method for steam cracking.

....

....

[2]

2.2   State one way in which the method for catalytic cracking is different to steam cracking.

....

[1]

2.3   Dodecane is an alkane with the formula $C_{12}H_{26}$. It can be cracked to produce heptane (C_7H_{16})
and one other hydrocarbon. Give the formula of this other hydrocarbon.

....

[1]

2.4   Dodecane can also be cracked to produce hexane (C_6H_{14}) and one other hydrocarbon.
Balance the equation for cracking dodecane.

$$C_{12}H_{26} \quad \rightarrow \quad C_6H_{14} \quad + \quad 2C_{.......}H_{.......}$$

[2]

2.5   A scientist has a sample of hexane (an alkane) and a sample of pentene (an alkene).
Describe a test that can be used to identify which sample is pentene.
Include the test results that you would expect the scientist to see.

....

....

....

....

[3]

[Total 9 marks]

Target AO3

3   A student conducted an experiment in order to measure the volume of gas produced
    when they crack a long-chain hydrocarbon. The student's set-up is shown in **Figure 1**.

Figure 1

Boiling tube   Silica catalyst   Bung

Inverted test tube
filled with water

Delivery tube

Mineral wool soaked with
liquid long-chain hydrocarbon

Bunsen
burner

Water

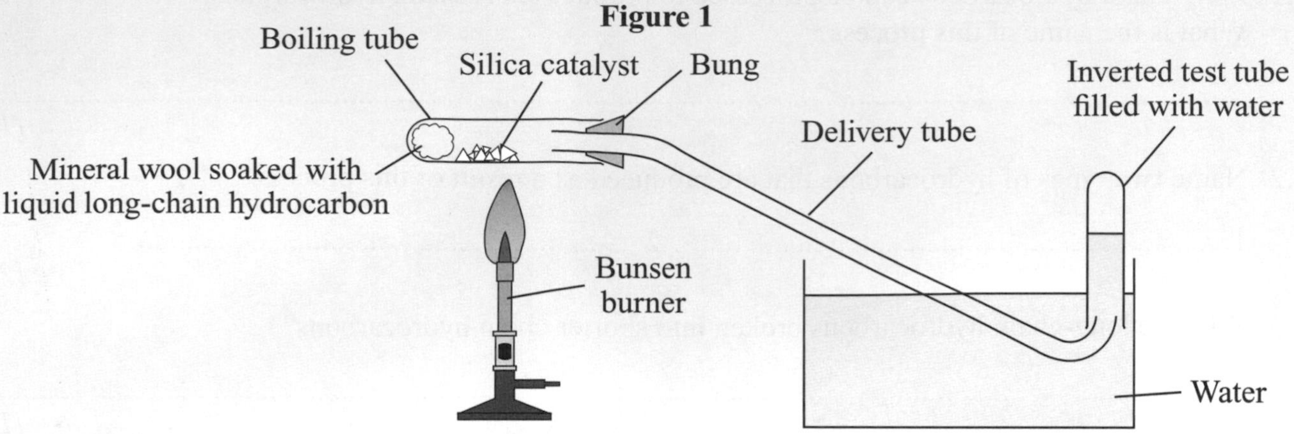

3.1 The bung is used to prevent any hydrocarbon vapour from escaping the boiling tube.
     Explain why this is an important safety precaution when using a Bunsen burner
     to heat the boiling tube.

     ....

     ....
                                                                                                                            [2]

3.2 Explain how filling the test tube with water allowed the student to measure the volume of gas
     produced by the cracking reaction.

     ....

     ....
                                                                                                                            [1]

3.3 Suggest why replacing the test tube with a measuring cylinder would produce more accurate results.

     ....

     ....
                                                                                                                            [1]

3.4 During the experiment, some water was sucked back into the delivery tube.
     Suggest why the water should not be allowed to reach the boiling tube.

     ....
                                                                                                                            [1]

3.5 Suggest **one** variable that the student should change to increase the rate of the reaction.

     ....
                                                                                                                            [1]

                                                                                                              [Total 6 marks]

Exam Tip

In the exam, you might be asked about experiments and reactions that you've never seen before. Firstly — don't panic.
Secondly — think about the information you've been given and if you can link it to your existing knowledge in some way.

Topic C7 — Organic Chemistry

Purity and Formulations

1   A paint was made up of 20% pigment, 35% binder, 25% solvent, and 20% additives.   (Grade 3-4)

1.1   Which of the statements below does **not** explain why the paint is a formulation? Tick **one** box.

It is a mixture that has been designed for a certain use.   ☐

Each part contributes to the properties of the formulation.   ☐

The mixture is made up of less than five parts.   ☐

Each part of the mixture is present in a measured amount.   ☐

[1]

1.2   Other than paint, name **one** example of a formulation.

....

[1]

[Total 2 marks]

2   This question is about purity.   (Grade 4-5)

2.1   How is a pure substance defined in chemistry? Tick **one** box.

A single element not mixed with any other substance.   ☐

A single compound not mixed with any other substance.   ☐

A single element or compound not mixed with any other substance.   ☐

An element that has not been reacted with anything.   ☐

[1]

2.2   The melting point of two samples of copper were measured. Sample **A** had a melting point of 1085 °C and sample **B** melted over the range 900 – 940 °C. Suggest which of the two samples was pure. Explain your answer.

....

....

[2]

2.3   The boiling point of water is 100 °C.
A scientist adds some salt to a sample of water and measures the boiling point of the solution. How will the addition of salt affect the boiling point of the water?

....

[1]

[Total 4 marks]

Exam Tip

A formulation is a mixture but a mixture isn't always a formulation. For the exam make sure you know what the difference is. Formulations are designed for a particular use and contain ingredients in specific amounts.

            Topic C8 — Chemical Analysis

Using Paper Chromatography

Use the words to label the different parts of the chromatography experiment shown on the right.

baseline   filter paper   ....

spots of chemicals   ....

solvent front

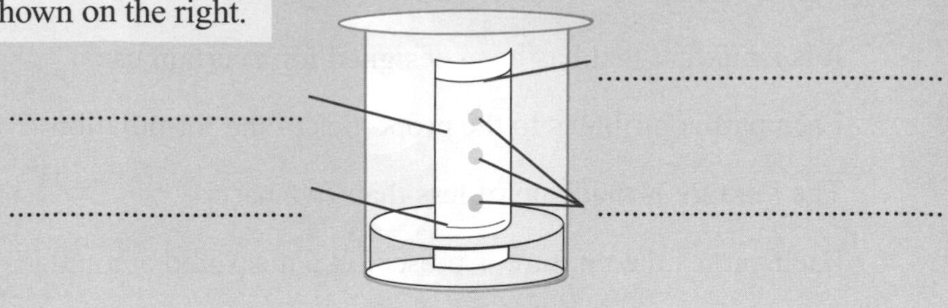

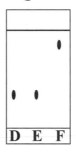

....

....

1   Paper chromatograms were produced for three dyes, **D**, **E** and **F**, using different solvents. **Figure 1** shows a chromatogram produced using ethanol as the solvent.

Figure 1

D E F

1.1 The chromatography experiment that produced the chromatogram in **Figure 1** had two phases. Which of the following statements describing the mobile phase is **true**? Tick **one** box.

The dyes moved in the mobile phase.   ☐

The mobile phase was the filter paper.   ☐

The stationary phase moved up the mobile phase.   ☐

The least soluble dye spent a longer time in the mobile phase.   ☐

[1]

1.2 Why do different substances travel different distances along the paper?

....

....

[1]

1.3 In all solvents, each dye only has one spot. What does this suggest about the dyes?

....

[1]

[Total 3 marks]

There are lots of different type of chromatography, but paper chromatography is the only one you need to know how to carry out. It's not just about knowing how to set up the apparatus — you also need to know how to analyse the results.

2 A scientist used chromatography to analyse the composition of five food colourings. Four of the colourings were unknown (**A – D**). The other was sunrise yellow. The results are shown in **Figure 2**.

Grade
4-5

Figure 2

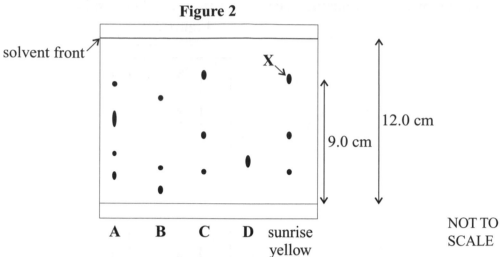

NOT TO
SCALE

2.1 Which food colouring definitely contains at least four different substances?

....
[1]

2.2 Which of the food colourings, **A-D**, could be made of the same substances as sunrise yellow?

....
[1]

2.3 How could you check whether the food colouring you identified in question 1.2 is made of the same substances as sunrise yellow?

....

....

....
[2]

2.4 Calculate the R_f value for the spot of chemical labelled **X** in **Figure 2**.

Use the equation: $R_f = \dfrac{\text{distance moved by substance}}{\text{distance moved by solvent}}$

R_f = ...
[2]

2.5 Describe how the scientist could use chromatography to find out whether food colouring **A** contained a particular substance.

....

....

....
[2]

[Total 8 marks]

Topic C8 — Chemical Analysis

Target AO3

3   A student set up a chromatography experiment to investigate a sample of ink which contained a mixture of several different compounds.

3.1 The chromatogram from the student's experiment is shown in **Figure 3**.

Figure 3

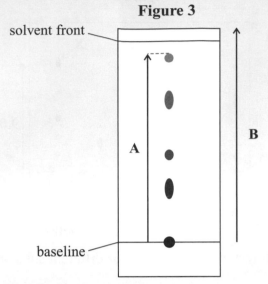

The student observes that there is a spot present on the baseline.
What could the student conclude from this observation?

....

....

[1]

3.2 The student concludes that because there are five spots on the chromatogram, there must be exactly five compounds in the ink.
Suggest and explain **one** reason why the student's conclusion is incorrect.

....

....

[2]

3.3 The student used the lengths of arrows **A** and **B** to calculate the R_f value for one of the compounds. However, they made one mistake when drawing each arrow.
Explain the mistakes that the student has made when drawing arrows A and B and what they should have done instead.

Arrow A: ....

....

Arrow B: ....

....

[4]

[Total 7 marks]

Exam Tip

If you're asked to suggest possible conclusions about an experiment, be careful that you don't assume something that isn't mentioned. You'll only get marks for conclusions that can be worked out from the information you're given.

Topic C8 — Chemical Analysis

Tests for Gases

 PRACTICAL

1   A student wants to identify a gaseous product.   Grade 3-4

Figure 1 shows the gas being tested.

Figure 1

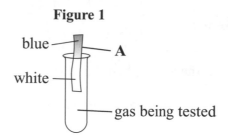

blue ——
white ——
A
gas being tested

1.1   Name the item labelled **A** in **Figure 1**.

....

[1]

1.2   Suggest which gas was present in the test tube.

....

[1]

[Total 2 marks]

2   A student performs an experiment that produces a colourless gas. To identify the gas, she collects it and carries out tests.   Grade 4-5

2.1   Suggest why the student should perform the experiment in a fume cupboard.

....

[1]

2.2   The student bubbles some of the gas through limewater. What gas is this test used to identify?

....

[1]

2.3   When a lighted splint was placed into a sample of the gas, it was **not** accompanied by a popping sound. What does this tell you about the gas?

....

[1]

2.4   When the student placed a glowing splint into a sample of the gas, the splint relighted. Name the gas that was produced by her experiment.

....

[1]

[Total 4 marks]

Exam Tip

There are only four tests for gases you need to know. But, you'll also need to know any precautions that need to be taken to carry out the tests safely. The test for carbon dioxide is also important for testing for carbonate ions.

Topic C8 — Chemical Analysis

Topic C9 — Chemistry of the Atmosphere

The Evolution of the Atmosphere

Warm-Up

Write the numbers 1-4 in the boxes below to put the events in the order in which they happened.

Animals evolved. ☐   The oceans formed. ☐

The early atmosphere formed. ☐   Plants evolved. ☐

1   The composition of gases in the atmosphere has varied during Earth's history. **(Grade 3-4)**

1.1   What are the approximate proportions of oxygen and nitrogen in the atmosphere today?
Tick **one** box.

Four-fifths oxygen and one-fifth nitrogen. ☐   Three-fifths oxygen and two-fifths nitrogen. ☐

One-fifth oxygen and four-fifths nitrogen. ☐   Two-fifths oxygen and three-fifths nitrogen. ☐

[1]

1.2   Other than oxygen and nitrogen, name **two** gases in the atmosphere today.

....

[2]

1.3   How was the oxygen in the atmosphere produced?

....

[1]

1.4   How was nitrogen in the atmosphere produced?

....

[1]

[Total 5 marks]

2*   Describe how the amount of carbon dioxide in the atmosphere got to the level that it is at today. **(Grade 4-5)**

Include ideas about:

- How carbon dioxide originally became part of the atmosphere.
- How the amount of carbon dioxide in the early atmosphere was different to how it is today.
- Reasons why the amount of atmospheric carbon dioxide has changed.

....

....

....

....

....

....

....

....

[Total 6 marks]

Greenhouse Gases and Climate Change

1   Greenhouse gases in the atmosphere help maintain life on Earth.   (Grade 4-5)

1.1   Which of the following is **not** a greenhouse gas? Tick **one** box.

Nitrogen ☐   Carbon dioxide ☐   Water vapour ☐   Methane ☐

[1]

1.2   Use the words in the box below to complete the paragraph describing the greenhouse effect.

long	absorbed	cools	short	reflected	warms

The sun gives out .... wavelength radiation.

The Earth reflects this as .... wavelength radiation.

This radiation is .... by greenhouse gases and then given out in all directions.

Some heads back to Earth and .... the Earth's surface.

[4]

[Total 5 marks]

2   **Figure 1** shows how the concentration of CO_2 in the atmosphere has changed over time.   (Grade 4-5)

2.1   Outline what **Figure 1** tells you about the concentration of atmospheric carbon dioxide.

....

....

[1]

Figure 1

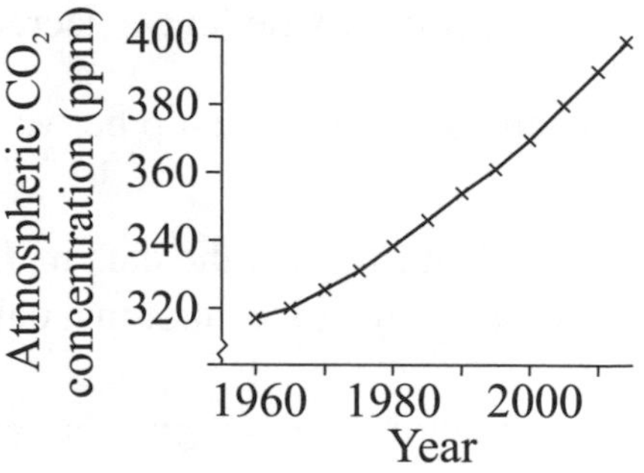

2.2   Give **one** example of a type of human activity which has contributed to the change in atmospheric carbon dioxide concentration, shown in **Figure 1**.

....

[1]

2.3   Over the same time period, the global temperature has increased. Suggest **one** reason why it's hard to prove that the change in carbon dioxide is causing the increase in temperature.

....

[1]

2.4   Increased global temperature could cause climate change. Give **one** possible effect of climate change.

....

[1]

[Total 4 marks]

Exam Tip

Examiners love to provide unfamiliar data and then ask questions about whether it shows a link between two factors, especially when it comes to greenhouse gases and climate change. Make sure you know how to interpret data in both graph and table form, and how to use the data to support your answer — if not for the exam, then for the next page...

Target AO3

3   Scientists in Antarctica use ice cores to measure how the
     Earth's atmosphere and temperature have changed over time.

3.1 **Table 1** shows the carbon dioxide concentration from one Antarctic ice core,
     as well as the global temperature anomaly for the same period. The global temperature anomaly
     is the difference between the average temperature for each year and the average temperature
     for the whole of the 20th century.

Table 1

Year	CO_2 concentration (ppm)	Global temperature anomaly (°C)
1960	319	+0.1
1970	324	+0.1
1980	340	+0.3
1990	355	+0.5
2000	374	+0.6

Which of the following is a valid conclusion that could be made from **Table 1**? Tick **one** box.

As carbon dioxide levels increased, the global temperature also increased.   ☐

The global temperature decreased as carbon dioxide levels increased.   ☐

As carbon dioxide levels decreased, the global temperature also decreased.   ☐

There is no relationship between changes in CO_2 levels and global temperature.   ☐

[1]

3.2 A student says that the data in **Table 1** shows that CO_2 levels increased throughout the 20th century.
     Explain why you cannot make this conclusion from the data in **Table 1**.

     ....

     ....

     ....

[2]

3.3 Explain why an increase in the global temperature might affect the
     scientists' ability to collect new ice cores from polar ice caps in the future.

     ....

     ....

     ....

[2]

[Total 5 marks]

Exam Tip

Exam questions about greenhouse gases and climate change often involve looking at a table or graph and using the data
to work out if a conclusion is true or false. Only make conclusions from the data given in the question and not from
information that you've learnt before — questions like this are a great opportunity to show off your brilliant analysis skills.

Topic C9 — Chemistry of the Atmosphere

Carbon Footprints

1 In recent years, governments and businesses have tried to reduce their carbon footprints. *(Grade 3-4)*

1.1 The following statements describe some of the difficulties in reducing carbon footprints. Which of the statements is **false**? Tick **one** box.

Governments are worried that their economies will be affected if they try to reduce carbon footprints. ☐

Countries cannot always make agreements about reducing emissions. ☐

Governments are worried that reducing carbon footprints could lead to sea levels rising. ☐

Technologies with lower carbon footprints need more development. ☐

[1]

1.2 Complete **Table 1** to show whether each action would increase or decrease a carbon footprint. Tick **one** box in each row.

Table 1

Action	Increase	Decrease
Producing more waste		
Using more renewable energy resources		
Using more fossil fuels		
Using processes that require more energy		
Capturing carbon dioxide and storing it underground		

[3]

[Total 4 marks]

2 Individuals have an annual carbon footprint. *(Grade 4-5)*

2.1 What is meant by the term 'carbon footprint'?

....

....

[2]

2.2 Suggest **two** reasons why an individual may not try to reduce their carbon footprint.

....

....

[2]

[Total 4 marks]

Exam Tip

Learning the definitions for all the different terms that crop up in GCSE Science may be a bit of a bore, but it might be really useful in the exams. Learning all the itty bitty details is worth it if it means you get all the marks available.

☹ ☐   ☺ ☐   ☺ ☐   Topic C9 — Chemistry of the Atmosphere

Air Pollution

1 Draw **one** line from each pollutant to show how it's formed. **Grade 1-3**

Pollutant	How Pollutant is Formed
sulfur dioxide	Incomplete combustion of hydrocarbons.
nitrogen oxides	Reaction of gases in the air caused by the heat of burning fossil fuels.
particulates	Combustion of fossil fuels that contain sulfur impurities.

[Total 2 marks]

2 Some of the pollutants that are released when fuels burn can cause acid rain. **Grade 3-4**

2.1 Name **one** pollutant that can lead to acid rain.

....

[1]

2.2 State **two** ways in which acid rain can be damaging.

....

....

[2]

[Total 3 marks]

3 Combustion of fuel in cars is a major contributor to air pollution. **Grade 4-5**

3.1 Nitrogen oxides can be formed from the combustion of fuels in cars.
Give **two** problems caused by nitrogen oxides in the environment.

....

....

[2]

3.2 Fuel combustion can produce particulates. What impact do particulates have on human health?

....

[1]

3.3 Combustion of fuels can also produce a gas that prevents blood from carrying oxygen around the body. Inhaling it can cause health problems, and sometimes death.

Name the gas and give the reason why it is difficult to detect it.

Name: ....

Reason: ....

[2]

[Total 5 marks]

Topic C9 — Chemistry of the Atmosphere

Finite and Renewable Resources

1   This question is about sustainable use of the Earth's resources.
     Table 1 shows the time it takes to form various materials.

Table 1

Material	Time to form (years)
Wood	2-20
Coal	3×10^8
Cotton	0.5

1.1 Using the data in **Table 1**, state **one** finite resource. Explain your answer.

Resource: ....

Reason: ....

[2]

1.2 What is meant by the term 'renewable resource'?

....

[1]

1.3 Name **one** other renewable resource that is not listed in **Table 1**.

....

[1]

[Total 4 marks]

2   Humans have developed items made from both natural and synthetic materials.

2.1 Give **one** example of how agriculture is used to increase the supply of a natural resource.

....

....

[1]

2.2 Give **one** example of a synthetic product which has replaced
     or is used in addition to a natural resource.

....

[1]

[Total 2 marks]

Exam Tip

If numbers are really big or small, they could be given in standard form, like the time taken for coal to form in Table 1 (3×10^8). You can tell how big the number is by looking at the little number next to the 10. If the little number is positive, then the whole number is greater than 1. The higher this little number is, the bigger the whole number will be. If the little number is negative, it means the whole number is between 0 and 1. The more negative this little number is, the smaller the whole number will be. Give this a read a few times until it makes sense.

Reuse and Recycling

1   Some materials can be recycled into new products.   (Grade 3-4)

1.1 Which of the following statements about the recycling of metals is **false**? Tick **one** box.

Recycling metals reduces the amount of waste sent to landfill. ☐

Recycling metals increases the finite amount of metals in the Earth. ☐

Recycling metals often uses less energy than making new metals. ☐

Recycling metals saves some of the finite amount of metals in the Earth. ☐

[1]

1.2 Glass can be recycled and made into new products.
Using the words in the box, complete the sentences below.

melted	reshaped	less	crushed	more

Glass products are .... and then ....

They are then .... to make other products for a different use.

This process uses .... energy than making new glass.

[4]

[Total 5 marks]

2   Cups and mugs for hot drinks can be made from different materials.
Two possible materials are stainless steel and paper.
Table 1 gives some information about these materials.   (Grade 4-5)

Table 1

	Stainless Steel Mug	**Paper Cup**
Source of raw material	Metal ores and coal	Plant fibre
Can it be reused or recycled?	Both	Possible but not widely done.

2.1 Using the information in **Table 1**, state which of the two raw materials is more sustainable.
Give a reason for your answer.

Raw material: ....

Reason: ....

[2]

2.2 The stainless steel mug can be reused many times.
Suggest why this may make it more sustainable than the paper cup.

....

....

[1]

[Total 3 marks]

Topic C10 — Using Resources

Life Cycle Assessments

Draw one line between each stage of a product's life and the correct example of that stage.

Life cycle stage	Example
Getting the Raw Materials	Coal being mined from the ground.
Manufacturing and Packaging	Plastic bags going to landfill.
Using the Product	A car using fuel while driving.
Product Disposal	Books being made from wood pulp.

1 What is the purpose of a life cycle assessment? Tick **one** box. (Grade 1-3)

It looks at how many different chemicals are used during the life cycle of a product. ☐

It looks at the total amount of greenhouse gases produced during the life cycle of a product. ☐

It looks at every stage of a product's life to assess the impact on the environment. ☐

It looks at the total economic impact of each stage of a product's life. ☐

[Total 1 mark]

2 A mobile phone company is carrying out a life cycle assessment for one of their products. (Grade 3-4)

2.1 Suggest **one** environmental problem associated with using metals as a raw material.

....
[1]

2.2 The mobile phone is powered by a battery which needs to be recharged regularly. Most electricity comes from burning fossil fuels. Suggest **one** environmental problem that this may cause.

....
[1]

2.3 Mobile phones can be recycled. However, some still get sent to landfill.
Give **two** disadvantages of disposing of rubbish in landfill.

1 ....

2 ....
[2]
[Total 4 marks]

Topic C10 — Using Resources

Using Life Cycle Assessments

1   A company carries out a life cycle assessment (LCA) for a new product. The LCA only shows some of the environmental impacts that are caused by the product. How can this type of LCA be described? Tick **one** box.

Grade 1-3

limited life cycle assessment ☐

selective life cycle assessment ☐

incomplete life cycle assessment ☐

exclusive life cycle assessment ☐

[Total 1 mark]

2   A new shop is deciding whether to stock plastic bags or paper bags for their customers' shopping. To help them decide, they carry out a life cycle assessment for each type of bag. Some information about each bag is shown in **Table 1**.

Grade 4-5

Table 1

	Plastic bag	**Paper bag**
Raw materials	Crude oil	Wood
Manufacture	A little waste produced.	Lots of waste produced.
Using the product	Can be reused several times.	Usually only used once.
Disposal	Recyclable Not biodegradable	Recyclable Biodegradable

2.1   Using the information in **Table 1**, give **two** advantages of plastic bags over paper bags.

1 ....

2 ....

[2]

2.2   Suggest **two** other pieces of information, that are not given in **Table 1**, that would be needed to help decide which bag has the least impact on the environment.

1 ....

2 ....

[2]

[Total 4 marks]

Exam Tip

Life cycle assessments are a useful way to compare the sustainability of different products. It's useful to know what sort of information you should expect to see in each part of the assessment. If you meet an LCA in the exam, you might need to use that knowledge to do a bit of detective work and figure out if there are some important details missing.

Target AO3

3   **Table 2** contains life cycle assessment data for two types of soft drink container.

Table 2

	Glass Bottles	Aluminium Cans
Raw Materials	Sand, soda ash and limestone	Aluminium ore
Manufacturing	• Has to be produced at very high temperatures • Their production releases greenhouse gases	• Require large amounts of electricity to extract aluminium from the ore • Their production releases greenhouse gases
Usage	Can be refilled and reused	Usually only used once
Disposal	Widely recycled and used to produce new glass	Can be continually recycled as a source of aluminium

3.1 Use information from **Table 2** to suggest **one** reason why glass bottles are more environmentally friendly than aluminium cans.

....

[1]

3.2 Recycling aluminium cans saves large amounts of energy compared to producing new cans. Explain why this would have a positive impact on their life cycle assessment.

....

....

[2]

3.3 Certain glass objects cannot be recycled with the glass bottles, so glass has to be sorted and separated before it can be recycled.
Explain why this negatively affects the life cycle assessment of the glass bottles.

....

....

[1]

3.4 A researcher says that the disposal section of the assessment is incomplete because it only contains information about recycling.
Suggest one other piece of information that the disposal section of the life cycle assessment could contain.

....

....

[1]

[Total 5 marks]

            Topic C10 — Using Resources

Potable Water

1   This question is about potable water.   *Grade 1-3*

1.1   Which of the following is a correct description of potable water? Tick **one** box.

Pure water   ☐

Water with a pH between 4.5 and 6.5   ☐

Water that is safe to drink   ☐

Water with a high concentration of salt   ☐

[1]

1.2   In the warmer areas of the UK, surface water can dry up. Suggest a suitable source
of fresh water that could be used instead for the production of potable water.

....

[1]

[Total 2 marks]

2   Fresh water needs to be treated before it is safe to drink.   *Grade 4-5*

2.1   Draw **one** line between each treatment of water and the substances removed by the process.

| Passing water through filter beds | | Solid Waste |

| | Microbes |

| Sterilisation | | Chemicals |

[2]

2.2   Name **three** things that can be used to sterilise fresh water.

1 ....

2 ....

3 ....

[3]

[Total 5 marks]

Topic C10 — Using Resources

Desalination

1   **Figure 1** shows a set of equipment that could be used to desalinate sea water through a process known as distillation.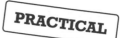

Figure 1

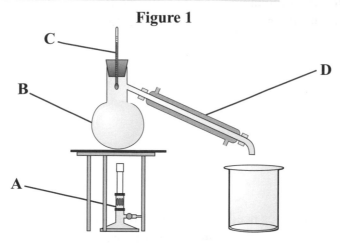

Name the components labelled **A** to **D** in **Figure 1**. Use the words in the box.

round bottomed flask	condenser	thermometer	Bunsen burner

A ....   B ....

C ....   D ....

[Total 4 marks]

2   Before seawater can be used for drinking water, it needs to go through desalination. Desalination is the process of removing salts.

2.1   Reverse osmosis is a type of desalination that uses membranes. Which of the following statements describes how membranes help to purify seawater? Tick **one** box.

The membranes let salt molecules pass through but stop the water from passing. ☐

The membranes let water molecules pass through but trap the salts. ☐

The salt molecules stick to the membranes which are then removed from the water. ☐

The membranes heat the water causing it to evaporate. ☐

[1]

2.2   Although it is surrounded by the sea, the UK produces potable water from fresh water sources, rather than from sea water. Explain why the UK chooses to use fresh water sources.

....

....

[2]

[Total 3 marks]

Exam Tip

Some water costs a lot to make potable, some not so much. Make sure you understand the different processes that salty water and fresh water undergo to make it safe to drink and why the different processes are used in different places.

Topic C10 — Using Resources

Waste Water Treatment

1   Waste water must be treated before being reused or released into the environment.   **Grade 3-4**

1.1   Which **two** of the following pollutants must be removed
from sewage and agricultural waste water? Tick **two** boxes.

Calcium ions, Ca^{2+} ☐

Organic matter ☐

Harmful microbes ☐

Sodium ions, Na^+ ☐

[2]

1.2   Industrial waste water sometimes needs further treatment compared to
sewage and agricultural waste water. Suggest why this is.

....

[1]

[Total 3 marks]

2   This question is about the treatment of waste water in the form of sewage.
Figure 1 shows the different stages water goes through at a sewage treatment facility.   **Grade 4-5**

Figure 1

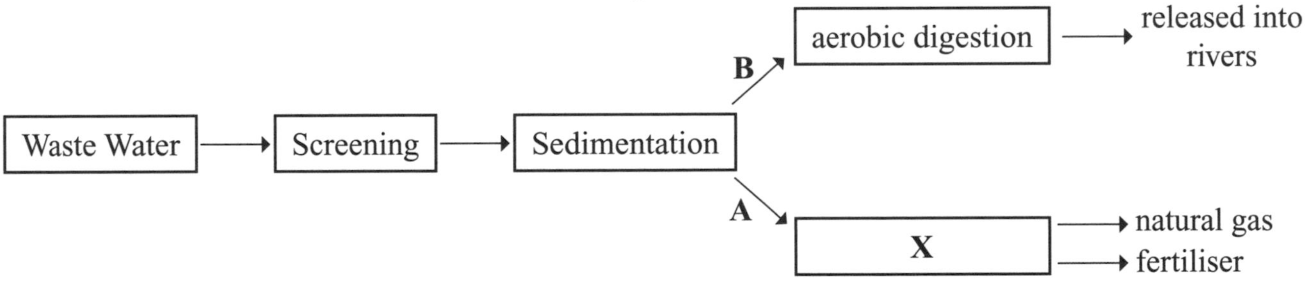

2.1   What is the purpose of the stage described as 'screening'?

....

....

[2]

2.2   What are the names given to the two substances produced by sedimentation?

Substance **A**: ....

Substance **B**: ....

[2]

2.3   What is the name of process **X**?

....

[1]

[Total 5 marks]

Topic C10 — Using Resources   ☹ ☐   ☺ ☐   ☺ ☐

Energy Stores and Systems

1   Draw **one** straight line from each object to the energy store that energy is being transferred **from**.

Object	Energy store
A car slowing down without braking.	chemical energy store
A mug of hot tea cooling down.	thermal energy store
A stretched spring returning to its original shape.	elastic potential energy store
A battery in a circuit.	kinetic energy store

[Total 3 marks]

2   Whenever a system changes, energy is transferred.

2.1 Define the term 'system'.

....

[1]

2.2 Complete **Table 1** to show whether each statement about closed systems is true or false. Tick **one** box in each row.

Table 1

Statement	True	False
Energy can only be transferred mechanically or electrically in a closed system.		
A closed system is one in which there is no net change in the system's total energy.		
Energy can be transferred into and out of a closed system.		

[3]

[Total 4 marks]

Exam Tip

Make sure you know the different types of energy store. Remember that energy can be transferred between stores mechanically (because of a force doing work), electrically, by heating or by radiation (e.g. light and sound waves).

Conservation of Energy and Energy Transfers

1 Which statements about energy are **false**? Tick **two** boxes. (Grade 1-3)

Energy can be transferred usefully. ☐

Energy can be created. ☐

Energy can be stored. ☐

Energy can be dissipated. ☐

Energy can be destroyed. ☐

[Total 2 marks]

2 An apple is hanging from a branch of a tree. (Grade 3-4)

2.1 The apple falls from the tree.
Give the **two** energy stores that energy is transferred between as the apple is falling.
You can assume there is no air resistance.

Energy is transferred from: ....

Energy is transferred to: ....
[2]

2.2 The passage below describes what is happening as the apple falls.
Use words from the box below to complete the passage.

electrostatic	mechanically	gravitational
work		energy

As the apple falls, ... is done on the apple by the

.... force. This means energy is transferred ....
[3]
[Total 5 marks]

3 A cyclist on a road applies his brakes to come to a stop.
Applying the brakes causes the brakes to warm up. (Grade 4-5)

Describe the energy transfer that has occurred.
You can ignore any friction between the bike and the ground.
You can also assume there is no air resistance.

....

....

....

[Total 3 marks]

Topic P1 — Energy

Kinetic and Potential Energy Stores

1   A student stretches a spring by 0.01 m.
The spring is not stretched past its limit of proportionality.
The spring has a spring constant of 20 N/m.

Calculate the energy stored in the elastic potential energy store of the spring as it is stretched.
Use an equation from the Equations List.

Energy = ... J

[Total 2 marks]

2   A girl kicks a ball resting on the ground into the air.
The ball reaches a height of 2.0 m. The ball has a mass of 0.50 kg.
Gravitational field strength = 9.8 N/kg.

2.1   Write down the equation that links the energy in an object's gravitational potential energy store,
the mass of the object, gravitational field strength and height.

....

[1]

2.2   Calculate the energy transferred to the ball's gravitational potential energy store.

Energy = ... J

[2]

2.3   The ball falls back down to the ground. All of the energy stored in the ball's
gravitational potential energy store is transferred to its kinetic energy store.
Calculate the speed of the ball when it hits the ground.
Give your answer to 2 significant figures.
Use the equation:

$$\text{kinetic energy} = \tfrac{1}{2} \times \text{mass} \times (\text{speed})^2$$

Speed = ... m/s

[3]

[Total 6 marks]

Energy Transfers by Heating

Warm-Up

Which of the following is the correct definition of specific heat capacity? Tick **one** box.

The energy transferred when an object is burnt. ☐

The maximum amount of energy an object can store before it melts. ☐

The energy needed to raise the temperature of 1 kg of a substance by 10 °C. ☐

The energy needed to raise the temperature of 1 kg of a substance by 1 °C. ☐

1   Use phrases from the box below to complete the passage.   (Grade 3-4)

| thermal | kinetic | electrically | mechanically | by heating |

An electric kettle is used to heat some water. When the kettle is on, energy is transferred

.... to the thermal energy store of the kettle's heating element.

The energy is then transferred .... to the water.

The energy is transferred to the water's .... energy store.

[Total 3 marks]

2   A block of aluminium is heated. The total amount of energy   (Grade 4-5)
transferred to the block is 9000 J. The mass of the block is 200 g.

2.1   Calculate the change in temperature of the block of aluminium when it is been heated.
The specific heat capacity of aluminium is 900 J/kg°C.
Use an equation from the Equations List.

Change in temperature = ... °C
[3]

2.2   Copper has a lower specific heat capacity than aluminium.
A 200 g block of copper is heated so its temperature changes by the same amount as
the aluminium. Use the correct phrase from the box below to complete the sentence.

| more than | less than | the same as |

The amount of energy needed to heat the copper block is ....

the amount of energy needed to heat the aluminium block.

[1]

[Total 4 marks]

Investigating Specific Heat Capacity

PRACTICAL

1   A student is investigating the specific heat capacities of three liquids. She uses the apparatus shown in **Figure 1**.

She places 60 g of a liquid into a 100 ml flask. She measures the initial temperature of the liquid. 3000 J of energy is supplied to the liquid using an immersion heater. She then measures the final temperature and calculates the temperature change. She repeats this method for each liquid.

Figure 1

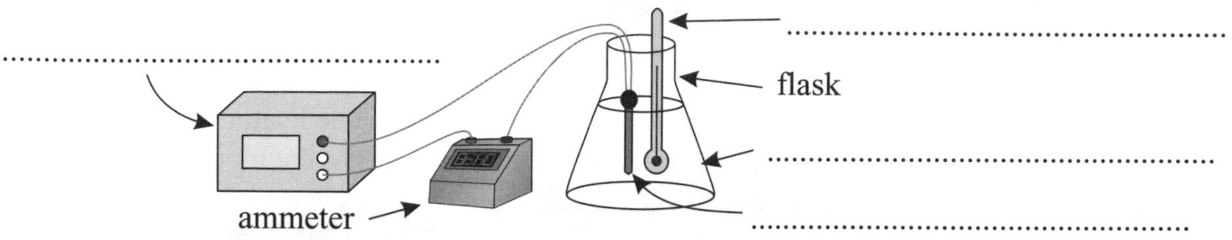

....

← flask

ammeter →

....

1.1   Use the phrases from the box to label the diagram in **Figure 1**.

thermometer	liquid	power supply	immersion heater

[3]

The student records her results, which are shown in **Table 1**.

Table 1

Liquid	Temperature change (°C)
A	12
B	23
C	25

1.2   Use the results in **Table 1** to list the liquids in order of increasing specific heat capacity.

Lowest specific heat capacity   ....

                                                    ....

Highest specific heat capacity   ....

[1]

1.3   Which of the following would improve the accuracy of the experiment?
Tick **one** box.

Putting insulation around the flask.   ☐

Using a more powerful power supply.   ☐

Testing more liquids.   ☐

[1]

[Total 5 marks]

Exam Tip

You may be asked about experiments you've never seen before in an exam, but don't panic. Take your time to read the experiment carefully. Work out what's going on before attempting any questions to get full marks.

170

2   A student is testing 3 materials, X, Y and Z, to find their specific heat capacities.

He uses the equipment shown in **Figure 2**.

Figure 2

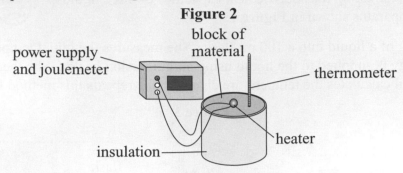

He heats a 300 g block of each material using an electric heater. The heater is connected to a joulemeter, which measures the amount of energy transferred to the block. The student measures the temperature of each block after 1500 J of energy has been transferred.

2.1 **Table 2** shows some of the variables that the student needs to consider during his experiment. Complete **Table 2** by putting one tick in the correct column for each row, to show what type of variable it is. The first row has been done for you.

Table 2

Variable	Control variable	Dependent variable	Independent variable
The energy transferred to the block			✓
The mass of the block			
The temperature of the block			
The temperature of the room			

[3]

2.2 After carrying out the experiment, the student realises he has read the scale of the thermometer incorrectly. This means that all his results are 1 °C higher than they should be. Name the type of error that this has caused.

....

[1]

2.3 Suggest how this error in the results could be corrected.

....

[1]

2.4 The student corrects the error, and repeats the experiment two more times. His results for material X are shown in **Table 3**. Calculate the mean temperature from the results in **Table 3**.

Table 3

	Trial 1	Trial 2	Trial 3
Temperature (°C)	31.0	29.5	32.5

mean temperature = ... °C

[2]

[Total 7 marks]

Power

1 Two lamps, A and B, are turned on for 1 minute. Lamp A is more powerful than lamp B. Choose the correct letter below to complete the sentence.

A transfer less energy
B transfer more energy
C transfer the same amount of energy

Lamp A will .... over 1 minute than lamp B.

[Total 1 mark]

2 A student heats a beaker of water using an immersion heater. The immersion heater has a power of 35 W.

2.1 Calculate the work done by the immersion heater when it is operated for 600 s.
Use the equation:

$$\text{power} = \frac{\text{work done}}{\text{time}}$$

Work done = ... J
[3]

2.2 The student then uses the immersion heater to heat a second beaker of water.
The heater transferred 16 800 J of energy to the system.
Calculate the time that the heater was on for.

Time = ... s
[4]
[Total 7 marks]

Reducing Unwanted Energy Transfers

1   **Figure 1** shows a well.
The handle is turned, which rotates the axle.
The rope attached to the bucket
wraps around the axle.
This raises the bucket in the well.

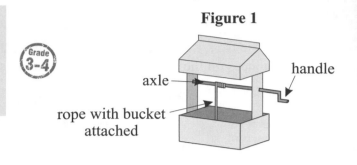

Figure 1

Use the correct words from the box
below to complete the sentence.

axle	more	less	always	lubricating
bucket		insulating		sometimes

Energy is .... wasted when the handle is turned. The bucket rises faster

when .... energy is wasted. The speed at which the bucket rises will be

increased by .... the ....

[Total 4 marks]

2   A builder is building an energy-efficient house.

She has four types of brick to choose
from to make the house walls.
Table 1 shows the thermal conductivity
and thickness of each type of brick.

Based on the information in **Table 1**,
state which type of brick she should use.
Explain your answer.

Table 1

Type	Thermal conductivity	Brick thickness (cm)
A	High	10
B	High	15
C	Low	10
D	Low	15

....

....

....

[Total 3 marks]

3   A student is charging her mobile phone.
She notices that the phone starts to heat up.
Explain why the phone starts to heat up.

....

....

[Total 2 marks]

Exam Tip

Sometimes a question will ask you to refer to a figure, such as a graph, table or diagram, in your answer. Make sure
you fully understand the figure before you start your answer, and pay attention to any labels. The examiners will find it
much easier to mark your answers if you refer to bits of the figure clearly, using the same terms they're labelled with.

Efficiency

1   All appliances have an efficiency.   (Grade 1-3)

   1.1   Which of the following statements is true?
Tick **one** box.

Some modern appliances are 100% efficient. ☐

The more energy wasted by a device, the more efficient it is. ☐

Whenever energy is transferred, some energy is wasted. ☐

[1]

   1.2   Choose the correct letter below to complete the sentence.

     A   Decreasing the energy transferred to a device
     B   Increasing the efficiency of a device
     C   Decreasing the efficiency of a device

     .... increases the amount of energy the device transfers to useful energy stores.

[1]

   1.3   A toaster has an efficiency of 68%. A kettle has an efficiency of 0.75.
State whether the toaster or the kettle is more efficient.

     ....

[1]

[Total 3 marks]

2   To fully charge a mobile phone battery, 20 000 J must be transferred to it.
The battery transfers 16 000 J of this energy usefully until it needs to be charged again.   (Grade 4-5)

   Which calculation can be used to find the efficiency of the battery as a percentage? Tick **one** box.

   (20 000 ÷ 16 000) ÷ 100   ☐

   (20 000 ÷ 16 000) × 100   ☐

   (16 000 ÷ 20 000) × 100   ☐

   (16 000 ÷ 20 000) ÷ 100   ☐

[Total 1 mark]

3   An electric motor has a useful power output of 57 W and an efficiency of 75%.   (Grade 4-5)

   3.1   Write down the equation that links efficiency, useful power output and total power input.

     ....

[1]

   3.2   Calculate the total power input for the motor.

Total power input = ... W

[3]

[Total 4 marks]

Target AO3

4   A student is investigating whether the efficiency of an electric kettle varies with the mass of water in the kettle.

The student carries out the following method:
1. Fill the kettle with 500 g of 20 °C water.
2. Turn on the kettle, and allow the water to heat up to 100 °C.
   The kettle automatically switches off when the water reaches this temperature.
3. Using a power consumption meter, record the energy transferred to the kettle while it was on.
4. Allow the kettle to cool.
5. Repeat steps 1-4 for different masses of water.

4.1 Suggest **two** risks associated with this experiment.

1. ....

2. ....

[2]

The student uses his results to calculate the efficiency of the kettle for each mass of water.
He plots a graph of efficiency against the mass of water, shown in **Figure 2**.

Figure 2

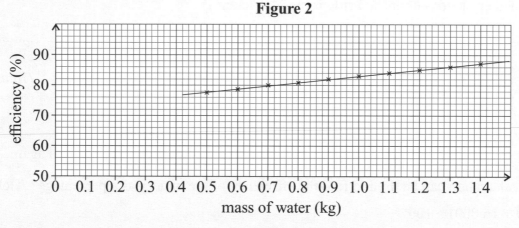

4.2 Which of the following is a valid conclusion for the experiment?
Tick **one** box.

The kettle is more efficient for lower masses of water. ☐

The kettle is more efficient for higher masses of water. ☐

The kettle's efficiency is independent of the mass of water. ☐

The kettle is most efficient for a mass of 1.0 kg of water. ☐

[1]

4.3 Justify your answer to 4.2, using **Figure 2**.

....

....

[1]

[Total 4 marks]

Exam Tip

If you're given an experimental method in the question, make sure you read it carefully, even though they can be quite long and tempting to skim over. Even if you don't think it contains crucial information, you wouldn't want to miss anything.

Topic P1 — Energy

Energy Resources and Their Uses

Warm-Up

Energy resources are either renewable or non-renewable.
Write the energy resources below in the correct column of the table.

bio-fuel   oil

coal   hydro-electricity

solar

wind

nuclear fuel

tidal   geothermal

wave power   gas

Renewable	Non-renewable

1   Petrol or diesel is used to power most cars. They are both made from a fossil fuel.   **Grade 1-3**

1.1   Name the **three** fossil fuels.

1. ....

2. ....

3. ....

[3]

1.2   Give **two** other everyday uses for fossil fuels.

1. ....

2. ....

[2]

1.3   Which of the following energy resources can be used to directly power some modern cars?
Tick **one** box.

Nuclear fuel   ☐

Geothermal power   ☐

Bio-fuel   ☐

Hydro-electricity   ☐

[1]

[Total 6 marks]

2   Describe the difference between renewable and non-renewable energy resources.   **Grade 3-4**

....

....

....

[Total 2 marks]

 ☐   ☐   ☐

Topic P1 — Energy

Wind, Solar and Geothermal

1 Wind turbines use wind power to generate electricity. (Grade 3-4)

1.1 Give **one** advantage and **one** disadvantage of using wind turbines to generate electricity.

Advantage: ....

....

Disadvantage: ....

....

[2]

1.2 Geothermal power uses hot rocks under the Earth's surface to generate electricity.
Give **one** advantage of using geothermal power to generate electricity.

....

....

[1]

[Total 3 marks]

2* A university wants to reduce their energy bills.
They want to build either a single wind turbine nearby,
or install solar panels on top of their buildings. (Grade 4-5)

The average wind speed for the university the previous year is shown in **Table 1**.
The average number of hours of sunlight per day is also given.

Table 1

	Average wind speed (m/s)	Average number of hours of daylight
October-March	8.0	9
April-September	4.3	15

The university decides to install both a wind turbine and solar panels.
Use the information in **Table 1** to suggest why.

....

....

....

....

....

....

....

....

[Total 4 marks]

Hydro-electricity, Waves and Tides

1 Wave-powered turbines are used to generate electricity. (Grade 1-3)

1.1 Which of the following statements about wave-powered turbines are true?
Tick **two** boxes.

They generate electricity all the time. ☐

They rely on light from the Sun to produce electricity. ☐

They must be placed near the coast. ☐

They produce pollution when generating electricity. ☐

They can disturb the habitats of animals. ☐

[2]

1.2 Hydro-electric power plants also use water to generate electricity.
Give **one** disadvantage of generating electricity from wave-powered turbines
compared to generating electricity from hydro-electric power plants.

....

[1]

[Total 3 marks]

2* An energy provider wants to build a new power plant.
They want to build either a hydro-electric power plant or a tidal barrage. (Grade 4-5)

Compare the reliability and the impact on the environment for generating
electricity from hydro-electric power plants and tidal barrages.

....

....

....

....

....

....

....

....

....

....

[Total 4 marks]

Exam Tip

If you're asked to compare two energy resources, then make sure you are comparing. For example, if you were asked to
compare the advantages and disadvantages of two resources, it's no good just listing the advantages and disadvantages
of each. You need to talk about the advantages and disadvantages of each energy resource in relation to the other.

 ☐   ☐   ☐

Topic P1 — Energy

Bio-fuels and Non-renewables

1   Complete **Table 1** to show to show whether each statement applies
to bio-fuels, fossil fuels, or both. Tick **one** box in each row.

Table 1

	Bio-fuels	Fossil fuels	Both
They release carbon dioxide when they are burnt.			
They are a renewable energy resource.			
They are slowly running out.			

[Total 3 marks]

2*   Describe the advantages and disadvantages of using fossil fuels to generate electricity.

....

....

....

....

....

....

....

....

....

....

....

[Total 6 marks]

Trends in Energy Resource Use

1   **Figure 1** shows the energy resources used to generate electricity in a country.

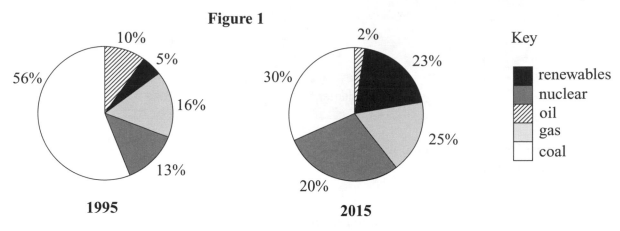

Figure 1

1995

2015

Key

■ renewables
▨ nuclear
▧ oil
▨ gas
□ coal

1.1   Determine what percentage of the country's electricity was generated by fossil fuels in 1995.

..........................%

[2]

1.2   Suggest **one** trend you can determine from the pie charts in **Figure 1**.

....

[1]

[Total 3 marks]

2   In the UK, the use of renewable energy resources is increasing. Some people say it is not increasing at a fast enough rate.

2.1   Suggest **one** reason for this increase in the use of renewable energy resources.

....

....

[2]

2.2* Suggest and explain the factors that may reduce the rate at which we decrease our use of fossil fuels and increase our use of renewable energy resources.

....

....

....

....

....

....

....

[4]

[Total 6 marks]

Topic P1 — Energy

Current and Circuit Symbols

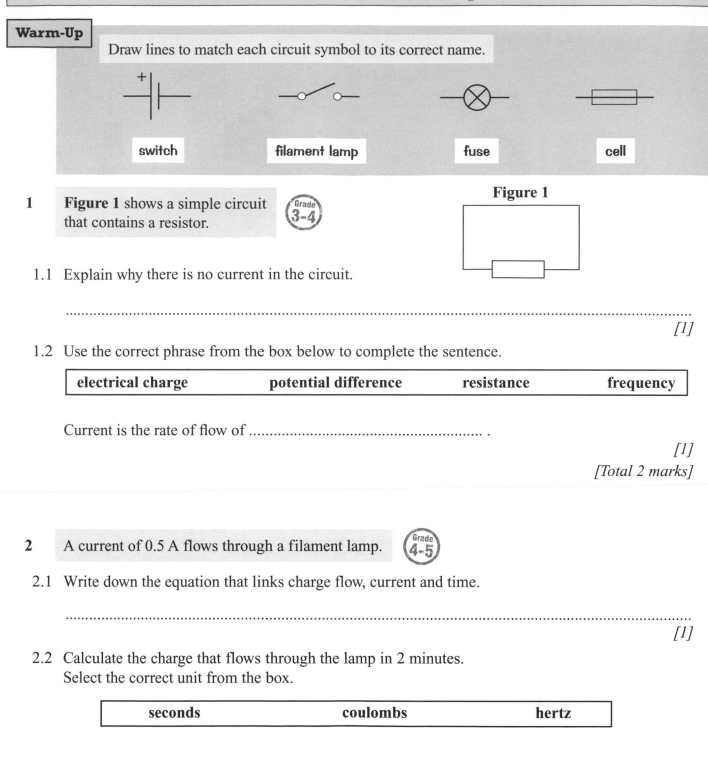

switch | filament lamp | fuse | cell

1 **Figure 1** shows a simple circuit that contains a resistor. _Grade 3-4_

Figure 1

1.1 Explain why there is no current in the circuit.

....

[1]

1.2 Use the correct phrase from the box below to complete the sentence.

electrical charge	potential difference	resistance	frequency

Current is the rate of flow of ....

[1]

[Total 2 marks]

2 A current of 0.5 A flows through a filament lamp. _Grade 4-5_

2.1 Write down the equation that links charge flow, current and time.

....

[1]

2.2 Calculate the charge that flows through the lamp in 2 minutes.
Select the correct unit from the box.

seconds	coulombs	hertz

Charge = ... Unit = ...

[4]

[Total 5 marks]

Resistance and V = IR

1 A current of 3 A flows through a 6 Ω resistor. *(Grade 1-3)*

Calculate the potential difference across the resistor.
Use the equation:

$$\text{potential difference} = \text{current} \times \text{resistance}$$

Potential difference = ...V

[Total 2 marks]

2 A wire is an ohmic conductor. *(Grade 3-4)*

The passage below describes ohmic conductors.
Use phrases from the box below to complete the passage.

changed	potential difference	resistance	constant

At a fixed temperature, the .... of an ohmic conductor will

remain .... as the current through it is ....

[Total 3 marks]

3 When a potential difference of 25 V is applied across a filament lamp, a current of 3.0 A flows through it. *(Grade 4-5)*

3.1 Calculate the resistance of the filament lamp. Give your answer to 2 significant figures.
Use the equation:

$$\text{potential difference} = \text{current} \times \text{resistance}$$

Resistance = ... Ω

[3]

3.2 Over time, the filament gets hotter. Explain why the current through the lamp begins to decrease.

....

....

....

[2]

[Total 5 marks]

Topic P2 — Electricity

PRACTICAL — Investigating Resistance

1   A student investigated how the resistance of a piece of wire depends on its length.
    The circuit she used is shown in **Figure 1**. Her results are displayed in **Table 1**.   Grade 3-4

Figure 1

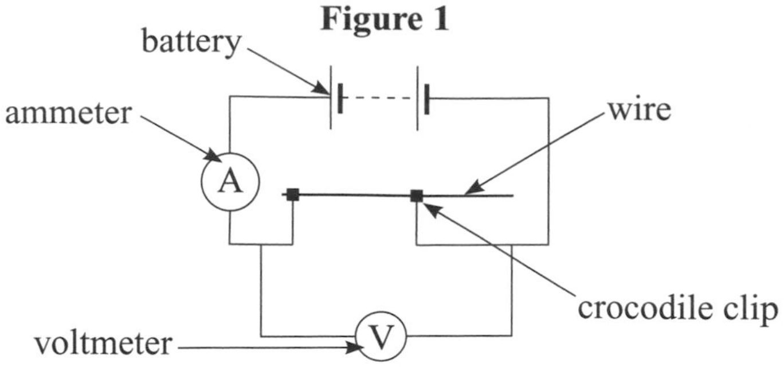

battery
ammeter
wire
A
crocodile clip
voltmeter — V

Table 1

Length / cm	Resistance / Ω
10	0.6
20	1.2
30	1.8
40	2.4
50	3.0

1.1 Complete the description of how the student used the results from her
     investigation in **Table 1** to calculate the resistance of each wire length.
     Use phrases from the box below to complete the sentence.

divided	ammeter	multiplied	power supply

The reading on the voltmeter was .... by the reading on the ....

[2]

1.2 Complete the graph in **Figure 2**, by plotting
     the remaining data points from **Table 1**.
     Draw a line of best fit on the graph.

[3]

1.3 What does the graph in **Figure 2** show?
     Tick **one** box.

Resistance is directly proportional to length.   ☐

There is no relationship between resistance
and length.   ☐

Resistance is inversely proportional to length.   ☐

Resistance increases with length up to a point,
and then starts decreasing.   ☐

[1]

[Total 6 marks]

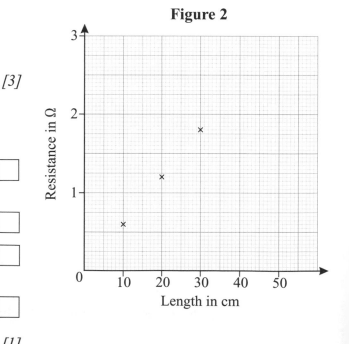

Figure 2

(graph: Resistance in Ω vs Length in cm)

Exam Tip

The shape of a graph shows you what the relationship is between the two variables on the axes. Take some time to
learn the graphs for the most common relationships (e.g. directly proportional), so you can pick up some marks easily.

I-V Characteristics

1 Electrical components can be linear or non-linear.

1.1 Which of the graphs below, **A**, **B**, **C** or **D**, is an *I-V* characteristic of a linear component?

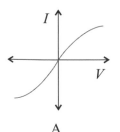 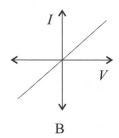 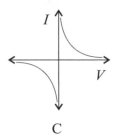 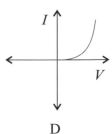

A   B   C   D

Your answer = ...
[1]

1.2 Give **one** example of a linear component.

....
[1]

[Total 2 marks]

PRACTICAL

2 A student is investigating the *I-V* characteristic of a filament lamp. She uses the circuit shown in **Figure 1**.

Figure 1

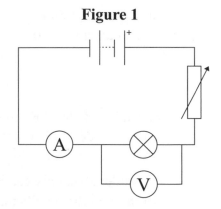

2.1 Describe a method the student could use to determine the *I-V* characteristic of the filament lamp.

....

....

....

....

....

....
[3]

2.2 **Figure 2** shows the *I-V* characteristic plotted from her results.

Using **Figure 2**, calculate the resistance of the filament lamp when the current through it is 2.0 A.

Figure 2

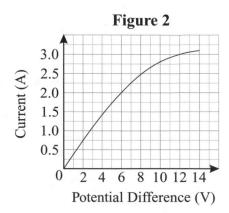

Resistance = ... Ω
[4]

[Total 7 marks]

Topic P2 — Electricity

Target AO3

3   A student creates a test circuit containing a diode, as shown in **Figure 3**. The student carries out an experiment to investigate how the resistance of the diode changes with current. She records the current through the circuit using a digital ammeter. She plots her results on a graph, shown in **Figure 4**.

Grade 4-5

Figure 4

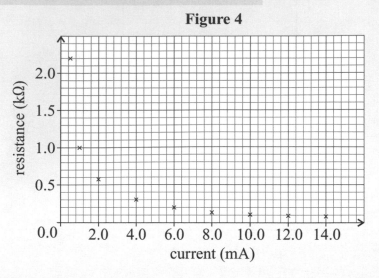

Figure 3

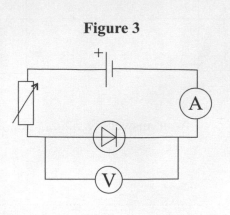

3.1 Draw a curve of best fit on **Figure 4**.

[1]

3.2 Using the graph in **Figure 4**, estimate the resistance of the diode when a current of 3.0 mA is passed through it.

Resistance = ... kΩ

[1]

3.3 The student states, "From my results, I can conclude that the greater the magnitude of the current through the diode, the lower the resistance". Why is it not possible for the student to make this conclusion from her results? Tick **one** box.

The student has only carried out the experiment for positive values of current, and the results may be different for negative values of current. ☐

The student has only carried out the experiment for a diode, and the results may be different for other components such as a filament lamp or thermistor. ☐

The student was using a digital ammeter, and the results may have been different if she'd used an analogue ammeter. ☐

[1]

3.4 Describe how the student could determine whether her experiment was reproducible.

....

....

....

[2]

[Total 5 marks]

Exam Tip

A lot of circuits that are used in experiments have quite similar looking diagrams. Make sure you pay close attention to what components are being used, and work out their purpose in the circuit, before you dive into answering any questions.

Circuit Devices

1 A thermistor is a special kind of resistor.

Which of the graphs below shows how the resistance of a thermistor changes with temperature?
Tick **one** box.

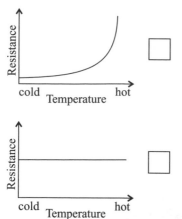

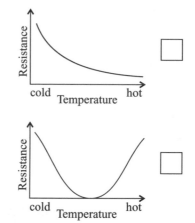

[Total 1 mark]

2 A student wants to measure the resistance of a light dependent resistor (LDR).

2.1 Draw the circuit diagram of a circuit that the student could use to measure
the resistance of an LDR. Use the circuit symbols shown in **Table 1**.

Table 1

battery	voltmeter	ammeter	LDR

[2]

2.2 The resistance of an LDR depends on its surroundings.
State what happens to the resistance of an LDR as the surrounding light intensity increases.

....

[1]

2.3 Give **one** example of a device that uses a light dependent resistor.

....

[1]

[Total 4 marks]

Topic P2 — Electricity

Series Circuits

1   **Figure 1** shows three circuits. **One** of the circuits has **all** of its components connected in series. Tick the box below this circuit.

Figure 1

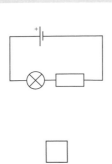

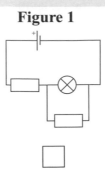

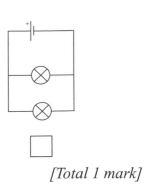

☐   ☐   ☐

[Total 1 mark]

2   **Figure 2** shows a circuit containing two resistors connected in series.

2.1 What is the total resistance of the circuit? Tick **one** box.

Figure 2

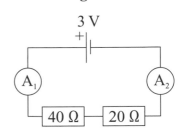

10 Ω   ☐

30 Ω   ☐

20 Ω   ☐

60 Ω   ☐

[1]

2.2 The reading on ammeter A_1 in **Figure 2** is 0.05 A.
Write down the reading on ammeter A_2.

Current = ... A
[1]

2.3 A third resistor is added in series to the circuit shown in **Figure 2**.
The potential difference across the 40 Ω resistor is 1.2 V.
The potential difference across the 20 Ω is 0.6 V.
Calculate the potential difference across the third resistor.

Potential difference = ... V
[2]
[Total 4 marks]

Topic P2 — Electricity

Parallel Circuits

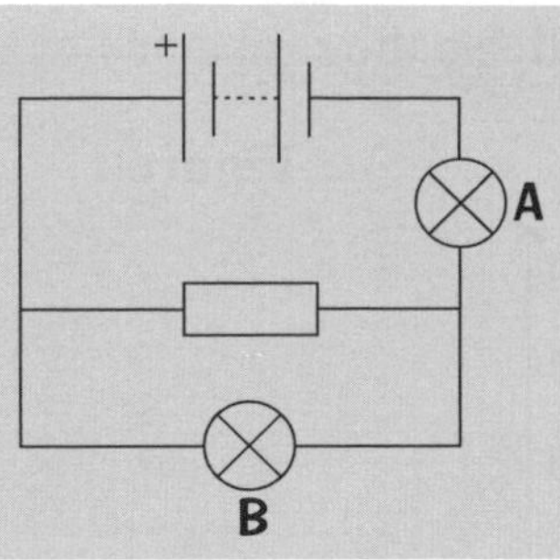

In the circuit diagram on the right, which filament lamp is connected in parallel with the resistor? Tick **one** box.

A ☐

B ☐

---

1 **Figure 1** shows a parallel circuit containing two identical resistors, R_1 and R_2. Grade 4-5

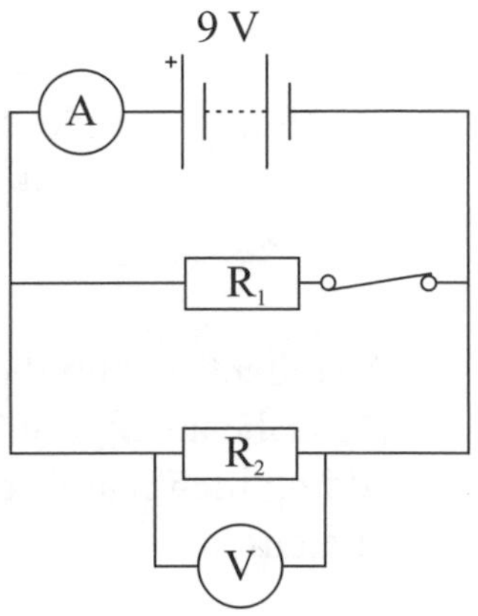

1.1 The current through R_1 in **Figure 1** is 3 A.
The current through R_2 in **Figure 1** is 3 A.
What is the reading on the ammeter in **Figure 1**?
Tick **one** box.

3 A ☐

1 A ☐

0 A ☐

6 A ☐

Figure 1

9 V

[1]

1.2 What is the reading on the voltmeter in **Figure 1**?
Tick **one** box.

3 V ☐

0 V ☐

9 V ☐

1 V ☐

[1]

Figure 2

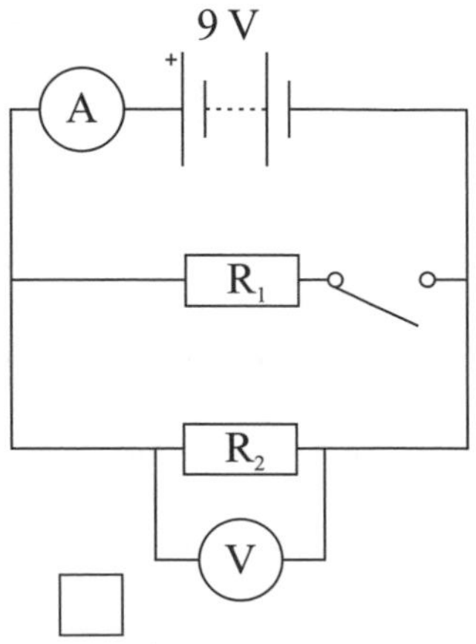

9 V

1.3 The switch is opened, as shown in **Figure 2**.
Which of the following statements about the
circuits in **Figure 1** and **Figure 2** is **true**?
Tick **one** box.

The total resistance of the circuit in **Figure 1** is larger than in **Figure 2**. ☐

The total resistance of the circuit in **Figure 1** is smaller than in **Figure 2**. ☐

The total resistance of the circuit in **Figure 1** is the same as in **Figure 2**. ☐

[1]

[Total 3 marks]

Investigating Circuits

1 A student investigates how adding identical fixed resistors in series affects the resistance of the circuit. **Figure 1** shows his results.

Figure 1

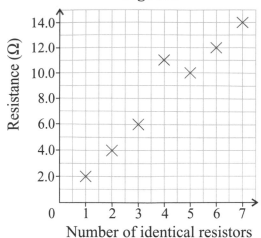

The result for four resistors is anomalous.

1.1 Draw a line of best fit for the student's data on **Figure 1**.
[1]

1.2 Use your line of best fit to predict the correct resistance for the anomalous result.

Resistance = ... Ω
[1]
[Total 2 marks]

2* A student sets up the basic circuit shown in **Figure 2**.
Describe an experiment the student could do to investigate how adding identical fixed resistors in parallel affects the overall resistance of a circuit. You may draw a circuit diagram as part of your answer.

Figure 2

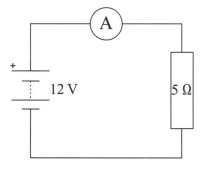

....

....

....

....

....

....

....

....

[Total 6 marks]

Electricity in the Home

Warm-Up

Choose from the words below to complete the sentences about mains electricity in the UK.

| alternating | 50 | 0 | 230 | direct |

Mains electricity is a supply of .... current.

It is at .... V and has a frequency of .... Hz.

---

1   Most electrical appliances have an electrical cable containing a live wire, a neutral wire, and an earth wire.   *(Grade 1-3)*

1.1   Name this type of cable.

....

  [1]

1.2   Each wire is coated in plastic insulation.
Draw **one** line from each wire to the colour of its insulation.

Wire

    neutral

    earth

    live

Colour of insulation

    green and yellow

    brown

    blue

  [2]

1.3   The earth wire is a safety wire used in appliances that have metal cases.
Use words from the box below to complete the passage.

| current | live | resistance | neutral | frequency | earth |

When an appliance is working normally, ... flows to the appliance through

the .... wire and the .... wire.

The .... wire will only carry current if there is a fault.

  [4]

1.4   State what could happen if a person touched an exposed live wire.

....

  [1]

  [Total 8 marks]

Exam Tip

Learning the potential difference and frequency of the UK mains supply could get you some easy marks in the exam.

Topic P2 — Electricity

Power of Electrical Appliances

1 The power source for a remote-controlled car is a battery. (Grade 1-3)

Which of the following is the main energy transfer from the battery to the toy car?
Tick **one** box.

By heating to the electrostatic energy store of the car's motor. ☐

Electrically to the nuclear energy store of the car's motor. ☐

Electrically to the kinetic energy store of the car's motor. ☐

Mechanically to the elastic potential energy store of the car's motor. ☐

[Total 1 mark]

2 Use the correct phrases from the box to complete the sentences below. (Grade 3-4)

charges	power	in total	per second	potential difference	safety

The .... of an appliance is the energy transferred ....

Energy is transferred because the .... do work against the appliance's resistance.

[Total 3 marks]

3 A student uses a 700 W microwave to heat a bowl of soup. (Grade 4-5)

3.1 Write down the equation that links energy transferred, power and time.

....

[1]

3.2 The microwave transfers 140 000 J to heat the bowl of soup.
Calculate the time it takes to heat the soup.

Time taken = ... s

[3]

3.3 The student buys a new microwave. The new microwave has a power rating of 900 W.
Explain why the 900 W microwave heats the soup faster than the 700 W microwave.

....

....

....

[2]

[Total 6 marks]

Topic P2 — Electricity

4 A student carries out an experiment to compare the useful power output of three different motors. A diagram of her experimental set-up is shown in **Figure 1**.

Figure 1

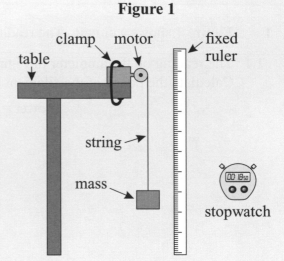

For each motor, the student follows these instructions:

- Turn on the motor.
- Use the stopwatch to measure the time taken for the motor to lift the mass through a height of 60 cm.
- Repeat this two more times.
- Calculate an average value of the time taken.
- Use the results to calculate the motor's useful power output.

4.1 Name the independent variable in this experiment.

....

[1]

4.2 Which of the following **wouldn't** increase the accuracy of the student's results? Tick **one** box.

Timing how long it takes the mass to travel 30 cm instead of 60 cm. ☐

Adding a marker to the mass that points to the ruler. ☐

Using two light gates instead of a stopwatch to measure the time taken. ☐

[1]

The student's results are shown in **Table 1**.

Table 1

Motor	Time taken / s			
	Repeat 1	**Repeat 2**	**Repeat 3**	**Mean**
A	1.9	2.1	2.2	2.1
B	5.1	4.8	4.5	....
C	3.7	3.7	3.2	3.5

4.3 Complete **Table 1** by calculating the mean time taken for motor B to lift the mass.

[2]

4.4 By lifting the mass through the same height each time, each motor transfers the same amount of energy to the mass. Use the results to determine which motor has the highest useful power output. Explain your answer.

....

....

....

....

[3]

[Total 7 marks]

Topic P2 — Electricity

More on Power

1 **Figure 1** shows a circuit. The reading on the voltmeter is 6 V.

Figure 1

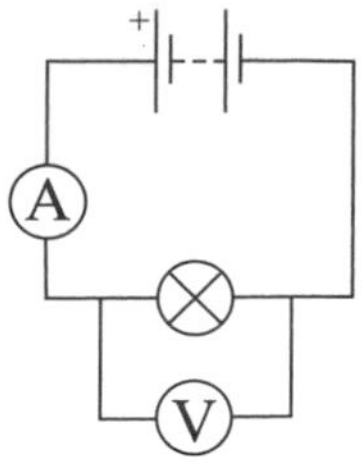

1.1 The reading on the ammeter in **Figure 1** is 2 A.
Calculate the power of the filament lamp. Use the equation:

$$\text{power} = \text{potential difference} \times \text{current}$$

Power = ... W

[2]

1.2 Write down the equation that links energy transferred, charge flow and potential difference.

....

[1]

1.3 Calculate the energy transferred to the lamp when 4 C of charge passes through it.

Energy transferred = ... J

[2]

[Total 5 marks]

2 A motor with a power of 1.5 kW has a resistance of 70 Ω.

The equation that links power, current and resistance is:

$$\text{power} = (\text{current})^2 \times \text{resistance}$$

Which calculation gives the current flowing through the motor in amps?
Tick **one** box.

$\text{current} = \sqrt{\dfrac{1500}{70}}$ ☐

$\text{current} = \sqrt{\dfrac{1.5}{140}}$ ☐

$\text{current} = \sqrt{\dfrac{70}{1500}}$ ☐

$\text{current} = 1500 \times 70$ ☐

[Total 1 mark]

Exam Tip

There's a lot of equations to do with power, but try not to panic about them. If you're not sure which one to use, look at the values you've been given, or have already calculated in the question. Then use the equation which involves those.

Topic P2 — Electricity

The National Grid

Use the words given below to label the diagram.

cables   power station   step-up transformer   step-down transformer

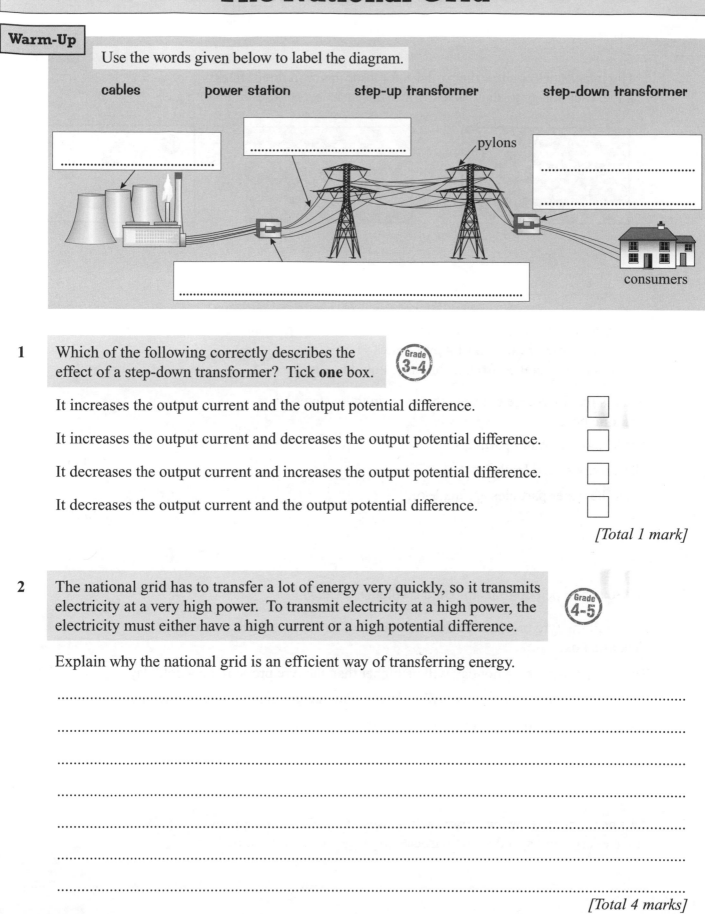

pylons

consumers

---

1 Which of the following correctly describes the effect of a step-down transformer? Tick **one** box.

Grade 3-4

It increases the output current and the output potential difference. ☐

It increases the output current and decreases the output potential difference. ☐

It decreases the output current and increases the output potential difference. ☐

It decreases the output current and the output potential difference. ☐

[Total 1 mark]

2 The national grid has to transfer a lot of energy very quickly, so it transmits electricity at a very high power. To transmit electricity at a high power, the electricity must either have a high current or a high potential difference.

Grade 4-5

Explain why the national grid is an efficient way of transferring energy.

....

....

....

....

....

....

....

[Total 4 marks]

You don't need to understand how transformers work, just what they're used for and the difference between the two types.

 ☐   ☐   ☐

The Particle Model and Motion in Gases

Warm-Up

The images below show the particles for a substance in three states.
Label each image to show whether the substance is a solid, a liquid or a gas.

....

1   A sample of ice is heated so that it melts.
The water is then heated until it evaporates.
The water has changed from a solid to a liquid to a gas.

Grade 1-3

What is the difference between the water in these states?
Tick **one** box.

The size of the water particles. ☐

The energy stored by the particles. ☐

What the water particles are made of. ☐

[Total 1 mark]

2   A tyre is pumped up to its maximum volume.   *Grade 3-4*

How will the tyre pressure be different on a hot day compared to a cold day?
Tick **one** box.

The tyre pressure on a hot day will be higher than the tyre pressure on a cold day. ☐

The tyre pressure on a hot day will be lower than the tyre pressure on a cold day. ☐

The tyre pressure on a hot day will be the same as the tyre pressure on a cold day. ☐

[Total 1 mark]

3   As a gas is cooled, its temperature decreases. Explain what happens
to the energy and speed of the particles in the gas when it is cooled.   *Grade 4-5*

....

....

....

[Total 2 marks]

😐 ☐   🙂 ☐   😊 ☐

Density of Materials

1 An irregularly shaped stone has an unknown volume. *(Grade 1-3)*

What equipment can be used for finding the volume of the stone?
Tick **one** box.

a thermometer ☐

a eureka can ☐

a mass balance ☐

a ruler ☐

a stopwatch ☐

[Total 1 mark]

2 A 1.5 m³ block of tungsten has a mass of 28 875 kg. *(Grade 4-5)*

2.1 Write down the equation that links density, mass and volume.

....
[1]

2.2 Calculate the density of tungsten. Give your answer to 2 significant figures.

Density = ... kg/m³
[2]
[Total 3 marks]

PRACTICAL

3* A student has a mass balance, a measuring cylinder and some acid (a liquid). *(Grade 4-5)*
She wants to use the equipment to find the density of the acid.

Describe an experiment the student could do to calculate the density of the acid.

....

....

....

....

....
[Total 4 marks]

Exam Tip

You might be asked to explain an experiment that is used to find the density of an object. Make sure you know the different equipment you would need for finding the density of a solid or a liquid. You should be able to explain how the equipment is used. You also need to be able to explain how the results are used to calculate the density.

 ☐ ☐ 😊 ☐

Topic P3 — Particle Model of Matter

Internal Energy and Changes of State

1 Use words from the box below to complete the passage.

| mass | increases | temperature | density | decreases |

When a system is heated, the internal energy of the system .... This either

increases the .... of the system or causes a change of state. During a change

of state the temperature and the .... of the substance remain constant.

[Total 3 marks]

2 Heating or cooling a substance can lead to a change of state.

2.1 Name the following changes of state:

Gas to liquid: ....

Liquid to gas: ....

[2]

2.2 A change of state is a physical change. Define the term 'physical change'.

....

....

[1]

[Total 3 marks]

3 A student fills a test tube with 30 g of water. He then heats the water.
Heating the water increases the internal energy of the water.

3.1 Define the term 'internal energy'.

....

....

[1]

3.2 The student continues to heat the water so that it starts to boil.
When the water boils it becomes water vapour.
He collects all of the water vapour produced.
He stops boiling the water. The mass of the water in the test tube is now 20 g.

State the mass of the water vapour the student collected.
Explain your answer.

....

....

....

[2]

[Total 3 marks]

Topic P3 — Particle Model of Matter

Specific Latent Heat

1   A sealed box containing a solid substance is heated.
    Figure 1 shows a graph of temperature against time as the substance is heated.

Figure 1

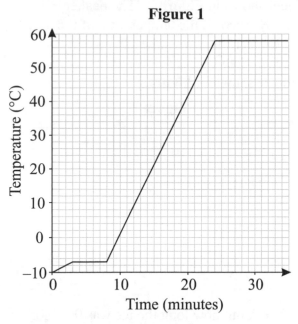

1.1 Draw straight lines to match the time period on the left
     to what is happening with the substance on the right.

Time period

| Between 3 and 8 minutes. |

| Between 24 and 35 minutes. |

| Between 8 and 24 minutes. |

Substance

| Substance is a liquid being heated. |

| Substance is melting. |

| Substance is boiling. |

| Substance is a solid being heated. |

| Substance is freezing. |

[3]

1.2 The substance has a mass of 0.50 kg.
     34 000 J of energy is transferred to the substance to completely melt it.
     The temperature of the substance does not change during this time.

Calculate the specific latent heat of fusion of the substance.
Use an equation from the Equations List.

Specific latent heat = ... J/kg
[3]

[Total 6 marks]

Topic P3 — Particle Model of Matter

Target AO3

2 A student is carrying out an experiment to determine how long it takes for ice to melt at room temperature.

The student uses the equipment shown in **Figure 2**. The beaker contains 250 g of crushed ice. He records the temperature of the ice every minute. He stops the experiment when he first records a temperature greater than 0 °C.
A graph of the student's results is shown in **Figure 3**.

Figure 2

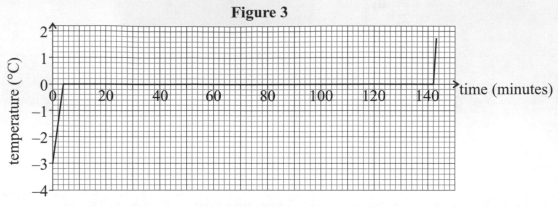

Figure 3

The student uses his graph to work out how long the ice was 0 °C for.
This is the time it took for the ice to melt.

2.1 The total energy required to melt 250 g of ice at 0 °C is 83 500 J. Using **Figure 3**, calculate the average rate of energy transfer to the ice from the surroundings in J/min.

rate of energy transfer = ... J/min
[3]

2.2 The student wants to improve his measurement of the time it took for the ice to melt.
Which of the following changes to the experiment could make this measurement more accurate?
Tick **one** box.

Taking temperature measurements every 30 s instead of every minute. ☐

Putting insulation around the beaker. ☐

Using a thermometer that can measure a lower minimum temperature. ☐

[1]

When the student stopped the experiment, he noticed that there was still some solid ice left in the beaker, so the whole 250 g of ice had not melted during the experiment.

2.3 Suggest how the student could find the actual mass of ice that melted during the experiment.

....

....

....

[2]

[Total 6 marks]

Topic P3 — Particle Model of Matter

The Current Model of the Atom

Warm-Up

What is the typical radius of an atom?

☐ 1×10^{-10} m   ☐ 1×10^{10} m   ☐ 1×10^{-20} m   ☐ 1×10^{-15} m

1 Scientists currently agree that a nuclear model is the best description of the atom we have. *(Grade 1-3)*

1.1 The passage below describes the nuclear model of the atom.
Use words from the box below to complete the passage.

| electrons | neutrons | size | protons | positively | mass | negatively |

An atom is made of a ....-charged nucleus, surrounded by ....

The nucleus contains .... and ....

The nucleus makes up most of the .... of the atom.

[5]

1.2 How many times smaller is the radius of the nucleus compared to the radius of the atom?
Tick **one** box.

10 000   ☐

100 000   ☐

10   ☐

[1]

[Total 6 marks]

2 Niels Bohr discovered that electrons within an atom can only exist in defined energy levels. *(Grade 4-5)*

2.1 Atoms can emit and absorb electromagnetic radiation.
Describe how this affects the positions of electrons in the atom.

....

....

....

....

[3]

2.2 An atom loses an electron. Is the new particle positively, negatively or neutrally charged?
Explain why.

....

....

[2]

[Total 5 marks]

Isotopes and Nuclear Radiation

1 Some isotopes are unstable. They emit nuclear radiation. (Grade 3-4)

1.1 Draw **one** line from each term to the correct definition.

Term | **Definition**

Isotopes

Gamma

Alpha particles

Atoms with the same number of protons but different numbers of neutrons.

Particles made up of two neutrons and two protons.

Nuclear radiation made up of electromagnetic waves.

[2]

1.2 An unstable isotope decays. It releases a high-speed electron from its nucleus. Name this type of radioactive decay.

....
[1]
[Total 3 marks]

2 One isotope of sodium is $_{11}^{23}$Na. (Grade 4-5)

2.1 Write down the mass number of this isotope.

....
[1]

2.2 Calculate the number of neutrons in the sodium nucleus.

Number of neutrons = ...
[1]

2.3 Which of the following is another isotope of sodium? Tick **one** box.

$_{23}^{11}$Na ☐ $_{24}^{11}$Na ☐ $_{12}^{23}$Na ☐ $_{11}^{24}$Na ☐
[1]
[Total 3 marks]

3 Beta sources are used when making paper. Beta particles pass through the paper and the count-rate is measured. The paper is then made thicker or thinner depending on the count-rate measured. (Grade 4-5)

Explain why a source that emits alpha particles or gamma rays couldn't be used for this purpose.

....
....
....
[Total 2 marks]

Target AO3

4 An engineer is investigating how the thickness of paper placed between a source of beta radiation and a detector affects the amount of radiation that reaches the detector.

Grade 4-5

The engineer uses a Geiger-Muller tube to measure the amount of radiation emitted from the source that makes it through different thicknesses of some sheets of paper.
A top-down view of their experimental set-up is shown in **Figure 1**.

Figure 1

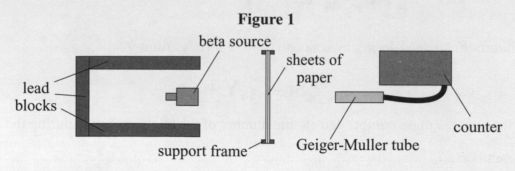

4.1 Identify **one** safety feature in **Figure 1**. Explain how it reduces the risk of harm to the engineer.

....

....

....
[2]

Table 1 shows the engineer's results for one thickness of the set of paper sheets.

Table 1

thickness of paper (mm)	count-rate detected (cps)		
	Trial 1	Trial 2	Trial 3
0.5	101	122	105

4.2 Calculate the uncertainty in the count-rate measurements in **Table 1**.

uncertainty = ... cps
[2]

4.3 Calculate the mean value of count-rate detected for a paper thickness of 0.5 mm.

mean count-rate = ... cps
[2]

[Total 6 marks]

Exam Tip

In the exam, you could be given some raw data from an experiment. You need to know how to process the data, e.g. find the mean or the uncertainty, and you may also be asked to interpret the results. For example, you might need to draw a conclusion or comment on how accurate the results are. So it's important you're comfortable with what these terms mean.

Topic P4 — Atomic Structure

Nuclear Equations

Warm-Up

The nuclear equation below shows an atom releasing a gamma ray.
Complete the nuclear equation by filling in the missing number.

$$^{99}_{44}Ru \rightarrow {}^{99}_{44}Ru + {}^{0}_{.....}\gamma$$

1 A strontium-90 nucleus decays by beta emission to form yttrium-90.

$$^{90}_{38}Sr \rightarrow {}^{90}_{39}Y + {}^{0}_{-1}e$$

1.1 Describe how the mass number and atomic number of the nucleus change during the decay.

Mass number: ....

Atomic number: ....

[2]

1.2 How does the charge of the nucleus change after this decay? Tick **one** box.

It increases. ☐

It decreases. ☐

There is no change. ☐

[1]

[Total 3 marks]

2 A student writes down the following nuclear decay equation: (Grade 4-5)

$$^{226}_{88}Ra \rightarrow {}^{a}_{b}Rn + {}^{4}_{2}X$$

2.1 What particle is represented by **X** in the nuclear decay equation above?

....

[1]

2.2 Calculate the values of a and b.

a = ...

b = ...

[2]

2.3 The radon (Rn) isotope then undergoes an alpha decay to form an isotope of polonium (Po).
Write a balanced nuclear equation to show this.

....

[3]

[Total 6 marks]

Topic P4 — Atomic Structure

Half-life

1 The passage below describes terms relating to radioactive decay. Use words from the box below to complete the passage.

| activity | becquerels | half-life | radiation | watts |

The .... is the time taken for the number of nuclei of a radioactive

isotope in a sample to halve. The rate of decay of a radioactive isotope is called

its .... and it is measured in ....

[Total 3 marks]

2 The graph in **Figure 1** shows how the count-rate of a radioactive sample changes over time.

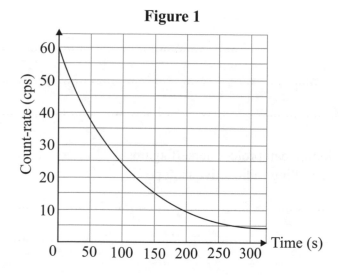

Figure 1

2.1 Using **Figure 1**, determine the half-life of the sample.

Half-life = ... s

[1]

2.2 At first, the sample contains approximately 800 undecayed nuclei.
Predict how many of these nuclei will have decayed after two half-lives.

Number of decayed nuclei = ...

[2]

[Total 3 marks]

Exam Tip

If you come across a half-life question in the exam, if you're given a graph, it should look similar to the one in Figure 1. The numbers will change from example to example, but if you can understand that curve, you'll be halfway there.

Topic P4 — Atomic Structure

Irradiation and Contamination

1 Workers in a nuclear power station are at risk of being irradiated by nuclear radiation. Which of the following methods would reduce their risk of irradiation? Tick **one** box. *(Grade 1-3)*

Work behind barriers that absorb radiation. ☐

Keep fire extinguishers close by. ☐

Wear clean clothes. ☐

[Total 1 mark]

2 A scientist is looking at the safety plans to be used in her lab while using radioactive isotopes. She is worried about **contamination** and **irradiation**. *(Grade 4-5)*

2.1 Explain the difference between contamination and irradiation.

....

....

....

....

[2]

2.2 Give **two** ways the scientist can protect herself against **contamination** when handling radioactive isotopes.

1. ....

2. ....

[2]

[Total 4 marks]

3 Radium-226 is an alpha source. Radium-226 was used in clocks until the 1960s. *(Grade 4-5)*

Should a clockmaker be more worried about contamination or irradiation when working on clocks made before 1960? Explain your answer.

....

....

....

....

....

[Total 3 marks]

Exam Tip

Make sure you learn the differences between irradiation and contamination and how to lower the risks of both. Remember, the dangers of irradiation or contamination depend on the type of radiation.

Contact and Non-Contact Forces

Warm-Up

Each quantity below is either a scalar or a vector.
Write each word in the correct place in the table.

acceleration   time   temperature

mass   velocity   force

Scalar	Vector

---

1 Which of the following correctly describes a vector? Tick **one** box.

Vector quantities only have magnitude. ☐

Vector quantities have direction but not magnitude. ☐

Vector quantities have both magnitude and direction. ☐

[Total 1 mark]

---

2 A child is pulling a toy train along the floor using a piece of string.
State **one** contact force and **one** non-contact force that acts on the toy.

Contact force: ....

Non-contact force: ....

[Total 2 marks]

---

3 **Figure 1** shows two pairs of identical magnets. There is a force of repulsion between
Magnet A and Magnet B. There is a force of attraction between Magnet C and Magnet D.

Figure 1

Magnet A and Magnet B

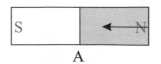
A

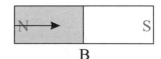
B

Magnet C and Magnet D

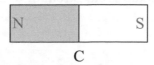
C

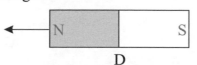
D

Complete the diagram in **Figure 1** by drawing an arrow that
represents the force Magnet D exerts on Magnet C.

[Total 2 marks]

Weight, Mass and Gravity

1   Draw **one** line from each property to the unit it is measured in.   (Grade 1-3)

Property	Unit
mass	kilograms
weight	newtons

[Total 1 mark]

2   Which of the following correctly describes the relationship between mass and weight? Tick **one** box.   (Grade 3-4)

Mass and weight are inversely proportional. ☐

Mass and weight are directly proportional. ☐

Mass and weight are the same thing. ☐

There is no relationship between mass and weight. ☐

[Total 1 mark]

3   Opportunity is a robot which is currently on the surface of the planet Mars. The total mass of Opportunity is 185 kg.   (Grade 4-5)

3.1 Write down the equation that links weight, mass and gravitational field strength.

....

[1]

3.2 Calculate the weight of Opportunity when it was on the Earth.
(The gravitational field strength on the surface of Earth = 9.8 N/kg.)
Give your answer to 2 significant figures.

Weight = ... N

[2]

3.3 The weight of Opportunity on Mars is 703 N.
Calculate the gravitational field strength on the surface of Mars.

Gravitational Field Strength = ... N/kg

[3]

[Total 6 marks]

Exam Tip

Outside of physics, people often use the term weight when they mean mass. Make sure you understand the difference. You measure mass on a balance, but weight is a force measured by a spring-balance (newtonmeter).

Topic P5 — Forces

Target AO3

4 A student is doing an experiment to determine the gravitational field strength on Earth.

To do this, the student intends to measure the weight of a set of iron discs.
Each disc is labelled with its mass.

4.1 The student wants to check the mass of each disc.
Suggest how the student could do this.

....

....
[1]

To measure the weight of a disc, the disc is placed on
a small plastic tray that is hung from the newtonmeter,
as shown in **Figure 1**. The student records the weight
of the disc by writing down the reading on the newtonmeter.
However, the reading is actually the combined weight
of the disc and the tray.

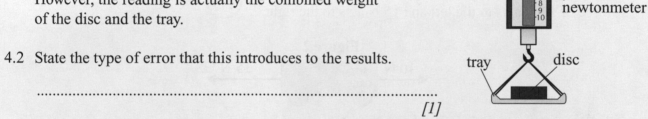

Figure 1

newtonmeter

tray   disc

4.2 State the type of error that this introduces to the results.

....
[1]

4.3 The student carries out the experiment, and records their results in **Table 1**.
The student then plotted their results on the grid shown in **Figure 2**.
Complete the graph in **Figure 2** by plotting the missing points. Draw a line of best fit on **Figure 2**.

Table 1

Mass (kg)	Weight (N)
0.2	2.2
0.3	3.2
0.4	4.2
0.5	5.0
0.6	6.4
0.7	7.2
0.8	8.2

Figure 2

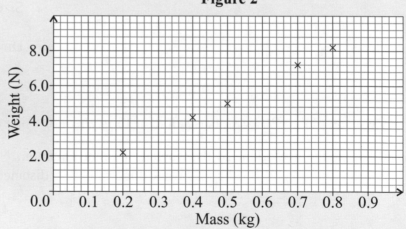

[2]

4.4 The gradient of the graph in **Figure 2** is equal to the Earth's gravitational field strength.
Calculate a value for the gravitational field strength using the graph in **Figure 2**.

Gravitational field strength = ... N/kg
[2]

[Total 6 marks]

Topic P5 — Forces

Resultant Forces and Work Done

1   **Figure 1** shows four runners who are running in windy weather.
Tick the box under the runner who is experiencing the largest resultant force.

Figure 1

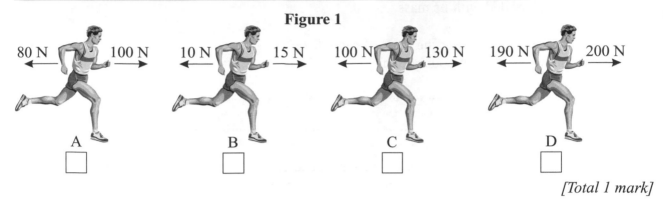

80 N ← → 100 N   10 N ← → 15 N   100 N ← → 130 N   190 N ← → 200 N

A ☐   B ☐   C ☐   D ☐

[Total 1 mark]

2   **Figure 2** shows two forces acting on a trolley.
A force of 10 N acts to the left and 15 N acts to the right.

Figure 2

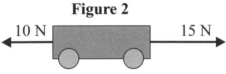

10 N ← → 15 N

Calculate the resultant force on the trolley. Give its size and direction.

Size of resultant force = ... N

Direction = ...
[Total 2 marks]

3   A woman pulls a 20 kg suitcase along a 15 m corridor using a horizontal force of 50 N.

3.1   Calculate the work done by the woman. Use the equation:
Work done = force × distance

Work done = ... Nm
[2]

3.2   Work is done against frictional forces acting on the wheels of the suitcase.
Describe the effect this has on the temperature of wheels. Explain this in terms of energy transfer.

....

....
[2]
[Total 4 marks]

Topic P5 — Forces

Forces and Elasticity

1 A student hangs masses from a spring. This causes the spring to stretch. (Grade 3-4)

1.1 Two forces are being applied to the spring to make it stretch.
Explain why more than one force is needed to make the spring stretch.

....

....

[1]

1.2 The student removes the masses. The spring returns to its original length and shape.
Name this type of deformation.

....

[1]

1.3 The student adds more masses to the spring.
When the masses are removed, the spring doesn't return to its original shape.
Name this type of deformation.

....

[1]

[Total 3 marks]

2 A child sits on the toy horse in **Figure 1**. His feet don't touch the floor. (Grade 4-5)

Figure 1

The child exerts a force of 240 N on the horse.
The height of the toy horse decreases by 0.20 m.
Calculate the spring constant of the spring.
Use the equation:

$$\text{force} = \text{spring constant} \times \text{extension}$$

Choose the correct unit from the box.

N/m	N/kg	kg m³

Spring constant = ... Unit = ...

[Total 4 marks]

Topic P5 — Forces

Investigating Springs

1   A student investigated the relationship between the force exerted on, and the extension of, a spring. He hung different numbers of masses from the bottom of the spring. Each time he measured the extension of the spring with a ruler. His set up is shown in **Figure 1**.

Figure 1

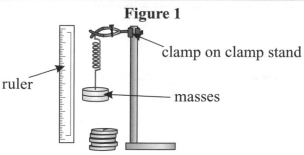

ruler

clamp on clamp stand

masses

Table 1

Force (N)	Extension (cm)
0	0
1	3.0
2	6.0
3	9.0
4	12.0
5	16.5
6	24.5

Figure 2

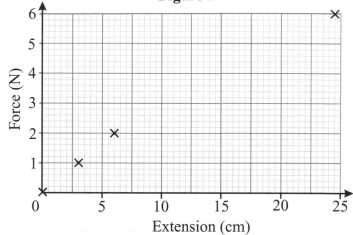

1.1   **Table 1** shows the results that the student obtained in his investigation. Complete the force-extension graph in **Figure 2** by plotting the **three** missing points from **Table 1** and drawing a line of best fit.

[3]

1.2   What name is given to the point on the graph where force and extension stop being directly proportional?

....

[1]

[Total 4 marks]

2   A spring is extended elastically by 8.0 cm. The spring constant of the spring is 25 N/m.

Calculate the work done on the spring. Use an equation from the Equations List.

Work done = ... J

[Total 3 marks]

Distance, Displacement, Speed and Velocity

1 **Figure 1** shows the path taken by a football kicked by a child. When it is kicked at point A, the ball moves horizontally to the right until it hits a vertical wall at point B. The ball then bounces back horizontally to the left and comes to rest at point C.

Figure 1

Scale 1 cm = 1 m

A   C   B

1.1 What is the total distance travelled by the ball as it moves from A to B?

Distance = ... m

[1]

1.2 Calculate the total distance travelled by the ball.

Distance = ... m

[1]

1.3 What is the magnitude of the displacement of the ball after it has come to rest?

Displacement = ... m

[1]

[Total 3 marks]

2 A man has just got a new job and wants to know how long it will take to get to work. His route to work is along a 6 km path.

2.1 What is the typical walking speed of a person?

Typical speed = ... m/s

[1]

2.2 Give **three** factors that can affect a person's walking speed.

1. ....

2. ....

3. ....

[3]

2.3 Write down the formula that links distance travelled, speed and time.

....

[1]

2.4 Estimate how long it would take the man to walk to work.

Time taken = ... s

[3]

[Total 8 marks]

Topic P5 — Forces

Acceleration

Circle the value below that is the acceleration of an object falling freely on Earth.

9800 m/s²   98 m/s²   0.0098 m/s²

1   An object is decelerating. Tick **one** box which describes its motion.

Moving with increasing velocity ☐   Moving with decreasing velocity ☐

Moving with a uniform velocity ☐   Stationary ☐

[Total 1 mark]

2   **Table 1** shows how the velocity of a car changes with time as it accelerates uniformly.

Table 1

Time (s)	0	1	2	3
Velocity (m/s)	0	4	8	12

2.1   Write down the formula that links acceleration, velocity and time.

....

[1]

2.2   Calculate the acceleration of the car.

Acceleration = ... m/s²

[2]

[Total 3 marks]

3   A train is travelling at 18 m/s. It speeds up to 32 m/s over a distance of 350 m. Calculate the acceleration of the train over this distance. Use an equation from the Equations List.

Acceleration = ... m/s²

[Total 3 marks]

Distance-Time Graphs

1 A boat is being rowed along a straight canal. Some students use a watch to time how long after setting off the boat passes markers spaced 100 metres apart. **Table 1** shows their results.

Table 1

Distance (m)	0	100	200	300	400	500
Time (s)	0	85	170	255	340	425

Figure 1

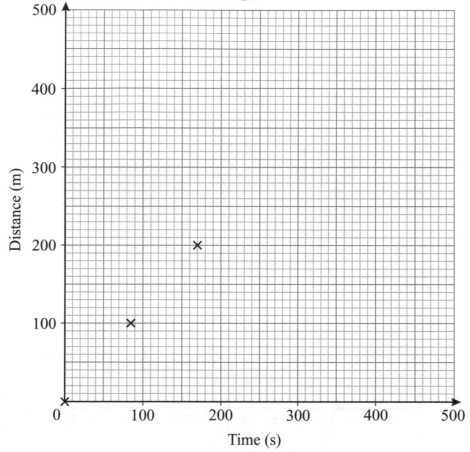

1.1 Complete the distance-time graph in **Figure 1** using the results in **Table 1**.

[3]

1.2 Using the graph in **Figure 1**, estimate how far the boat travelled in 300 s.

Distance = ... m

[1]

1.3 Using the graph in **Figure 1**, estimate how long it took the boat to travel 250 m.

Time = ... s

[1]

1.4 Describe the boat's speed during the first 500 m of its journey.

....

[1]

[Total 6 marks]

Topic P5 — Forces

Velocity-Time Graphs and Terminal Velocity

1 Any object falling for long enough reaches its terminal velocity.
Which statements correctly describe terminal velocity? Tick **two** boxes.

Terminal velocity is the minimum velocity an object can fall at. ☐

The resultant vertical force on an object falling at its terminal velocity is zero. ☐

The resultant vertical force on an object falling at its terminal velocity equals its weight. ☐

Terminal velocity is the maximum velocity an object can fall at. ☐

[Total 1 mark]

2 **Figure 1** shows a velocity-time graph for a roller coaster car.

Figure 1

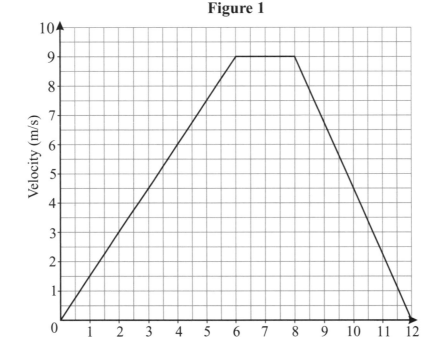

2.1 The car is accelerating between 0 s and 6 s.
Using the graph in **Figure 1**, calculate the acceleration for the ride between 0 s and 6 s.

Acceleration = ... m/s²
[3]

2.2 Between what times is the car travelling at a constant speed?

....
[1]

[Total 4 marks]

Target AO3

3   A teacher did an experiment to investigate how the speed of a rechargeable remote-controlled car varies with how well charged it is.

The teacher set the car going in a straight line along a straight track.
He measured the speed of the car at fixed distances as it travelled along the track.
He repeated his experiment 3 times — once when the car was 100% charged,
once when it was 75% charged, and once when it was 50% charged.

3.1   Identify the independent variable in the teacher's experiment.

....

[1]

3.2   Which of the following pieces of equipment would be the most suitable for the teacher to use to measure the speed of the car accurately? Tick **one** box.

A stopwatch and a tape measure.   ☐

A protractor and a metre ruler.   ☐

A set of light gates, connected to a data-logger.   ☐

[1]

The teacher uses his results to plot a velocity-time graph for each of his experiments on the same grid, shown in **Figure 3**.

Figure 3

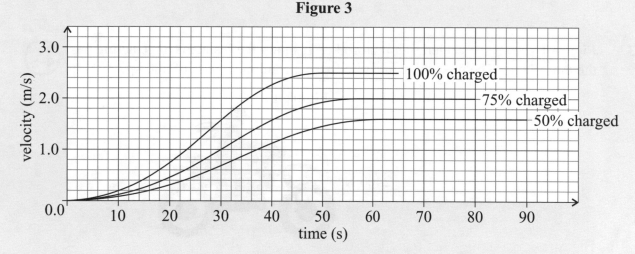

3.3   The teacher makes the following statement based on his results:
"When the car was 100% charged, it reached its maximum speed in the shortest time."
Explain how the graphs in **Figure 3** show that his statement is correct.

....

....

....

[2]

[Total 4 marks]

Exam Tip

A handy way to tackle velocity-time graph questions is to split the graph up into sections with different shapes or gradients.
You can then work out what is happening in each of those sections, and piece them together to get the full picture.

 ☐   ☐   ☐

Topic P5 — Forces

Newton's First and Second Laws

1 State Newton's First Law for a stationary object.

....

....

[Total 1 mark]

2 The passage below describes Newton's Second Law.
Use words from the box below to complete the passage.

area	weight	mass	driving	resistive	resultant

Newton's Second Law states that the acceleration of an object is directly

proportional to the .... force acting on the object.

Newton's Second Law also says that the acceleration is inversely proportional to the

.... of the object.

[Total 2 marks]

3 **Figure 1** shows an accelerating motorbike. It shows the resultant force acting on
the motorbike. The motorbike and rider have a combined mass of 400 kg.

Figure 1

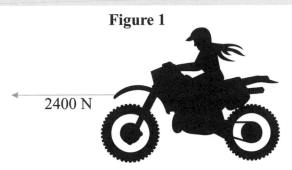

2400 N

Calculate the acceleration of the motorbike. Use the equation:

Force = mass × acceleration

Choose the correct unit from the box.

N	kg	m/s²

Acceleration = ... Unit = ...

[Total 4 marks]

Topic P5 — Forces

Newton's Third Law

Warm-Up

Which of the following is Newton's Third Law? Tick **one** box.

A resultant force is inversely proportional to the mass of an object. ☐

When two objects interact, they exert equal and opposite forces on each other. ☐

A resultant force of zero leads to an equilibrium situation. ☐

1   **Figure 1** shows skater A pushing on skater B with a force of 100 N. Using Newton's Third Law, what force does skater B exert on skater A? Tick **one** box.

Figure 1

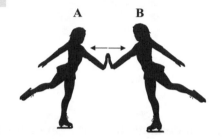

50 N   ☐

150 N   ☐

200 N   ☐

100 N   ☐

[Total 1 mark]

2   **Figure 2** shows the forces acting on a gymnast balancing on two beams. The gymnast is in equilibrium.

Figure 2

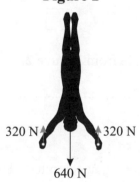

320 N↑   ↑320 N

↓
640 N

2.1   State the size of the force exerted by each of the gymnast's hands on the balance beams.

Force = ... N

[1]

2.2   State the size of the attractive force exerted on the Earth by the gymnast.

Force = ... N

[1]

[Total 2 marks]

Exam Tip

If you're struggling to see what's going on in a question, try drawing a quick diagram. Make sure it shows all the forces mentioned in the question. Then look at each force one at a time to work out what effect it's having.

 ☐   ☐   ☐

PRACTICAL   Investigating Motion

1   **Figure 1** shows the equipment used by a student to investigate how changing the force on a trolley changes its acceleration. The trolley is on a frictionless, flat surface.

Figure 1

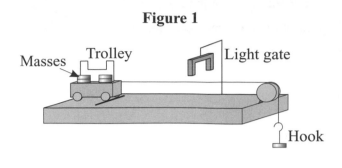

Figure 2

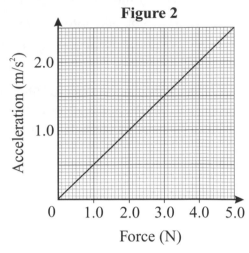

The student changes the force on the trolley by moving a mass from the trolley to the hook. The acceleration for different forces is recorded.
Figure 2 is a graph of acceleration against force for the trolley.

1.1   For this experiment, what is the mass being accelerated? Tick **one** box.

The mass of the hook.   ☐

The mass of the hook and the trolley.   ☐

The mass of the trolley.   ☐

[1]

1.2   Give **one** conclusion that can be made from **Figure 2**.

....

....

[1]

1.3   Using **Figure 2**, calculate the mass being accelerated. Use the equation:
$$\text{Force} = \text{mass} \times \text{acceleration}$$

Mass = ... kg

[3]

1.4   The mass on the hook was kept the same. 50 g of mass was added to the trolley.
What effect will this have on the acceleration of the trolley?

....

[1]

[Total 6 marks]

Topic P5 — Forces

Stopping Distance and Thinking Distance

1 A car is travelling at 40 mph. The thinking distance of the driver is 12 m. The braking distance of the car is 24 m. Calculate the car's stopping distance when it is travelling at 40 mph. Tick **one** box.

Grade 1-3

36 m ☐

12 m ☐

24 m ☐

[Total 1 mark]

2 Define the following terms: *Grade 3-4*

2.1 Thinking distance

....

[1]

2.2 Braking distance

....

[1]
[Total 2 marks]

3 Give **three** things that could affect a person's reaction time. *Grade 3-4*

1. ....

2. ....

3. ....

[Total 3 marks]

4 Explain why a driver with a slower than average reaction time has an increased risk of being in an accident. *Grade 4-5*

....

....

....

[Total 2 marks]

Exam Tip

A good habit to get into is learning how to keep your longer explanation and description answers clear and to the point. Most of the time, you won't get any marks for bonus information. If you stick to the key points, then you'll be sorted.

220

Braking Distance

Warm-Up

Circle the factors below which affect the braking distance of a vehicle.

Drinking alcohol   Broken headlights   Snow on the road

Bald tyres   Drug use

Driver distractions

Ice on the road   Smooth road surface

1   A heavy vehicle travelling quickly can have a very large deceleration.
    State **two** dangers of large decelerations.

Grade 1-3

1. ....

2. ....

[Total 2 marks]

2   When a vehicle's brakes are applied, friction between the wheels and brakes
    causes work to be done. Explain how this affects the temperature of the brakes.
    You should include a description of the energy transfers that occur.

Grade 4-5

....

....

....

....

[Total 2 marks]

3* Explain the importance of car tyres that are in good condition when driving in the rain.
    Explain the effect this will have on the stopping distance and the overall safety of the car.

Grade 4-5

....

....

....

....

....

....

....

....

[Total 4 marks]

Topic P5 — Forces

Reaction Times

1 What is the typical reaction time for a person? Tick **one** box.

☐ 1.3 – 1.8 s   ☐ 0.2 – 0.9 s   ☐ 0.01 – 0.02 s   ☐ 2.0 – 3.0 s

[Total 1 mark]

2 A teacher tests the reaction times of three of her students.
She measures how far a ruler vertically falls before the student catches it.

2.1 Describe **one** other method that can be used to test people's reaction times.

....

....

[1]

2.2 **Table 1** shows the teacher's results.
The values in the table show the distance the ruler falls in cm during each attempt.
Complete the table by working out the average distance fallen by the ruler for each student.

Table 1

	Attempt 1	Attempt 2	Attempt 3	Average
Student A	7.0	7.1	6.9	....
Student B	8.4	8.2	8.3	....
Student C	6.5	7.0	6.0	6.5

[2]

2.3 Which student has the fastest average reaction time?

....

[1]

2.4 Suggest **two** ways the teacher could make the experiment a fair test.

1. ....

2. ....

[2]

2.5 The teacher then repeats the experiment. This time, she has a fourth student talk to the student being tested. Suggest how you would expect this to affect the reaction times of the students.

....

[1]

[Total 7 marks]

Topic P5 — Forces

Transverse and Longitudinal Waves

1   **Figure 1** shows a displacement-distance graph of a wave.

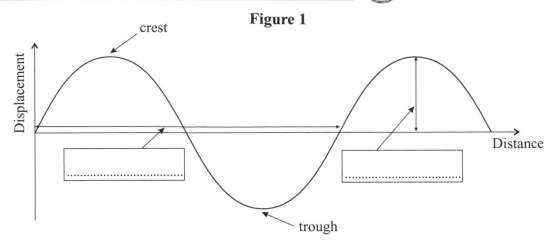

Figure 1

1.1   Use phrases from the box to complete the labels in **Figure 1**.

wavelength	period	rest position	amplitude

[2]

1.2   What is meant by the term 'frequency'?

....

[1]

1.3   Describe the difference between longitudinal waves and transverse waves.

....

....

....

[2]

[Total 5 marks]

2   A child throws a stone into a pond. The stone creates ripples when it hits the water. These ripples spread across the pond.

The child thinks that a leaf floating on the pond will move to the edge of the pond with the ripples. Explain whether or not she is correct.

....

....

....

[Total 2 marks]

Frequency, Period and Wave Speed

1 A wave has a period of 2 s.

Calculate the frequency of the wave. Use the equation:

$$\text{frequency} = 1 \div \text{period}$$

Frequency = ... Hz

[Total 2 marks]

2 A student investigated the speed of sound in air.
The equipment she used is shown in **Figure 1**.

The sound waves detected by each microphone were shown
as separate traces on the oscilloscope screen.

Figure 1

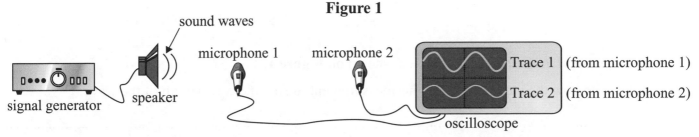

2.1 Her method is described below in steps **A** to **E**.
Steps **A** to **E** are not in the correct order.

A Measure the distance between the microphones. This is the wavelength.
B Stop moving microphone 2 when the traces line up, as shown in **Figure 1**.
C Use the measured distance and the frequency of the signal generator to find the wave speed.
D Begin with both microphones at an equal distance from the speaker.
E Keeping microphone 1 fixed, slowly move microphone 2
away from the speaker, causing trace 2 to move.

In the spaces below, write down the correct order of steps.
The first one has been done for you.

D ⟶ .... ⟶ .... ⟶ .... ⟶ ....

[3]

2.2 Write down the equation that relates wave speed, frequency and wavelength.

....

[1]

2.3 The signal generator is set to 50.0 Hz. The wavelength of the sound waves
is measured to be 6.80 m. Calculate the speed of the sound waves.

Wave speed = ... m/s

[2]

[Total 6 marks]

Topic P6 — Waves

Investigating Waves

1   A student produces a wave on a string using a vibration generator.
A snapshot of the wave on the string is shown in **Figure 1**.

Figure 1

d

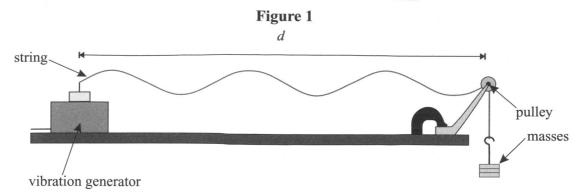

1.1   How many wavelengths are shown on the string in **Figure 1**?

Number of wavelengths = ...
[1]

1.2   The student measures the distance, *d*, shown on **Figure 1**.

Explain how the student can use this measurement to find the wavelength of the wave.

....

....
[1]

[Total 2 marks]

2   A student is investigating water waves in a ripple tank.
She sets up the equipment shown in **Figure 2**.

Figure 2

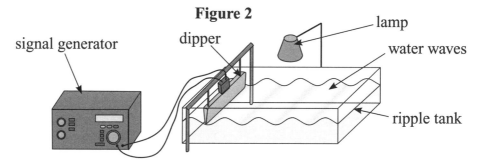

Explain how the student could use this equipment to find the speed of the water waves.

....

....

....

....

....

....

[Total 4 marks]

Topic P6 — Waves

Refraction

1   **Figure 1** shows a ray of light refracting as it passes into a glass block.

Figure 1

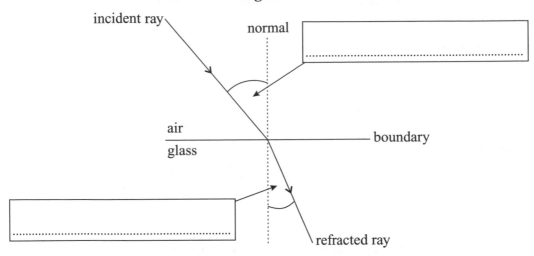

1.1 Label the angle of incidence and the angle of refraction on **Figure 1**.

[1]

1.2 Give the angle between the normal and the boundary.

Angle = ... °

[1]

[Total 2 marks]

2   A light ray travelling through air hits the boundary of a clear plastic block. The angle of incidence at the air to plastic boundary is 30°. The angle of refraction is 20°.

Draw a ray diagram to show the refraction of the light ray at the boundary.
The boundary has been drawn for you.

[Total 4 marks]

Topic P6 — Waves

Electromagnetic Waves

1   All electromagnetic waves are part of the electromagnetic spectrum.   (Grade 1-3)

Which of the following electromagnetic waves has the highest frequency?
Tick **one** box.

infrared radiation ☐

visible light ☐

gamma rays ☐

ultraviolet radiation ☐

[Total 1 mark]

2   **Table 1** shows the electromagnetic spectrum. It is incomplete.   (Grade 4-5)

2.1   Complete **Table 1** by filling in the missing types of electromagnetic waves.

[2]

Table 1

Radio Waves	....	Infrared	Visible Light	Ultraviolet	....	Gamma Rays

2.2   Draw an arrow beneath **Table 1** that points from the electromagnetic waves with the shortest wavelength towards the electromagnetic waves with the longest wavelength.

[1]

2.3   Use phrases from the box below to complete the following sentences.

a vacuum	glass	sound	longitudinal	transverse	water

All waves in the electromagnetic spectrum are .... waves.

All electromagnetic waves travel at the same speed in ....

[2]

2.4   Changes in atoms can create different types of electromagnetic waves.
What type of electromagnetic wave is generated by changes in the nucleus of an atom?

....

[1]

[Total 6 marks]

Exam Tip

You need to know each type of electromagnetic radiation in the EM spectrum for your exam. You also need to be able to put them in order of increasing frequency or wavelength. Remember, visible light is in the middle of the EM spectrum.

Uses of EM Waves

The phrases below show parts of a passage describing the uses of radio waves. Number each phrase 1 to 5 to show the correct order of parts. The first one has been done for you.

☐ ...can send signals very long distances.   **1** Radio waves can be used to...

☐ ...transmit TV signals...   ☐ ...and radio signals.   ☐ Some wavelengths...

1 Microwave radiation can be used to cook food. (Grade 3-4)

1.1 Use words from the box below to complete the sentences.

| emits | reflects | increase | absorbs | decrease |

When food is cooked in a microwave oven, water in the food .... microwaves.

This causes the temperature of the food to ....

[2]

1.2 Give **one** other use of microwave radiation.

....

[1]

[Total 3 marks]

2 Infrared cameras are used to create images of objects in the dark. They work by detecting the amount of infrared radiation given out by an object. (Grade 3-4)

2.1 Which phrase, **A**, **B** or **C**, should be used to complete the sentence below? Write the correct letter, **A**, **B** or **C**, in the space below.

A more infrared radiation than

B the same amount of infrared radiation as

C less infrared radiation than

Hotter objects give out .... cooler objects.

[1]

2.2 Give **two** other devices that use infrared radiation.

1. ....

2. ....

[2]

[Total 3 marks]

Topic P6 — Waves

More Uses of EM Waves

1 Visible light and ultraviolet radiation are parts of the electromagnetic spectrum. *Grade 1-3*

1.1 Which of the following is a use of visible light? Tick **one** box.

fibre-optic cables for communication ☐

suntanning lamps ☐

cooking food ☐

[1]

1.2 Which of the following is a use of ultraviolet light? Tick **one** box.

cooking food ☐

communicating by satellite ☐

energy efficient lamps ☐

sending TV signals ☐

[1]

1.3 Name **one** other use of ultraviolet light.

....

[1]

[Total 3 marks]

2 Electromagnetic waves can be used to treat illnesses. *Grade 3-4*

2.1 Give **two** types of electromagnetic wave that can be used to treat cancer

1. ....

2. ....

[2]

2.2 Describe **one** other use of an electromagnetic wave in medicine.

....

....

[1]

[Total 3 marks]

Exam Tip

Electromagnetic radiation has a lot of uses. Make sure you know at least one use for each part of the EM spectrum. Being able to remember the different uses is an easy way to get yourself some marks in the exam.

Topic P6 — Waves

Investigating IR Radiation

1 A student is investigating the amount of infrared radiation emitted by different surfaces.

The equipment the student uses is shown in **Figure 1**.

She uses a Leslie cube with four different surfaces.

The student places an infrared detector in front of each face of the Leslie cube.
Each detector is placed the same distance from the cube.

Figure 1

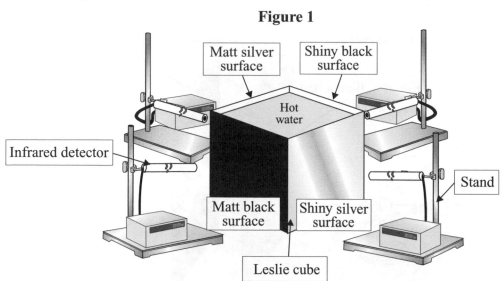

The student recorded how much radiation was detected by each infrared detector.
Her results are shown in **Table 1**.

Table 1

	Matt silver surface	Shiny silver surface	Matt black surface	Shiny black surface
Reading on infrared detector	63	45	90	74

1.1 Suggest a suitable graph or chart the student could use to present their results.
Give a reason for your answer.

Suggestion ....

Reason ....

....

[2]

1.2 Use the information in **Table 1** to place the surfaces in order
from the best to worst emitter of infrared radiation.

Best emitter ....

↑ ....

↓ ....

Worst emitter ....

[1]

[Total 3 marks]

Topic P6 — Waves

PRACTICAL | **Investigating IR Absorption**

1* A student is investigating how well different surfaces absorb infrared radiation. Grade 4-5

The student has the equipment shown in **Figure 1**.

The silver plates are identical apart from one surface.
One plate has a shiny silver surface, the other plate has a matt black surface.
Both plates have a small metal ball stuck to a shiny silver side with wax.

Figure 1

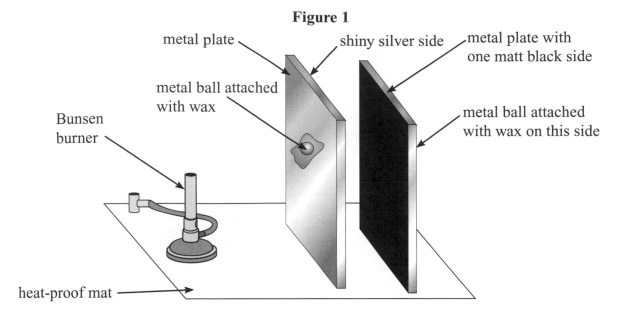

metal plate — shiny silver side — metal plate with one matt black side

metal ball attached with wax

Bunsen burner

metal ball attached with wax on this side

heat-proof mat

The student wants to find out whether the shiny silver or matt black surface is better at absorbing infrared radiation.

Describe an experiment the student could carry out to investigate this using the equipment in **Figure 1**.

....

....

....

....

....

....

....

....

....

....

....

....

[Total 6 marks]

Dangers of Electromagnetic Waves

Radiation dose is measured in sieverts (Sv). It can also be measured in millisieverts (mSv).
Draw a ring around the value below which is equal to 1 Sv.

50 mSv   1000 mSv   1 000 000 mSv

100 mSv   0.001 mSv

1 Some types of electromagnetic radiation can be harmful to people. (Grade 3-4)

1.1 The amount of radiation absorbed affects the amount of harm caused to a person.
Give **one** other factor that affects the amount of harm caused.

....
[1]

1.2 One type of harmful electromagnetic radiation is ultraviolet radiation.
Give **two** damaging effects of ultraviolet light on humans.

1. ....

2. ....
[2]
[Total 3 marks]

2* **Table 1** lists the radiation doses for two medical procedures done to a patient. (Grade 4-5)

Table 1

Procedure	Typical radiation dose (mSv)
X-ray image of skull	0.07
X-ray image of lower spine	1.4

Compare the risk of harm to the patient from both procedures.
Your answer should include a description of the harmful effects that the patient
may experience due to the radiation used in each of these procedures.

....

....

....

....

....

....
[Total 4 marks]

Topic P6 — Waves

Permanent and Induced Magnets

Warm-Up

Circle the type of force each pair of magnets experiences when brought close together.

| N | S | N | S | | N | S | S | N |

attractive / repulsive   attractive / repulsive

1 Which of the following is always true for a permanent magnet and a magnetic material? **Grade 1-3**
Tick **one** box.

the force between them is always repulsive ☐

the force between them is always attractive ☐

the force between them can be either attractive or repulsive ☐

[Total 1 mark]

2 The passage below describes magnetic forces. **Grade 3-4**
Use words from the box below to complete the passage.

| strongest | north | non-contact | weakest | south | contact |

Magnetic forces are examples of .... forces. The direction of the magnetic

field shows the direction that the force would act on a .... pole at that point.

The field is .... at the poles of the magnet.

[Total 3 marks]

3 **Figure 1** shows two bars of metal. One is a permanent magnet. One is made **Grade 4-5**
from a magnetic metal. The magnetic field pattern around the bars is shown.

Permanent bar magnet   **Figure 1**   Magnetic material

| N | S |

3.1 Explain why there is a magnetic field pattern around the magnetic material.

....

....

[2]

3.2 Suggest what the magnetic material might be.

....

[1]

[Total 3 marks]

☹ ☐   🙂 ☐   😊 ☐

Electromagnetism

1 **Figure 1** shows a current-carrying wire and the magnetic field pattern around it. Three points are labelled **X**, **Y** and **Z**.

Grade 4-5

1.1 Draw an arrow on each magnetic field line to show its direction.

[1]

1.2 State at which point, **X**, **Y** or **Z**, the magnetic field is strongest.

....
[1]

Figure 1

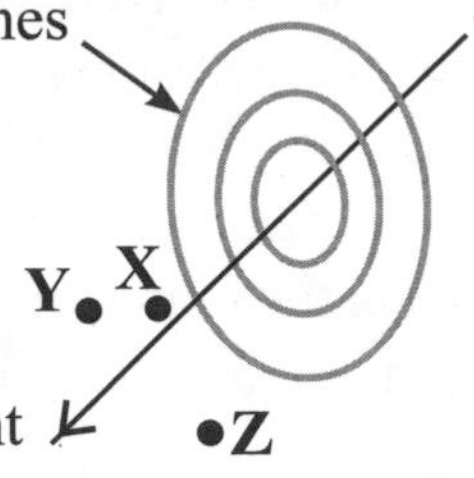

magnetic field lines → ⊙ ← wire

Y• •X

direction of current ↙ •Z

1.3 The wire above is carrying a current of 0.5 A. A second wire is carrying a current of 0.2 A. Explain which wire has the strongest magnetic field around it.

....

....
[2]

[Total 4 marks]

2 **Figure 2** shows a solenoid carrying a current. A magnetic field is produced inside and around the solenoid.

Grade 4-5

Figure 2

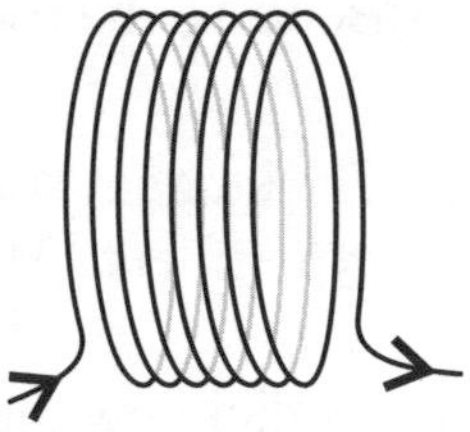

2.1 Describe the magnetic field produced inside the solenoid.

....

....
[2]

2.2 The two changes listed below are made to the solenoid. What happens to the magnetic field around the solenoid in each case? Tick **one** box for each change.

	It increases	It decreases	It reverses
Change 1: The current is reversed.	☐	☐	☐
Change 2: An iron core is added.	☐	☐	☐

[2]

2.3 What is the solenoid known as once an iron core has been added?

....
[1]

[Total 5 marks]

Exam Tip

A wire with a current flowing through it always has a magnetic field around it, no matter what shape it is bent into. Make sure you know how you can change the strength and the direction of a magnetic field around a wire.

Topic P7 — Magnetism and Electromagnetism

Target AO3

3 A student is testing the properties of an electromagnet. **Figure 3** shows her experimental set-up.

Grade 4-5

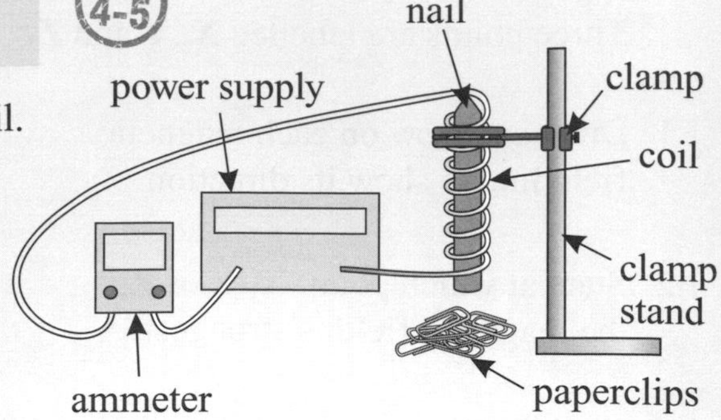

The student wraps a length of wire around an iron nail. She then runs a current of 200 mA through the wire to create an electromagnet and records how many paperclips are picked up by the electromagnet. She then increases the current by 200 mA and repeats the experiment, up to a maximum current of 1000 mA.

Figure 3

power supply, nail, clamp, coil, clamp stand, ammeter, paperclips

3.1 Increasing the current also causes the temperature of the electromagnet to increase. Suggest a safety precaution that the student could take to reduce the risk from this hazard.

....

[1]

3.2 During the experiment, the wire falls off the nail. When the student replaces the wire, she increases the number of turns in the wire. Why will this make her results less valid? Tick **one** box.

Because the wire may fall off again. ☐

Because the experiment is no longer a fair test. ☐

Because the results will be more accurate. ☐

[1]

The student fixes her mistake, and repeats the experiment. Her results are shown in **Table 1**.

3.3 Predict how the results would be likely to change if the student replaced the iron nail with a piece of plastic that is the same size and shape as the nail.

....

....

....

[1]

Table 1

Current (mA)	Number of paperclips
200	3
400	9
600	15
800	22
1000	24

3.4 The student thinks she has recorded some anomalous results, so she decides to repeat the experiment. This time, she increases her current in steps of 100 mA. Explain why the student may find it easier to spot anomalous results in the repeated results.

....

....

....

....

[3]

[Total 6 marks]

Topic P7 — Magnetism and Electromagnetism

☹ ☐   😐 ☐   🙂 ☐

Biology Mixed Questions

1   **Figure 1** shows a type of animal cell. *Grade 1-3*

Figure 1

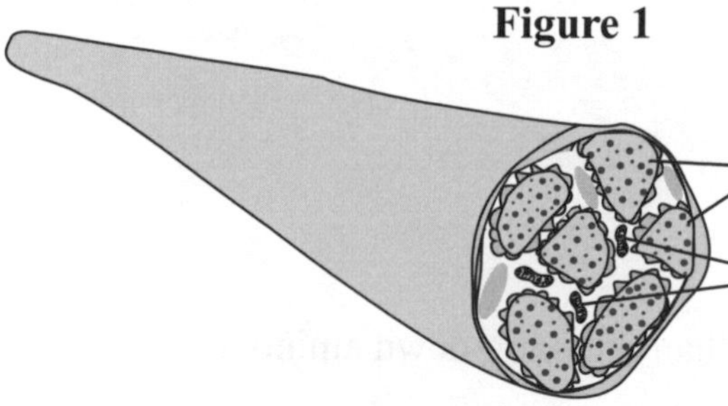

tissues that contract

mitochondria

1.1   What type of cell is the cell in **Figure 1**?
      Tick **one** box.

      sperm cell ☐   nerve cell ☐   muscle cell ☐   xylem cell ☐

      [1]

1.2   Why does this type of cell have lots of mitochondria?
      Tick **one** box.

      To provide the energy the cell needs to carry out its function. ☐

      To allow the cell to carry out photosynthesis. ☐

      To allow the cell to produce lots of proteins. ☐

      To strengthen the cell. ☐

      [1]

Figure 2 shows a single-celled organism called *Euglena*, found in pond water.
Euglena is a eukaryote.

Figure 2

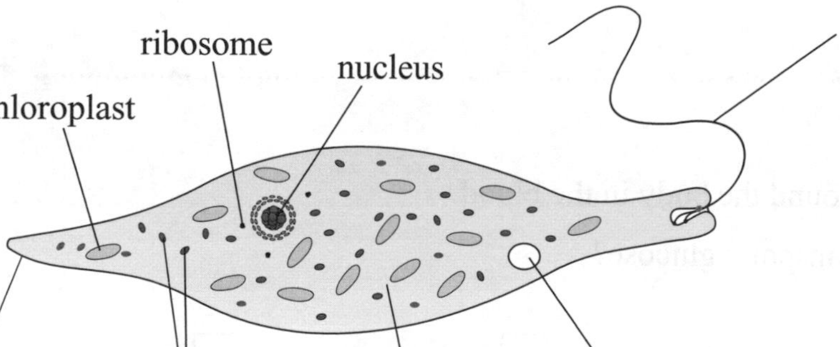

ribosome

nucleus

chloroplast

flagellum
(hair-like structure that
allows the cell to move)

cell
membrane   mitochondria   cytoplasm   vacuole

1.3   Give **one** piece of evidence from **Figure 2** which shows that *Euglena* is a eukaryote
      and not a prokaryote.

      ....

      [1]

1.4   Which of the following is an example of a **prokaryote**?
      Tick **one** box.

      sperm cell ☐   nerve cell ☐   fruit fly ☐   *E. coli* bacterium ☐

      [1]

      [Total 4 marks]

2   One of the functions of the liver is to break down excess amino acids.   (Grade 1-3)

2.1   Which of the following molecules is made up of amino acids?
Tick **one** box.

a carbohydrate   ☐

a protein   ☐

a lipid   ☐

glycerol   ☐

[1]

2.2   State **one** function of the liver, other than breaking down amino acids.

....

[1]

2.3   Urea is a waste product from the breakdown of amino acids.
Which organ removes urea from the body? Tick **one** box.

brain   ☐

pancreas   ☐

kidney   ☐

lung   ☐

[1]

[Total 3 marks]

3   Aerobic respiration transfers energy from glucose.   (Grade 3-4)

3.1   Complete the word equation for aerobic respiration.

glucose + ... → .... + water

[2]

Glucose is transported around the body in the blood.

3.2   What part of the blood transports glucose?
Tick **one** box.

red blood cells ☐   white blood cells ☐   plasma ☐   platelets ☐

[1]

3.3   The steps below describe what happens when the blood glucose level gets too high.

Put the steps in order by writing the correct number (**1, 2, 3** or **4**) in the space provided.

.... The pancreas releases insulin.

.... Glucose is converted into glycogen for storage.

.... Glucose moves into the liver and muscle cells.

.... Receptors in the pancreas detect that the blood glucose level is too high.

[2]

[Total 5 marks]

Biology Mixed Questions

4   **Figure 3** shows a plant cell with one of its subcellular structures magnified. The overall movement of four molecules into and out of the subcellular structure is also shown.

Figure 3

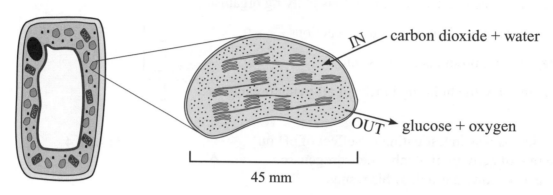

45 mm

4.1 Look at the movements of carbon dioxide, water, glucose and oxygen in **Figure 3**.
What reaction do these movements suggest is taking place in the magnified subcellular structure?

....

[1]

4.2 What is the name of the magnified subcellular structure in **Figure 3**?

....

[1]

4.3 The width of the subcellular structure when viewed using a microscope is 45 mm.
What is the width of the magnified image in μm?
Tick **one** box.

45 000 μm ☐

0.045 μm ☐

4500 μm ☐

4.5 μm ☐

[1]

The cell in **Figure 3** is from a leaf.
4.4 Describe how carbon dioxide enters a leaf.

....

....

[2]

4.5 What is the name of the process which transports water up a plant and into the leaves?

....

[1]

4.6 After glucose has been produced by a plant cell, some of it leaves the cell to be transported around the plant. What is the name of the transportation process?

....

[1]

[Total 7 marks]

Biology Mixed Questions

238

5 Alcohol dehydrogenase enzymes break down alcohol in the body. (Grade 4-5)

5.1 Which of the following sentences about enzymes is correct?
Tick **one** box.

Enzymes speed up chemical reactions in living organisms. ☐

Enzymes are used up in chemical reactions. ☐

Enzymes are products of digestion. ☐

Enzymes are the building blocks of all living organisms. ☐

[1]

A scientist was investigating the effect of pH on the rate of activity of alcohol dehydrogenase. **Figure 4** shows a graph of his results.

Figure 4

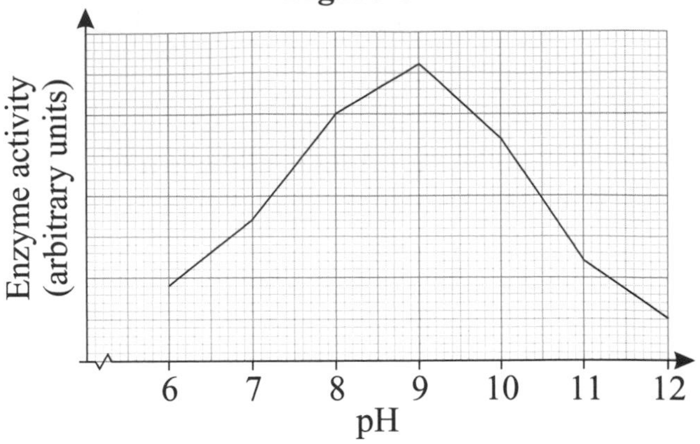

5.2 What is the optimum pH for the enzyme?

....
[1]

5.3 Suggest and explain the effect an acid with a pH of 1 would have on the enzyme.

....

....

....
[3]

5.4 Which of the following statements about alcohol is correct?
Tick **one** box.

Alcohol is a risk factor for several communicable diseases. ☐

Alcohol is a risk factor for lung cancer. ☐

Alcohol can cause liver damage. ☐

Alcohol has no effect on brain function. ☐

[1]

5.5 Alcohol can be produced by yeast cells when they respire.
What type of respiration is involved in the production of alcohol?

....
[1]
[Total 7 marks]

Exam Tip

In your exam, you could be asked to 'suggest and explain' something. 'Suggest' is just asking you to take what you know and apply it to a new situation. Then 'explain' your thinking — say why you made the suggestion that you did.

Biology Mixed Questions

6   **Figure 5** shows an example of a grassland food chain.

Figure 5

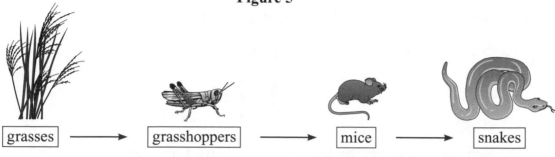

grasses → grasshoppers → mice → snakes

6.1 Grasses are the producer in this food chain.
     What is meant by the term producer?

     ....

     ....
                                                                                              [1]

6.2 Give **one** biotic factor that may reduce the amount of grass in this food chain.

     ....
                                                                                              [1]

6.3 Mice are also eaten by owls.
     What might happen to the population of **snakes** if owls were introduced into the ecosystem?
     Give a reason for your answer.

     ....

     ....

     ....
                                                                                              [2]

     A scientist is investigating the grassland ecosystem.

6.4 Describe a method that the scientist could use to investigate whether
     the distribution of grasses changes across the ecosystem.

     ....

     ....

     ....
                                                                                              [3]

6.5 The scientist says: "The grassland is a stable community."
     What is meant by a stable community?

     ....

     ....

     ....
                                                                                              [2]
                                                                              [Total 9 marks]

Chemistry Mixed Questions

1   **Figure 1** shows the nuclear symbol of a Group 1 element.   *(Grade 1-3)*

Figure 1

$$^{7}_{3}\text{Li}$$

1.1   Write the name of the element that the symbol in **Figure 1** represents.

....

[1]

1.2   Name another element in the same group as the element shown in **Figure 1**.

....

[1]

1.3   Atoms contain protons, neutrons and electrons. Draw **one** line from each of these particles to show how many there are in an atom of the element shown in **Figure 1**.

Particle	Number in one atom of Li
proton	3
electron	4
neutron	3

[1]

1.4   The element in **Figure 1** is a metal. Which of the following diagrams shows the structure of a metal? Tick **one** box.

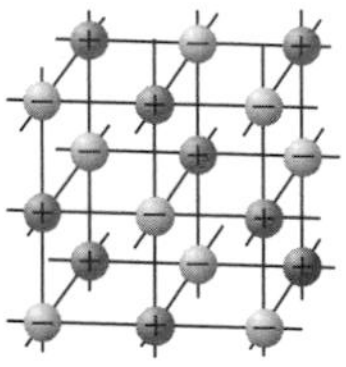

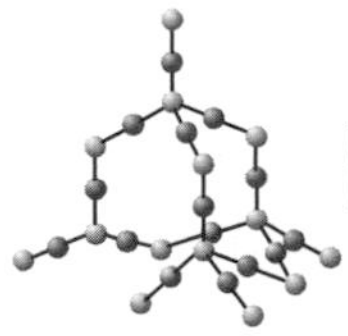

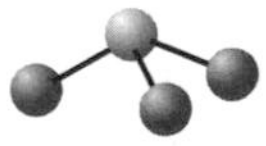

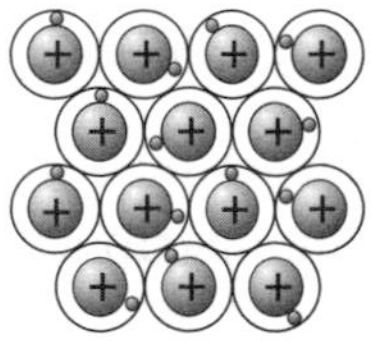

[1]

1.5   The element in **Figure 1** reacts with water. One of the products of this reaction is a gas. When a lit splint is placed in the gas, a squeaky popping noise is made. What gas was produced? Tick **one** box.

Carbon dioxide ☐   Chlorine ☐   Oxygen ☐   Hydrogen ☐

[1]

1.6   LiOH is also produced in the reaction between the element in **Figure 1** and water. Complete the sentence below. Use a word from the box.

oxide	hydroxide	carbonate

When a Group 1 element reacts with water a metal .... is formed.

[1]

[Total 6 marks]

2 Hydrochloric acid and sodium hydroxide react in a neutralisation reaction.

2.1 A student carries out an experiment to find the volume of hydrochloric acid needed to neutralise 25 cm³ of sodium hydroxide. She does the experiment three times. Her results are in **Table 1**.

Complete **Table 1** to show the mean volume of hydrochloric acid needed.

Table 1

Repeat	1	2	3	mean
Volume (cm³)	35.60	35.90	35.75	....

[2]

2.2 Calculate the uncertainty of the mean.
Use the equation: uncertainty = range ÷ 2

Uncertainty = ... cm³

[2]

2.3 The products of the reaction between hydrochloric acid and sodium hydroxide are sodium chloride and water. Complete the equation below to show this reaction.

.... + NaOH → .... + H₂O

[2]

2.4 The student measures the pH of the sodium hydroxide at the start of the experiment. She then measures the pH as the hydrochloric acid is added and the pH at the end of the reaction.

Describe how the pH of the reaction mixture would change during the experiment.

....

....

....

[3]

2.5 **Figure 2** is a dot and cross diagram showing the formation of sodium chloride. Complete the right-hand side of **Figure 2**. You should add any charges and electrons that are needed.

Figure 2

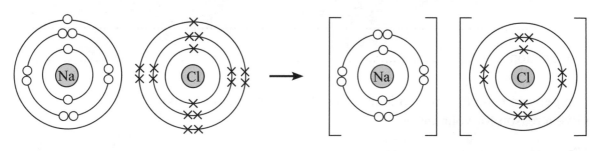

[2]

2.6 State the type of bonding in sodium chloride.

....

[1]

[Total 12 marks]

Exam Tip

Make sure that you carefully read each question before answering it so that you understand what the examiner is asking you to do. There's nothing worse than rushing through the questions and then realising you've made loads of mistakes.

Chemistry Mixed Questions

242

3 A substance can be classified as an element, a compound or a mixture.   (Grade 3-4)

3.1 Draw a line to connect each type of substance with an example of it.

Type of Substance   **Example**

| compound | | salt water |

| element | | nitrogen |

| mixture | | iron oxide |

[2]

3.2 Calcium carbonate is a compound with the formula $CaCO_3$.
Name the elements that make up calcium carbonate.

....

[2]

3.3 In terms of the substances they contain, what is the
difference between pure water and potable water?

....

....

[2]

3.4 Mixtures can be separated by physical methods.
Name **two** techniques that can be used to separate mixtures

1 ....

2 ....

[2]

[Total 8 marks]

4 Oxygen atoms have the electronic structure 2, 6.   (Grade 4-5)

4.1 State which group of the periodic table oxygen is in.
Explain your answer with reference to the electronic structure of oxygen.

Group: ....

Explanation: ....

[2]

4.2 Oxygen can react to form oxide ions. Predict the charge on an oxide ion.
Give a reason for your answer.

Charge: ....

Reason: ....

[2]

4.3 When magnesium reacts with oxygen, it forms magnesium oxide.
What type of reaction does magnesium take part in? Tick **one** box.

Displacement ☐   Oxidation ☐   Electrolysis ☐   Reduction ☐   *[1]*

[Total 5 marks]

Chemistry Mixed Questions

5   Alkanes are hydrocarbon compounds found in crude oil. **Table 2** shows
    how the boiling points of some alkanes change as the molecules get bigger.

Table 2

Alkane	Propane	Butane	Pentane	Hexane	Heptane
Molecular formula	C_3H_8	C_4H_{10}	C_5H_{12}	C_6H_{14}	C_7H_{16}
Boiling point (°C)	−42	−0.5		69	98

5.1 Using the data in **Table 2**, plot a graph of the number of carbon atoms in an alkane molecule
     against boiling point on the axes below. Draw a smooth curve through the points that you plot.

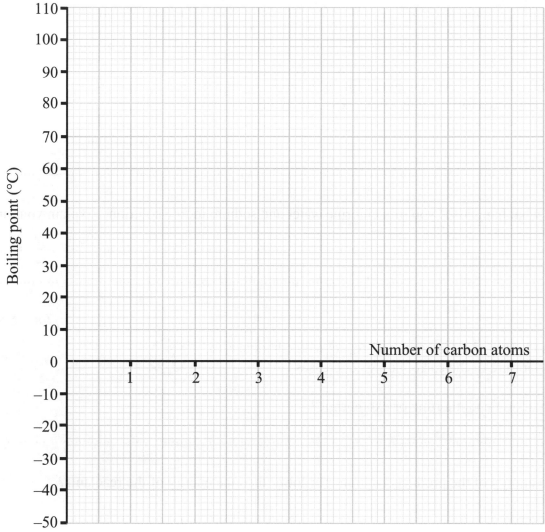

[2]

5.2 Use your graph to estimate the boiling point of pentane.   .... °C
                                                                        [1]

5.3 What is the general formula of the alkanes? Tick **one** box.

     C_nH_{2n} ☐ C_nH_{2n+1} ☐ C_nH_{2n+2} ☐ $C_nH_{2n−1}$ ☐
                                                                        [1]

5.4 Calculate the relative formula mass (M_r) of propane, C_3H_8.
     Relative atomic masses (A_r): C = 12, H = 1

                                        Relative formula mass = ...
                                                                        [1]
                                                        [Total 5 marks]

Chemistry Mixed Questions

6 Chlorine is a Group 7 element that exists as molecules of Cl_2.

6.1 Complete the dot-and-cross diagram below to show the bonding in Cl_2.
You only need to show the outer electron shells.

Cl ( ) Cl

[2]

6.2 Chlorine has two main isotopes — ^{35}Cl and ^{37}Cl. Explain the term 'isotope'.

....

....

[2]

6.3 Describe a test you could carry out for chlorine.
Include any observations you would expect to make.

....

....

[2]

6.4 Predict what happens if you mix chlorine water and sodium iodide solution. Explain your answer.

....

....

[2]

[Total 8 marks]

7 When sodium hydrogen carbonate reacts with ethanoic acid, the temperature of the surroundings decreases.

7.1 Is this reaction endothermic or exothermic?

....

[1]

7.2 Will the energy of the products be higher or lower than the energy of the reactants?

....

[1]

7.3 What effect will increasing the concentration of ethanoic acid have on the rate of the reaction?
Give a reason for your answer.

Effect: ....

Reason: ....

....

[3]

[Total 5 marks]

Exam Tip

Look out for questions that test your knowledge of scientific words, such as isotope, endothermic and concentration.
These marks are simple ones to pick up, provided you know each term inside out. Don't miss out by not learning them.

Chemistry Mixed Questions

8 Aluminium and iron can be obtained by extracting them from their ores. Both metals can also be obtained from recycling aluminium and iron items.

Table 3

Material	Extraction process	Energy saved by recycling
Aluminium	Electrolysis	Around 95%
Iron	Reduction with carbon	Around 60%

8.1 Look at **Table 3**. Suggest whether the extraction of aluminium or iron will have a larger carbon footprint. Give a reason for your answer.

Extraction process: ....

Reason: ....

....

....

[4]

8.2 **Table 3** shows that energy is saved when aluminium and iron are obtained from recycled metals rather than being extracted from their ores. Give **two** other advantages of recycling metals.

1 ....

2 ....

[2]

[Total 6 marks]

9* The structure and bonding of substances affects their properties.

Table 4

	Hardness	Melting point	Conducts electricity?
Diamond	Hard	High	No
Graphite	Soft	High	Yes

Explain how the structure and bonding of diamond and graphite give them the properties listed in **Table 4**.

Your answer should include details of how the atoms are arranged and how they're held together.

....

....

....

....

....

....

....

[Total 6 marks]

Physics Mixed Questions

1   The three states of matter are solid, liquid and gas.   *(Grade 1-3)*

1.1   Materials can change state if they are heated or cooled.
Draw **one** line from each change of state to its correct name.

Change of state   **Name**

| freezing |

| solid to liquid |

| condensing |

| liquid to solid |

| melting |

[2]

1.2   Use a phrase from the box below to complete the sentence.

| as dense as | denser than | less dense than |

Gases are usually .... liquids.

[1]

[Total 3 marks]

2   **Figure 1** shows a displacement-distance graph for a sound wave.   *(Grade 1-3)*

Figure 1

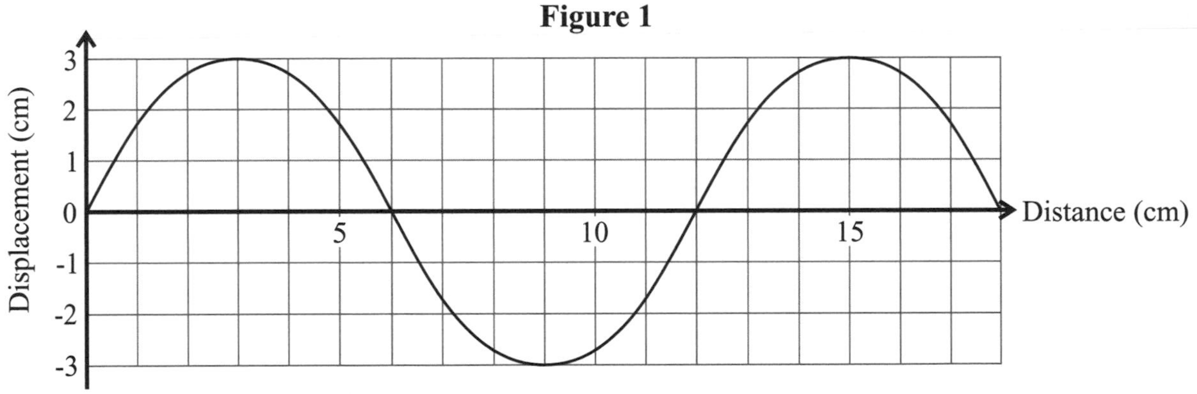

2.1   What is the amplitude of the wave? Tick **one** box.

3 cm   ☐

6 cm   ☐

12 cm   ☐

[1]

2.2   What is the approximate speed of sound in air? Tick **one** box.

3 m/s   ☐

330 m/s   ☐

330 000 m/s   ☐

[1]

[Total 2 marks]

3   A cyclist accelerates from rest.   (Grade 3-4)

3.1   What is the typical speed of a cyclist? Tick **one** box.

1.5 m/s ☐   3 m/s ☐   6 m/s ☐   14 m/s ☐

[1]

3.2   It takes the cyclist 10 seconds to reach this speed.
Calculate his acceleration during these 10 seconds. Use the equation:

$$\text{acceleration} = \text{change in velocity} \div \text{time taken}$$

Acceleration = ... m/s²

[2]

[Total 3 marks]

4   A student is investigating the relationship between mass and weight.   (Grade 3-4)

4.1   Mass is a scalar quantity. Weight is a vector quantity.
Explain what is meant by a scalar quantity.

....

[1]

4.2   Use words from the box below to complete the passage.

weight	kilograms	force	newtons	mass	newton metres

The force on an object due to gravity is called its ....

It is measured in .... You can think of weight as acting from a single

point on an object. This point is called the centre of ....

[3]

4.3   The student measures the mass of her full pencil case.
She then measures its weight.

What piece of equipment could she use to directly measure the weight of the pencil case?
Tick **one** box.

mass balance ☐

thermometer ☐

newtonmeter ☐

measuring cylinder ☐

[1]

4.4   The student states that the pencil case would weigh the same on a planet with
a smaller gravitational field strength. Is she correct? Explain your answer.

....

....

[1]

[Total 6 marks]

Physics Mixed Questions

248

5 A girl walks her dog.
She records the total distance she has travelled every 5 minutes. (Grade 3-4)

5.1 She uses the information she collects to draw a distance-time graph for her walk.
State what quantity the gradient of a distance-time graph gives.

....
[1]

5.2 She walked a distance of 420 m in 5.0 minutes.
Calculate the average speed at which she walked.
Use the equation:

speed = distance travelled ÷ time

Speed = ... m/s
[3]

5.3 Whilst walking, the girl throws a ball for her dog to chase.
Each time she throws the ball, she transfers energy to the ball's kinetic energy store.
How is energy transferred to the ball? Tick **one** box.

electrically ☐

mechanically ☐

by heating ☐

by radiation ☐
[1]
[Total 5 marks]

6 Gamma rays are a type of electromagnetic wave. (Grade 3-4)

6.1 State **one** use of gamma rays.

....
[1]

6.2 The equation shows a nucleus emitting a gamma ray.
Determine the values of A and B.

$$^{99}_{43}\text{Tc} \rightarrow ^{A}_{43}\text{Tc} + ^{B}_{0}\gamma$$

A = ...
B = ...
[2]

6.3 A scientist works with gamma radiation. He uses a shield to protect himself from being irradiated by gamma rays. Suggest what material this shield is made from.

....
[1]
[Total 4 marks]

Physics Mixed Questions

PRACTICAL

7 A student tests the relationship between the potential difference across a diode and the current through it.

7.1 Which of the following shows an *I-V* graph for a diode? Tick **one** box.

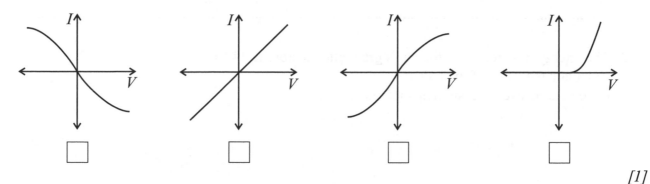

☐ ☐ ☐ ☐

[1]

When the potential difference across the diode is 2.4 V, the current through the diode is 0.4 A.

7.2 Write down the equation that links potential difference, current and resistance.

....

[1]

7.3 Calculate the resistance of the diode.

Resistance = ... Ω

[3]

[Total 5 marks]

8 Two beakers containing 0.5 kg of water are at room temperature. A student then heats the water using two different electric heaters. You can assume both heaters are 100% efficient. Heater A takes 340 s to heat the water in one of the beakers to 100 °C. Heater B takes 170 s to heat the water in the other beaker to 100 °C.

8.1 In terms of energy transfer, which heater is more powerful, Heater A or Heater B? Explain your answer.

....

....

[2]

8.2 Heater A is used to heat 0.5 kg of water from 20 °C to 50 °C.
The specific heat capacity of water is 4200 J/kg °C.
Calculate the energy transferred to the water.
Use an equation from the Equations List.

Energy = ... J

[3]

[Total 5 marks]

Physics Mixed Questions

9 A student carries a bag of magnets to a classroom. **(Grade 4-5)**

The change in height of the bag is 9.0 m. The Earth's gravitational field strength is 9.8 N/kg.

9.1 Write down the equation which links energy in a gravitational potential energy store, mass, gravitational field strength and height.

....

[1]

9.2 The energy transferred to the bag's gravitational store is 440 J.
Calculate the mass of the bag.
Give your answer to 2 significant figures.

Mass = ... kg

[3]

9.3 The student wants to investigate the magnetic field produced by one of the magnets from the bag. She decides to use a compass to plot the magnetic field.

Figure 2 shows a bar magnet.
Draw the magnetic field lines around the magnet in **Figure 2**.

Figure 2

| N | S |

[2]

9.4 When the student moves the compass away from the magnet, the needle points north. Explain why this happens.

....

....

....

[2]

9.5 Describe the difference between a permanent and an induced magnet.

....

....

[2]

[Total 10 marks]

10 A child is playing with a remote-controlled toy car.
The car is travelling at a constant speed.

Figure 3

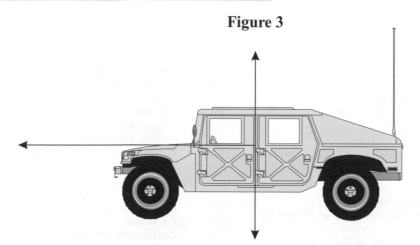

10.1 **Figure 3** shows an incomplete force diagram for the toy.
Complete the force diagram by drawing the missing resistive force acting on the car.

[2]

10.2 Write down the equation that links energy in a kinetic energy store, mass and speed.

....

[1]

10.3 The car travels at 5.0 m/s. The car has 7.5 J of energy in its kinetic energy store.
Calculate the mass of the car.

Mass = ... kg

[3]

10.4 The car's battery runs out of power and the car rolls up a hill and stops at the top.
Describe the energy transfers that take place after the battery stops working.

....

....

....

[2]

10.5 The car is powered by an electric motor. The efficiency of the motor is 0.65.
The total input energy transfer is 700 J.

Calculate the energy wasted by the motor.

Wasted energy = ... J

[3]

[Total 11 marks]

Answers

Topic B1 — Cell Biology

Page 1 — Cells
Warm-Up
These cells have a nucleus. — Eukaryotic cells
These are the smallest type of cells. — Prokaryotic cells
These cells can be bacteria. — Prokaryotic cells

1.1

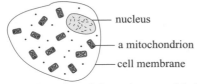

nucleus

a mitochondrion

cell membrane

[3 marks — 1 mark for each correct label]

1.2 Cell membrane — controls what goes in and out of the cell *[1 mark]*.
Mitochondria — where most aerobic respiration happens *[1 mark]*.
Nucleus — controls what the cell does / contains genetic material *[1 mark]*.

1.3 E.g. cytoplasm *[1 mark]*, ribosomes *[1 mark]*.

1.4 There is no cell wall/vacuole. / There are no chloroplasts. *[1 mark]*

Page 2 — Microscopy
1.1 24 mm *[1 mark]*
1.2 24 ÷ 0.012 = × **2000** *[1 mark]*
2.1 real size = 10 mm ÷ 1000 = **0.01 mm** *[1 mark]*
2.2 1 mm = 1000 μm
0.01 mm × 1000 = **10 μm**
[1 mark. Allow 1 mark for an incorrect answer to 2.1 × 1000.]
2.3 Electron microscopes have a higher magnification and resolution than light microscopes *[1 mark]*.
2.4 E.g. more subcellular structures can be seen under an electron microscope. / Subcellular structures can be seen with greater detail. *[1 mark]*

Page 3 — More on Microscopy
1.1 To make the specimen easier to see *[1 mark]*.
1.2 × 4 *[1 mark]*
Remember, you should always start with the objective lens with the lowest magnification — this makes it easier to get your specimen into view.
1.3 They bring the sample into focus by moving the stage up and down *[1 mark]*.
1.4 She should select the × 40 or × 10 objective lens *[1 mark]* and use the adjustment knobs to bring the sample back into focus *[1 mark]*.
1.5 Any two from: e.g. she should use a pencil with a sharp point. / She should make sure her drawing takes up at least half of the space available. / She should not colour or shade her diagram. / She should include a title. / She should write down the magnification that it was observed under. / She should label the important features of her drawing using straight, uncrossed lines. *[2 marks — 1 mark for each correct answer]*

Page 4 — Cell Differentiation and Specialisation
Warm-Up
differentiation
1 root hair cell — Long, hair-like shape. They absorb water and mineral ions.
xylem — Long hollow cells joined end to end. They transport water.
phloem — Long cells joined end to end, with very few subcellular structures. They transport food.
[2 marks for all three correct answers, otherwise 1 mark for one correct answer]
2.1 To carry the male DNA to the egg *[1 mark]*.
2.2 The tail helps the sperm to swim to the egg *[1 mark]*.
2.3 Mitochondria give the sperm energy for swimming *[1 mark]*.

Page 5 — Chromosomes and Mitosis
1.1 The chromosomes are being copied *[1 mark]*.
1.2 The number of mitochondria is increasing *[1 mark]*.
1.3 The cytoplasm is dividing *[1 mark]*.
The cell membrane is dividing *[1 mark]*.
1.4 They are genetically identical *[1 mark]*.

Page 6 — Stem Cells
1.1 A stem cell is an undifferentiated cell *[1 mark]*.
1.2 meristems *[1 mark]*
1.3 E.g. rare species can be cloned to prevent them from being wiped out. Crop plants with useful features (e.g. plants that aren't killed by a disease) can be grown quickly/cheaply.
[2 marks — 1 mark for each correct answer]
2.1 E.g. diabetes / paralysis *[1 mark]*
2.2 E.g. human embryos *[1 mark]*
2.3 E.g. some people think embryos shouldn't be used for research because each one could be a human life *[1 mark]*.
2.4 E.g. the stem cells may become infected with a virus that may then be passed on to the patient *[1 mark]*.

Page 7 — Diffusion
1.1 E.g.

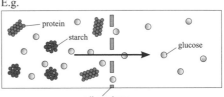

protein

starch

glucose

cell membrane

[1 mark for an arrow pointing in the correct direction.]

Remember, molecules diffuse from an area of higher concentration (where there are more of them) to an area of lower concentration (where there are fewer of them).

1.2 They are too big to fit through the membrane *[1 mark]*.
1.3 A decrease in the concentration gradient will decrease the rate of diffusion *[1 mark]*.
2.1 The ink will diffuse / spread out through the water *[1 mark]*. This is because the ink particles will move from where there is a higher concentration of them (the drop of ink) to where there is a lower concentration of them (the surrounding water) *[1 mark]*.
2.2 The ink particles will diffuse/spread out faster *[1 mark]*.

Pages 8-9 — Osmosis
1.1 water *[1 mark]*, less *[1 mark]*, more *[1 mark]*
1.2 A plant is absorbing water from the soil *[1 mark]*.
2.1 $\dfrac{(6.58 - 5.73)}{5.73} \times 100$
= **14.8 %** (3 s.f.) *[2 marks for the correct answer, otherwise 1 mark for correct working.]*
2.2 The concentration of the salt solution in beakers 4 and 5 must have been higher than the concentration of the solution inside the potato cells *[1 mark]* so the chips lost mass as water moved out of the cells by osmosis *[1 mark]*.
3.1 Any two from: e.g. the volume of sucrose solution the student puts in the Visking tubing. / The volume of sucrose solution the student puts in the beaker. / The temperature the beaker is kept at. / The size of the Visking tubing *[2 marks]*.
3.2 It will stay the same *[1 mark]*.
3.3 The solution in the Visking tubing is less concentrated than the solution in the beaker *[1 mark]*.
Water molecules will move by osmosis from a less concentrated solution (where there are lots of water molecules) to a more concentrated solution (where there are fewer water molecules).
3.4 The water concentration of the solutions in the Visking tubing and the beaker will have become the same *[1 mark]*, so there will be no net movement of water molecules *[1 mark]*.

Answers

Page 10 — Active Transport

1.1 The movement of a substance from a less concentrated solution to a more concentrated solution (against a concentration gradient) *[1 mark]*.

1.2 For energy/respiration *[1 mark]*.

1.3 It needs energy from respiration *[1 mark]*.

2.1 For healthy growth *[1 mark]*.

2.2 Because the concentration of minerals is usually higher inside the plant cells than in the soil (outside the plant cells) *[1 mark]* so the minerals won't move into the plant cells by diffusion *[1 mark]*.

2.3 Active transport occurs against a concentration gradient but diffusion occurs down a concentration gradient *[1 mark]*. Active transport needs energy from respiration but diffusion doesn't *[1 mark]*.

Page 11 — Exchanging Substances

Warm-Up

1 — blue whale, 2 — tiger, 3 — bacterium

1.1 125 μm³ *[1 mark]*

The volume of a cube is just length × width × height (5 × 5 × 5 in this case).

1.2 150 μm² *[1 mark]*

The surface area of a cube is the area of one face (length × width) × the number of faces. So here it is (5 × 5) × 6.

1.3 3:1 *[1 mark]*

The surface area of the cube is 24 μm² and the volume is 8 μm³. This gives the cube a surface area to volume ratio of 24:8. To get the answer here, you need to simplify the ratio by dividing both sides by the volume.

2 The Arctic hare *[1 mark]* because it is smaller than the polar bear *[1 mark]*. This means it will have a larger surface area to volume ratio, so it will lose heat the fastest *[1 mark]*.

Pages 12-13 — More on Exchanging Substances

Warm-Up

a thin membrane, a large surface area, a good blood supply, being ventilated

1 Villi increase the surface area of the small intestine *[1 mark]*.

2.1 A = carbon dioxide *[1 mark]*
B = oxygen *[1 mark]*

2.2 diffusion *[1 mark]*

2.3 gases a short distance to move — the walls of the alveoli are thin *[1 mark]*
a large surface area — lots of alveoli *[1 mark]*

3.1 Oxygen diffuses from the water into the blood *[1 mark]*.
Carbon dioxide diffuses from the blood into the water *[1 mark]*.

3.2 They give a large surface area for gas exchange *[1 mark]*.

3.3 E.g. it has a good blood supply *[1 mark]*, which speeds up diffusion *[1 mark]*. / It has a thin layer of surface cells *[1 mark]*, which means gases only have a short distance to diffuse *[1 mark]*.

4 How to grade your answer:
Level 0: There is no relevant information. *[No marks]*
Level 1: Adaptations of the leaf for gas exchange are described but not explained. *[1 to 2 marks]*
Level 2: A full explanation is given of the different adaptations of the leaf for gas exchange. *[3 to 4 marks]*
Here are some points your answer may include:
The lower surface of the leaf is a gas exchange surface.
It is covered in small holes called stomata.
Gases (such as carbon dioxide and oxygen) diffuse into and out of the leaf through the stomata.
The leaf has a flattened shape.
This increases its surface area for gas exchange.
The walls of the cells inside the leaf are another gas exchange surface.
Air spaces inside the leaf increase the area of this surface for gas exchange.

Topic B2 — Organisation

Page 14 — Cell Organisation

Warm-up

Organ system – 4, Tissue – 2, Cell – 1, Organ – 3

1.1 X — liver *[1 mark]*
Y — large intestine *[1 mark]*
Z — small intestine *[1 mark]*

1.2 A group of different tissues that work together to perform a certain function *[1 mark]*.

1.3 A group of organs working together to perform a function *[1 mark]*.

1.4 A group of similar cells that work together to carry out a function *[1 mark]*.

1.5 It breaks down and absorbs food *[1 mark]*.

Page 15 — Enzymes

1.1 active site *[1 mark]*

1.2 B *[1 mark]*

Remember, the substrate has to fit into the active site (like a key fitting into a lock).

2.1 The rate of reaction increases as temperature increases *[1 mark]*.

2.2 The temperature is too high *[1 mark]*, so the enzyme has been denatured / has changed shape so that the substrate no longer fits in the active site *[1 mark]*. This means the enzyme will no longer catalyse the reaction *[1 mark]*.

Page 16 — Investigating Enzymatic Reactions

1.1 Amylase helps to break down starch into sugar *[1 mark]*.

1.2 The iodine solution will turn from browny-orange *[1 mark]* to blue-black *[1 mark]*.

2.1 E.g. by using a water bath *[1 mark]*.

2.2

Test tube	Time (s)	Rate of reaction
X	110	9.1
Y	40	**25**
Z	190	**5.3**

[2 marks — 1 mark for each correct answer]

2.3 per second (s⁻¹) *[1 mark]*

Page 17 — Enzymes and Digestion

1.1 carbohydrate — sugars *[1 mark]*
lipid — glycerol *[1 mark]* + fatty acids *[1 mark]*
protein — amino acids *[1 mark]*

1.2 lipids *[1 mark]*

1.3 E.g. pancreas *[1 mark]*, small intestine *[1 mark]*

2.1 Bile is produced by the **liver**. It is stored in the **gall bladder**. It has an **alkaline** pH, so it **neutralises** acid from the stomach. It also **emulsifies** fats.
[5 marks — 1 mark for each correct answer in bold.]

2.2 Tiny droplets will have a larger surface area for enzymes to work on *[1 mark]*.

Answers

Page 18 — Food Tests

Warm-up
Benedict's test should be ticked.
1   Benedict's — turns brick-red *[1 mark]*
     Biuret — turns pink or purple *[1 mark]*
2   How to grade your answer:
     Level 0:   There is no relevant information. *[No marks]*
     Level 1:   There is a brief description of how the sample could be prepared or tested for protein. *[1 to 2 marks]*
     Level 2:   There is some description of how the sample could be prepared and tested for protein, but some details are missing. *[3 to 4 marks]*
     Level 3:   There is a clear and detailed description of how the sample could be prepared and tested for protein. *[5 to 6 marks]*
     Here are some points your answer may include:
     To prepare a sample, the student could first break up the beans using a pestle and mortar.
     He could then dissolve the mixture in distilled water.
     Finally, he could filter out any solid bits using a filter funnel lined with filter paper.
     To test for proteins in the sample, the student should add biuret solution to the sample.
     He should then mix the contents by gently shaking the test tube.
     If the beans contain protein, the solution will change from blue to pink or purple.

Page 19 — The Lungs

1.1   trachea *[1 mark]*
1.2   bronchus *[1 mark]*
2   Breathing rate = 495 ÷ 12 = 41.25
            = **41.3** breaths per minute (3 s.f.)
     [2 marks for the correct answer written to 3 s.f., otherwise 1 mark for 41.25.]
3

	Oxygen concentration	Carbon dioxide concentration
X	High	Low
Y	Low	**High**
Z	**High**	**Low**

[3 marks — 1 mark for each correct answer.]

Page 20 — Circulatory System — The Heart

1.1   pulmonary artery *[1 mark]*
1.2   C *[1 mark]*
1.3   E.g.

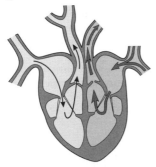

[1 mark for an arrow or arrows indicating the direction of blood flow into and out of the heart as shown.]
2.1   It controls the resting heart rate *[1 mark]*.
2.2   E.g. because they have an irregular heartbeat *[1 mark]*.
3   Because it consists of two circuits joined together *[1 mark]*.
     The first circuit pumps deoxygenated blood to the lungs to take in oxygen (and returns oxygenated blood to the heart) *[1 mark]*.
     The second circuit pumps oxygenated blood around all the other organs of the body (and returns deoxygenated blood to the heart) *[1 mark]*.

Pages 21-22 — Circulatory System — Blood Vessels

1   A *[1 mark]*
     Reason: e.g. A has much thicker walls than either B or C, so it's more likely to be an artery *[1 mark]*.
2.1

Feature	Capillary	Artery	Vein
Elastic fibres in blood vessel walls		✓	
Large lumen			✓
Thin walls, with gaps between the cells	✓		
Valves			✓

[3 marks — 1 marks for each column in the table correctly filled in]
2.2   To carry blood close to every cell in the body *[1 mark]*, so that substances can be exchanged with them *[1 mark]*.
2.3   Because they have different functions *[1 mark]*. Arteries carry blood away from the heart at high pressure, while veins carry blood back to the heart at a lower pressure *[1 mark]*.
3.1   The artery returned to its original length when the mass was removed *[1 mark]*.
3.2   E.g. the wrong mass may have been used / the length may have been measured incorrectly / the mass carrier may have been removed *[1 mark]*.

Page 23 — Circulatory System — Blood

1.1   nucleus *[1 mark]*
1.2   plasma *[1 mark]*
1.3   platelets *[1 mark]*
2.1   It gives them a large surface area for absorbing oxygen *[1 mark]*
2.2   This increases the space available for carrying oxygen in the cell *[1 mark]*.
2.3   E.g. they contain haemoglobin *[1 mark]*.

Page 24 — Cardiovascular Disease

Warm-up
heart, blood vessels (in any order)
1.1   They lower blood cholesterol levels *[1 mark]*.
1.2   E.g. statins must be taken regularly over a long time but a person could forget to take them. / Statins can cause unwanted side effects. / It takes time for their effect to work. *[1 mark]*
2.1   Stents are put inside coronary arteries to keep them open *[1 mark]*. This allows blood carrying oxygen to reach the heart muscle *[1 mark]*.
2.2   E.g. that the patient could have a heart attack during the operation / develop an infection after the surgery / develop blood clots near the stent *[1 mark]*.

Page 25 — More on Cardiovascular Disease

1.1   Leaky heart valves allow blood to flow in both directions through the heart *[1 mark]*.
1.2   E.g. a valve might not open properly *[1 mark]*.
1.3   E.g. the surgeons could replace the valve with another biological valve / a valve from another human/mammal. / The surgeons could replace the valve with a mechanical valve *[1 mark]*.
2.1   Because they have heart failure *[1 mark]*.
2.2   E.g. artificial hearts are less likely to be attacked by the body's immune system than a donor heart *[1 mark]*.
2.3   E.g. artificial hearts don't work as well as healthy donor hearts. / Blood doesn't flow through artificial hearts as smoothly as through natural hearts, which can cause blood clots. / Unlike with natural hearts, a patient with an artificial heart has to take drugs to thin their blood, which can mean they bleed more than usual if they have an accident. *[1 mark]*

Answers

Page 26 — Health and Disease

1.1   A state of physical and mental wellbeing *[1 mark]*.

1.2   Any two from: e.g. a poor diet. / Being under constant stress. / Your life situation.
[2 marks — 1 mark for each correct answer.]

1.3   Only communicable diseases can spread between people *[1 mark]*.

2.1   The immune system helps to fight off pathogens *[1 mark]*. So having a weakened immune system will mean that they are more likely to be infected with other pathogens / develop communicable diseases *[1 mark]*.

2.2   E.g. a pathogen may cause an immune system reaction that leads to an allergic reaction. / Some viruses can lead to certain types of cancer. *[1 mark]*

2.3   A communicable disease because it can spread between people / it is caused by a pathogen *[1 mark]*.

Pages 27-28 — Risk Factors for Non-Communicable Diseases

1.1   Risk factors are things that are linked to an increased chance of getting a certain disease *[1 mark]*.

1.2   E.g. parts of a person's lifestyle *[1 mark]*.
Substances in the body *[1 mark]*.

1.3   E.g. type 2 diabetes *[1 mark]*

2.1   Any two from: e.g. a high fat diet / a lack of exercise / smoking *[2 marks — 1 mark for each correct answer]*.

2.2   E.g. it can be expensive for individuals if they have to move/adapt their home. / If someone has to give up work because of a non-communicable disease, their income will reduce. *[1 mark]*

2.3   E.g. a reduction in the number of people able to work may affect a country's economy. / The cost of researching / treating non-communicable diseases is huge. *[1 mark]*

3.1   Similarity: E.g. the rate of obesity and the rate of diabetes both increased overall / show a positive correlation *[1 mark]*.
Difference: E.g. the rate of diabetes increased every year whereas there were periods when the rate of obesity decreased or stayed the same *[1 mark]*.

3.2   E.g. a correlation between the prevalence of obesity and the number of people with diabetes doesn't show that one causes the other. / Figure 1 shows that the percentage of people with obesity fell between 2015 and 2016, while the number of people with diabetes increased in the same year, which contradicts the student's statement. / The student is only comparing data for seven years — it may be that the trend is not present over a longer period of time *[1 mark]*.

Page 29 — Cancer

Warm-up

Malignant Tumours — Are cancerous

Benign Tumours — Are not cancerous

Can spread to other parts of the body

1.1   E.g. smoking *[1 mark]*.

1.2   E.g. genetic factors / having genes that make you more likely to get cancer *[1 mark]*.

2.1   uncontrolled cell division *[1 mark]*

2.2   Cells can break off from malignant tumours and travel in the bloodstream *[1 mark]*. Secondary tumours form when cells get into healthy tissues and form tumours *[1 mark]*.

Page 30 — Plant Cell Organisation

1.1   epidermal — covers the upper and lower surface of the leaf *[1 mark]*
meristem — causes growth at the tips of roots and shoots *[1 mark]*
xylem — transports water into the leaf *[1 mark]*

1.2   A *[1 mark]*

2.1   They get more light near the top of the leaf *[1 mark]*, which the cells need to carry out photosynthesis *[1 mark]*.

2.2   E.g. they have lots of chloroplasts *[1 mark]*.

2.3   spongy mesophyll *[1 mark]*

Page 31 — Transpiration and Translocation

Warm-up
A: phloem tube
B: xylem tube

1.1   mineral ions *[1 mark]*, water *[1 mark]*

1.2   It moves sugar around the plant *[1 mark]*.

2   The process by which water is lost from a plant is called **transpiration**. It is caused by the **evaporation** and diffusion of water from a plant's surface. The transport of sugars around the plant is called **translocation**.
[3 marks — 1 mark for each correct answer in bold.]

Page 32 — Transpiration and Stomata

1.1   X = stomata *[1 mark]*
Y = guard cells *[1 mark]*

1.2   They are responsible for opening and closing the stomata *[1 mark]* in order to control gas exchange and water loss from a leaf *[1 mark]*.

2.1   2.0 + 1.8 + 2.3 + 1.9 + 1.7 = 9.7
9.7 ÷ 5 = 1.94 = **1.9** (2 s.f.) *[2 marks for correct answer, otherwise 1 mark for mean = 1.94]*

2.2   The greater the air flow around the plant, the greater the transpiration rate *[1 mark]*.

2.3   E.g. increasing air flow means that more water vapour is swept away from the plant / reduces the concentration of water vapour outside the leaves *[1 mark]*. This increases the rate of diffusion of water out of the leaves *[1 mark]*.

Answers

Topic B3 — Infection and Response

Page 33 — Communicable Disease

Warm-up

'insects' should be circled

1   A microorganism that causes disease *[1 mark]*.

2.1   E.g. they can be killed / their habitats can be destroyed to stop them from breeding *[1 mark]*.

2.2   E.g. be hygienic/wash hands / isolate infected individuals / get vaccinated *[1 mark]*.

3.1   A communicable disease is a disease that can spread (between people and/or animals) *[1 mark]*.

3.2   The cold virus/pathogen is carried in the droplets made when he coughs/sneezes *[1 mark]*. A tissue will catch the droplets, so other people don't breathe them in *[1 mark]*.

Page 34 — Bacterial Diseases

1.1   toxins *[1 mark]*

1.2   E.g. eating food products from animals that were infected with *Salmonella* bacteria when they were alive *[1 mark]*. Eating food that has been made in unclean conditions / made in conditions where the bacteria are present *[1 mark]*.

1.3   The vaccination prevents the spread of the disease in poultry *[1 mark]*. This means that the poultry that humans eat won't be contaminated with the *Salmonella* bacteria *[1 mark]*.

2.1   Through sexual contact *[1 mark]*.

2.2   E.g. pain when urinating *[1 mark]*. A thick yellow or green discharge from the vagina *[1 mark]*.

2.3   penicillin *[1 mark]*

2.4   Strains of the gonorrhoea bacteria have become resistant to it *[1 mark]*.

2.5   condoms *[1 mark]*

Page 35 — Viral Diseases

1.1   fever *[1 mark]*, red skin rash *[1 mark]*

1.2   a vaccination *[1 mark]*

2.1   E.g. tomato plant *[1 mark]*

2.2   C *[1 mark]*

Tobacco mosaic virus causes a mosaic pattern of discolouration on the leaves of the plant, so there would be discoloured patches, rather than the whole leaf turning yellow or falling off.

3.1   antiretroviral drugs *[1 mark]*

3.2   the immune system *[1 mark]*

3.3   Viruses reproduce inside cells *[1 mark]*. Eventually, this causes the cell to burst open *[1 mark]*.

Page 36 — Fungal and Protist Diseases

Warm-up

protist, vectors, fever

1.1   rose black spot *[1 mark]*

1.2   In water / by the wind *[1 mark]*.

1.3   Treat the disease using fungicides *[1 mark]*. Strip the affected leaves off the plant *[1 mark]* and then destroy these leaves *[1 mark]*.

Page 37 — Fighting Disease

1   Some white blood cells engulf and **digest** pathogens. This is called **phagocytosis**. Other white blood cells produce proteins that lock onto invading pathogens. These proteins are called **antibodies**.
[3 marks — 1 mark for each correct answer.]

2   How to grade your answer:

Level 0:   There is no relevant information. *[No marks]*

Level 1:   There is a brief mention of one or two defences which reduce the number of pathogens entering the body. *[1 to 2 marks]*

Level 2:   There is some explanation of how at least three of the body's defences reduce the number of pathogens entering the body. *[3 to 4 marks]*

Level 3:   There is a full and clear explanation of how at least four defences reduce the number of pathogens entering the body. *[5 to 6 marks]*

Here are some points your answer may include:

The skin stops pathogens entering the body.

It also releases substances that kill pathogens.

Nose hairs trap particles that could contain pathogens.

This reduces the number of pathogens that can enter the airways through the nose.

The trachea and bronchi secrete mucus to trap pathogens.

The mucus is then swept up to the back of throat (where it can be swallowed) by tiny hair-like structures called cilia. This further reduces the number of pathogens entering the airways.

The stomach produces hydrochloric acid, which kills pathogens that have been swallowed.

Page 38 — Fighting Disease — Vaccination

Warm-up

To stop them getting ill in the future.

1.1   dead or inactive pathogens *[1 mark]*

1.2   They should produce antibodies *[1 mark]*.

2   Antibody production after infection in the vaccinated child happens much faster than in the unvaccinated child *[1 mark]* and more antibodies are also produced *[1 mark]*.

Page 39 — Fighting Disease — Drugs

Warm-up

heart conditions, foxgloves

1.1   Yes, because antibiotics don't destroy viruses *[1 mark]*.

1.2   E.g. a painkiller *[1 mark]*

2.1   The number of antibiotic-resistant infections increased between 2013 and 2015 *[1 mark]*.

2.2   E.g. antibiotic-resistant infections are hard to treat *[1 mark]* so if the trend continues more people may die from bacterial infections / more people may suffer serious effects from bacterial infections *[1 mark]*.

Page 40 — Developing Drugs

1.1   cells, tissues and live animals *[1 mark]*

In preclinical trials, animals are used to test the drug on a whole body or multiple body systems, so the animal needs to be alive. You wouldn't want to test on humans at this stage, just in case the drug is dangerous.

1.2   toxicity *[1 mark]*, dosage *[1 mark]*

1.3   A substance that's like the drug being tested but doesn't do anything *[1 mark]*.

1.4   So that doctors are able to compare the two groups *[1 mark]* to see if the drug makes a real difference to their condition *[1 mark]*.

1.5   C *[1 mark]*

Answers

Topic B4 — Bioenergetics

Page 41 — Photosynthesis
1.1 starch — storage *[1 mark]*, fats and oils — storage *[1 mark]*, amino acids — making proteins *[1 mark]*, cellulose — making cell walls *[1 mark]*
1.2 respiration *[1 mark]*
2.1 chloroplasts *[1 mark]*
2.2 **carbon dioxide** *[1 mark]* + water → glucose + **oxygen** *[1 mark]*
2.3 Energy is transferred from the environment during photosynthesis *[1 mark]*.

Pages 42-43 — The Rate of Photosynthesis
Warm-Up
carbon dioxide concentration, light intensity, temperature, amount of chlorophyll
1.1 Carbon dioxide stops being a limiting factor at a concentration of 0.10 units *[1 mark]*.
1.2 0.06 units *[1 mark]*
2.1 Dependent variable — volume of oxygen produced in 10 minutes *[1 mark]*.
Independent variable — relative light intensity *[1 mark]*.
2.2 Any two from: e.g. carbon dioxide concentration in the water / temperature / the plant being used *[2 marks — 1 mark for each correct answer]*.
2.3

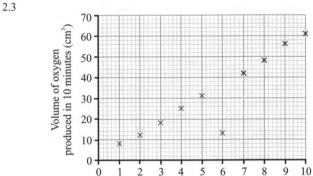

[2 marks for all four points plotted correctly, otherwise 1 mark for at least two points plotted correctly.]
2.4 6 *[1 mark]*
2.5 The rate of photosynthesis increases as light intensity increases *[1 mark]*.

Pages 44-45 — Respiration and Metabolism
1.1 glycerol *[1 mark]*
1.2 nitrate *[1 mark]*
1.3 cellulose *[1 mark]*
Cellulose is a component of plant cell walls.
1.4 urea *[1 mark]*
2.1 Respiration is a reaction carried out by **all** *[1 mark]* living organisms. Respiration is an **exothermic** *[1 mark]* reaction. It transfers energy **to** *[1 mark]* the environment.
2.2 E.g. to build up larger molecules from smaller ones. / To move about. / To keep warm. *[1 mark]*

3.1 Any one from: e.g. the mass of the peas in the flask / the size of the flask / the type of peas / the temperature outside of the flasks / the temperature of the peas at the start of the experiment *[1 mark]*.
3.2 The reading of 31 °C in Flask 2 on Day 1 should be circled *[1 mark]*.
3.3 The boiled peas will not germinate, so Flask 2 is included to show that the increase in temperature in Flask 1 is due to the peas germinating *[1 mark]*.
You get the mark here if you said something that meant the same as this, but said it in a different way — for example, you would get the mark for saying "Flask 2 was included as a control experiment."
3.4 The peas in Flask 1 released heat energy *[1 mark]*.
The temperature of Flask 1 rose by 8 °C. As the student controlled other variables that could have affected the results, it must have been the germinating peas that released the heat energy in Flask 1. The student didn't directly measure how much the peas respired each day so you can't say that the last option is a valid conclusion based on what you know.

Page 46 — Aerobic and Anaerobic Respiration
Warm-Up
glucose — $C_6H_{12}O_6$
carbon dioxide — CO_2
water — H_2O
1

Statement	Aerobic respiration	Anaerobic respiration
It transfers more energy.	✓	
It uses O_2.	✓	
It can produce ethanol and CO_2 as products.		✓
It is the incomplete breakdown of glucose.		✓

[3 marks for all four answers correct, otherwise 2 marks for three correct answers or 1 mark for two correct answers.]
2.1 The snail released carbon dioxide as it respired *[1 mark]*.
2.2 It will have decreased *[1 mark]* because the snail will have used up oxygen as it respired *[1 mark]*.

Page 47 — Exercise
1 During exercise your **muscles** may respire anaerobically. This causes a build up of **lactic acid**. It also leads to an **oxygen** debt. *[3 marks — 1 mark for each correct answer]*
2.1 (12 + 11 + 12) ÷ 3 = 11.6... = **12** breaths per minute *[1 mark]*
2.2 To get more oxygen into the blood *[1 mark]*, which was needed for increased respiration in the muscles *[1 mark]*.
2.3 The student had an oxygen debt / didn't get enough oxygen to the muscles during the exercise *[1 mark]*.
2.4 It would have increased *[1 mark]*.

Answers

Topic B5 — Homeostasis and Response

Page 48 — Homeostasis

Warm-up

The control systems **are** automatic.

If a control system detects the level of something is too high, it will **decrease** the level.

If a control system detects the level of something is too low, it will **increase** the level.

1   allowing large changes in conditions inside the body *[1 mark]*

2.1   E.g. to provide the right temperature for enzymes to work properly / the optimum temperature for enzymes *[1 mark]*.

2.2   The increase in body temperature is detected by **receptors**. Information is then sent to **a coordination centre**. The information is processed and a signal is sent to **effectors**, which produce a response. The man's body temperature is brought back to normal. *[3 marks — one mark for each correct answer.]*

2.3   the hormonal/endocrine system *[1 mark]*

Pages 49-50 — The Nervous System

1.1   motor neurone *[1 mark]*

1.2   Muscles — contract *[1 mark]*
       Glands — secrete hormones *[1 mark]*

2.1   X — brain *[1 mark]*
       Y — spinal cord *[1 mark]*

2.2   central nervous system/CNS *[1 mark]*

2.3   It receives information from receptors and coordinates a response *[1 mark]*.

3.1   mean = (25 + 20 + 15) ÷ 3 = 60 ÷ 3 = **20 mm**
       [2 marks for correct answer, otherwise 1 mark for correct working.]

3.2   The back of the hand is more sensitive than the forearm *[1 mark]*.

From this experiment, the student doesn't have enough information to make any of the other conclusions, because they haven't measured any other parts of the body. But they can compare two of the parts of the body that they have measured.

3.3   Any value between 5 and 20 mm *[1 mark]*.

The cheek is less sensitive than the palm, but more sensitive than the back of the hand — so the mean distance between toothpicks for the cheek should be between the values for the palm and the back of the hand.

3.4   E.g. the person being tested would be able to see how many toothpicks were touching their skin *[1 mark]*.

Page 51 — Synapses and Reflexes

Warm-up

Dropping a hot plate.

1   Reflex reactions are rapid and automatic. *[1 mark]*

2.1   X — sensory neurone *[1 mark]*
       Y — relay neurone *[1 mark]*

2.2   flame/fire *[1 mark]*

2.3   synapse *[1 mark]*

2.4   The stimulus is detected by receptors (in the hand) *[1 mark]*. The receptors send electrical impulses along structure X / the sensory neurone *[1 mark]*. When the impulses reach structure A / the synapse, chemicals are released *[1 mark]*. The chemicals move across structure A and trigger new electrical impulses in structure Y *[1 mark]*.

Page 52 — Investigating Reaction Time

1.1   Mean = (0.16 + 0.15 + 0.18 + 0.17) ÷ 4 = 0.165
       = **0.17 s** (2 s.f.) *[2 marks for correct answer or 1 mark for 0.165]*

1.2   Reaction time was faster after caffeine. *[1 mark]*

1.3   The results are repeatable. *[1 mark]*

1.4   Any two from: e.g. the amount of caffeine/the amount of drink that the volunteer was given. / The test used to measure reaction time. / The time between the volunteer having the caffeine and the test being done. / The time of day the tests were carried out. *[2 marks — 1 mark for each correct answer.]*

Page 53 — The Endocrine System

1   B *[1 mark]*

2.1   Glands secrete hormones directly into the blood. *[1 mark]*

2.2   Hormones are chemicals. *[1 mark]*

2.3   E.g. the effects of the endocrine system are slower *[1 mark]*. The effects of the endocrine system are longer lasting *[1 mark]*

3.1   pituitary gland *[1 mark]*

3.2   They act on other glands *[1 mark]* to make them release other hormones that bring about change *[1 mark]*.

Page 54 — Controlling Blood Glucose

1.1   pancreas *[1 mark]*

1.2   insulin *[1 mark]*

1.3   When there is too much glucose in the blood, some of it moves into the **liver**. The glucose is then changed into **glycogen** so it can be stored. *[2 marks — 1 mark for each correct answer.]*

2.1   The body produces little or no insulin. *[1 mark]*

2.2   With insulin injections *[1 mark]*.

2.3   E.g. eat a carbohydrate-controlled diet *[1 mark]*. Get regular exercise *[1 mark]*.

2.4   being overweight / obesity *[1 mark]*

Page 55 — Puberty and the Menstrual Cycle

1.1   testosterone *[1 mark]*

1.2   testes *[1 mark]*

1.3   stimulating sperm production *[1 mark]*

2.1   oestrogen *[1 mark]*

2.2   ovulation *[1 mark]*

2.3   Every 28 days. *[1 mark]*

2.4   luteinising hormone *[1 mark]*

3   The progesterone level will fall *[1 mark]*. Progesterone helps to maintain the uterus lining *[1 mark]*, so when the level falls the uterus lining will break down and the woman will bleed *[1 mark]*.

Page 56 — Controlling Fertility

Warm-up

contraceptive injection, contraceptive patch

1.1   As a tablet taken by mouth. *[1 mark]*

1.2   The hormones stop FSH production. *[1 mark]*

1.3   progesterone *[1 mark]*

1.4   It stops eggs maturing. / It stops eggs being released from the ovaries. *[1 mark]*

1.5   E.g. a woman doesn't have to think about using the implant every day (unlike taking an oral contraceptive) *[1 mark]* because the effects of the implant lasts for several years *[1 mark]*.

Page 57 — More on Controlling Fertility

Warm-up

diaphragm — worn over the entrance to the uterus

male condom — worn over the penis

female condom — worn inside the vagina

1.1   They stop sperm from getting to an egg. *[1 mark]*

1.2   condom *[1 mark]*

1.3   Spermicides kill or disable sperm *[1 mark]*. This prevents the sperm from being able to fertilise the egg, so the woman doesn't get pregnant *[1 mark]*.

1.4   E.g. not having intercourse when the woman is at the stage in her menstrual cycle when she is most likely to get pregnant *[1 mark]*.

Answers

Topic B6 — Inheritance, Variation and Evolution

Page 58 — DNA
1.1 DNA is found in the nucleus of animal and plant cells *[1 mark]*.
1.2 The structures that contain DNA *[1 mark]*.
2.1 A DNA molecule is made up of two strands of DNA coiled together *[1 mark]* into a double helix *[1 mark]*.
2.2 Genes code for particular sequences of amino acids *[1 mark]*, which are put together to make specific proteins *[1 mark]*.
2.3 The genome is all the genetic material in an organism *[1 mark]*.
2.4 E.g. it allows scientists to find genes that are linked to different types of diseases *[1 mark]*.

Page 59 — Reproduction
1 sperm — male gamete in animals
egg — female gamete
pollen — male gamete in plants
[2 marks for all three correct answers, otherwise 1 mark for 1 correct answer.]
2.1 meiosis *[1 mark]*
2.2 mitosis *[1 mark]*
2.3 They are genetically identical to the parent cell *[1 mark]*.
3

	Asexual reproduction	Sexual reproduction
There is only one parent.	✓	
There is no mixing of genes.	✓	
It results in genetic variation in the offspring.		✓
There is fusion of gametes.		✓

[3 marks for all four correct answers, otherwise 2 marks for three correct answers or 1 mark for two correct answers.]

You need to get two answers correct for 1 mark here. If you only get one answer correct (or you don't get any answers correct) you won't get any marks.

Page 60 — Meiosis
1.1 the reproductive organs *[1 mark]*
1.2 It is copied *[1 mark]*.
1.3 two *[1 mark]*
1.4 Four gametes are produced *[1 mark]*, each with only a single set of chromosomes *[1 mark]*. Each of the gametes is genetically different from the others *[1 mark]*.
2.1 mitosis *[1 mark]*
2.2 They differentiate into different types of specialised cell *[1 mark]*.

Page 61 — X and Y Chromosomes
1.1 23 *[1 mark]*
1.2 1 *[1 mark]*
2.1

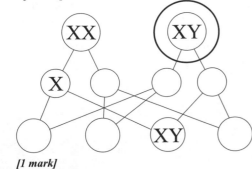

[1 mark]

2.2

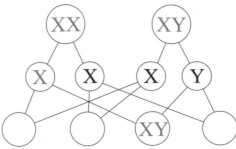

[1 mark for all gametes correct]

2.3

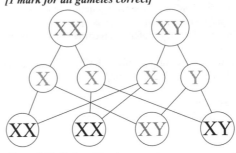

[1 mark if all the offspring genotypes are correct]
2.4 50:50 / 1:1 *[1 mark]*

Page 62 — Genetic Diagrams
Warm-up
alleles, homozygous, multiple genes
1.1

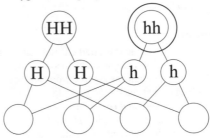

[1 mark]
1.2 Hh *[1 mark]*
1.3 The offspring all have short hair *[1 mark]*.
All the offspring have the genotype Hh. This means they all have the dominant allele (H), so they all have short hair.

Page 63 — Inherited Disorders
1.1 extra fingers or toes *[1 mark]*
1.2 It is caused by a dominant allele *[1 mark]*.
2.1

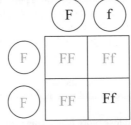

*[1 mark for correct genotypes of gametes.
1 mark for correct genotype of offspring.]*
2.2 half / 1 in 2 *[1 mark]*
2.3 none / 0 *[1 mark]*
Remember, cystic fibrosis is caused by a recessive allele, so two copies of the allele are needed for an individual to have it. None of the offspring in the Punnett square have two copies so none of them have it.

Answers

Page 64 — Family Trees and Embryo Screening

1.1   Hilda *[1 mark]*

Using the key next to the family tree, you can see that Freddy, Zelda and Buster are all carriers of the disease, whereas Hilda is not affected by it.

1.2   dd *[1 mark]*

The disorder is caused by a recessive allele. That means a person must have two copies of the recessive allele to be affected by it. Arthur is affected by the disorder, so he must have the genotype dd.

1.3   Dd *[1 mark]*

Zelda is a carrier of the disorder. This means she has one copy of the recessive allele and one copy of the dominant allele.

2.1   E.g. it could lead to people with genetic disorders being treated unfairly. / It could mean that one day people will screen embryos for features that they prefer. / Screening embryos is expensive. *[1 mark]*

2.2   E.g. it will help to stop people suffering. / Treating genetic disorders is expensive. *[1 mark]*

Page 65 — Variation

1.1   A random change in an organism's DNA that can be inherited *[1 mark]*.

1.2   B *[1 mark]*

2   E.g. flower shape / leaf shape / the size of the leaves/flowers / flower colour *[1 mark]*.

3   The difference in weight must be caused by the environment *[1 mark]*, because the twins have exactly the same genes *[1 mark]*.

In this case, the environment can mean the amount of food each twin eats or the amount of exercise they each do.

Page 66 — Evolution

1   Evolution is a change in the **inherited** characteristics of a population over time. According to the theory of evolution by natural selection, **all** organisms evolved from simple life forms that first evolved over **three** billion years ago.
       [3 marks — 1 mark for each correct answer.]

2.1   No individuals of the species are left *[1 mark]*.

2.2   Any two from: e.g. the environment changes too quickly. / A new predator kills them all. / A new disease kills them all. / They can't compete with another new species for food. / A catastrophic event happens that kills them all.
       [2 marks — 1 mark for each correct answer.]

3   How to grade your answer:
       Level 0:   There is no relevant information. *[No marks]*
       Level 1:   There is a brief explanation of how a population of hares with large ears could have evolved, but key information is missing. *[1 to 2 marks]*
       Level 2:   There is some explanation of how a population of hares with large ears could have evolved, but some detail is missing. *[3 to 4 marks]*
       Level 3:   There is a full explanation of how a population of hares with large ears could have evolved. *[5 to 6 marks]*
       Here are some points your answer may include:
       The original population of hares would have had variation in the sizes of ears.
       Those with larger ears would lose more heat. This would make them more likely to survive and reproduce in the warm climate than hares with smaller ears. So the genes for larger ears would be more likely to be passed on to offspring than genes for smaller ears.
       Over time, the genes for larger ears would become more common in the population until all the hares in the population had larger ears.

Page 67 — Antibiotic-Resistant Bacteria

Warm-up
False, True, False

1   C *[1 mark]*

2.1   Going down the table: 4, 2, 1, 3 *[2 marks for all four stages in the correct order, otherwise 1 mark for three stages in the correct order.]*

2.2   The person is less likely to be immune to MRSA than to a non-resistant strain of *S. aureus* *[1 mark]* and there is less likely to be an effective treatment for their illness *[1 mark]*.

Pages 68-69 — More on Antibiotic-Resistant Bacteria

1   By restricting the amount of antibiotics they give to their livestock *[1 mark]*.

2   E.g. the rate of development of new antibiotics is slow *[1 mark]*. The process of development is expensive *[1 mark]*.

3.1   By only prescribing antibiotics when they are needed. / By not prescribing antibiotics for non-serious conditions/infections by viruses *[1 mark]*.

3.2   It makes sure that all of the bacteria are destroyed *[1 mark]* and none are left to mutate and develop into antibiotic-resistant strains *[1 mark]*.

4.1   E.g. volume of nutrient broth solution / volume of ampicillin solution *[1 mark]*.

4.2   How to grade your answer:
       Level 0:   There is no relevant information. *[No marks]*
       Level 1:   There is a brief description of a method that could be used to carry out the investigation. Very little detail is included and some steps may be in the wrong order. *[1 to 2 marks]*
       Level 2:   There is a good description of a method that could be used to carry out the investigation. *[3 to 4 marks]*
       Here are some points your answer may include:
       Use a pipette to transfer some of strain A to one bottle with ampicillin in it and one bottle without ampicillin.
       Use a different pipette to transfer some of strain B to one bottle with ampicillin and one bottle without ampicillin.
       Put lids on all of the bottles.
       Store them all at the same temperature for a few days.
       Observe each bottle to see if the nutrient broth solution has gone cloudy.

4.3   E.g. if strain B is resistant to ampicillin, it is important that it is not allowed to escape into the general population, so it must be disposed of properly. / The bacteria used may pose a health risk to humans if not disposed of properly. / If the antibiotic used is not disposed of properly it may escape into the environment, where other bacteria may develop resistance to it *[1 mark]*.

Page 70 — Selective Breeding

1.1   When humans choose which plants or animals are going to breed *[1 mark]*.

1.2   artificial selection *[1 mark]*

1.3   B and C *[1 mark]*

1.4   E.g. to get cows that produce more milk *[1 mark]*.

2.1   It's less likely that individuals in an inbred population will have alleles that make them resistant to a disease *[1 mark]*, so if one individual gets a disease, the rest are also likely to get it *[1 mark]*.

2.2   E.g. genetic defects are more likely *[1 mark]*.

Answers

Page 71 — Genetic Engineering

1.1 The transfer of a gene from one organism's DNA into another organism's DNA *[1 mark]*.

1.2 They can be made to produce insulin *[1 mark]*.

2.1 It can increase crop yield *[1 mark]*.

2.2 Any two from: e.g. to be resistant to disease. / To be resistant to insects. / To produce bigger fruit. *[2 marks — 1 mark for each correct answer.]*

3.1 To find out whether a GM crop affects the number of wild flowers growing in a nearby area *[1 mark]*.

3.2 E.g. they could repeat their experiment with other meadows *[1 mark]*.

Page 72 — Fossils

Warm-up

False, True, True

1 C *[1 mark]*

2.1 Decay microbes need moisture and oxygen to survive *[1 mark]*. If these conditions are not present then decay can't happen *[1 mark]*.

2.2 Any two from: e.g. footprints / burrows / rootlet traces. *[2 marks — 1 mark for each correct answer.]*

2.3 They may be formed when parts of the organism are replaced by minerals when they decay *[1 mark]*.

Pages 73-74 — Classification

Warm-up

kingdom, **phylum**, class, **order**, family, genus, **species**

1.1 kingdom *[1 mark]*

1.2 physical characteristics *[1 mark]*

2.1 Carl Woese *[1 mark]*

2.2 Archaea *[1 mark]*

2.3 Any two from: protists / fungi / plants / animals. *[2 marks — 1 mark for each correct answer.]*

3 *Lophornis [1 mark]*

Remember, the binomial system puts the genus name followed by the species name, so the black-crested coquette's genus is Lophornis.

4 Our understanding of the internal structures of organisms has improved *[1 mark]*. Our understanding of the processes taking place inside organisms has improved *[1 mark]*.

5.1 E.g. current classification data *[1 mark]*. Information from the fossil record *[1 mark]*.

5.2 B *[1 mark]*

If you follow the lines from G and J back, you'll find that they meet at B, so B is their most recent common ancestor.

5.3 G and H *[1 mark]*

If you follow both of their lines back, G and H meet at B, and J and K meet at I. It's a shorter distance from J and K to I than it is for G and H to B, so G and H are more distantly related.

Topic B7 — Ecology

Page 75 — Competition

1.1 population *[1 mark]*

1.2 B *[1 mark]*

2.1 All the organisms in **Figure 1** are interdependent *[1 mark]*.

2.2 E.g. shelter *[1 mark]*

2.3 E.g. territory *[1 mark]*, mates *[1 mark]*

Pages 76-77 — Abiotic and Biotic Factors

Warm-up

'predators', 'pathogens' and 'competition' should be circled.

1.1 Light intensity and carbon dioxide level are examples of abiotic factors. *[1 mark]*

1.2 E.g. oxygen level *[1 mark]*

1.3 Any two from: e.g. moisture level / soil pH / soil mineral content / carbon dioxide level *[2 marks — 1 mark for each correct answer.]*

2.1 A new pathogen is likely to lead to a decrease in the population size of the flowering plants *[1 mark]*.

2.2 The bee population is likely to decrease *[1 mark]* because there will be fewer flowers available for them to feed from *[1 mark]*.

3.1 The heron population increased then decreased sharply, then increased again over the ten years *[1 mark]*.

3.2 Figure 2 shows that the average pH of the lake fell between years 4 and 5 *[1 mark]*, and Figure 1 shows that the population size of perch decreased during this time period *[1 mark]*.

3.3 There might have been an abiotic or biotic factor other than pH that affected the perch population *[1 mark]*.

3.4 E.g. the heron population is likely to decrease *[1 mark]* because Figure 1 shows that the perch and heron population follow the same trend / that the effect is likely to be similar to what was seen in year 5 when the perch population fell suddenly *[1 mark]*.

Page 78 — Adaptations

1.1 extremophiles *[1 mark]*

1.2 E.g. bacteria *[1 mark]*

1.3 E.g. high pressure *[1 mark]*

2.1 structural adaptation: long eyelashes / large surface area to volume ratio *[1 mark]*

These are both examples of physical features of the camel's body. So they are both structural adaptations.

behavioural adaptation: drinks large quantities of water when available *[1 mark]*

2.2 Functional adaptations are processes inside an organism's body *[1 mark]* that make the organism suited to its environment *[1 mark]*.

2.3 It prevents the camel losing too much water in its urine *[1 mark]*.

Remember to use the information that you are given in the question. It tells you that camels live in hot and dry conditions, so it is likely that concentrated urine is a way of coping with a lack of water.

Page 79 — Food Chains

Warm-up

The producer is seaweed.

1.1 photosynthesis *[1 mark]*

1.2 primary consumer *[1 mark]*

1.3 blue tits / sparrowhawk *[1 mark]*

Remember, only animals that eat other animals are predators. The greenflies are only consumers.

2.1 The population of the rabbits would decrease *[1 mark]* because there would be more foxes eating them *[1 mark]*.

2.2 If the number of rabbits decreases due to disease *[1 mark]*, then the number of foxes could decrease as there would be less food for them to eat *[1 mark]*.

Answers

Page 80 — Using Quadrats

1.1   mean = total number of organisms ÷ number of quadrats
= (26 + 23+ 18) ÷ 3 = 67 ÷ 3 = 22.33...
= **22** (2 s.f.) *[2 marks for correct answer to 2 significant figures, otherwise 1 mark for mean = 22.33...]*

1.2   Yes. If you arrange the results from quadrats 1 to 3 in order from smallest to largest, then 14 is the middle value *[1 mark]*.

Watch out: you get the mark for your explanation here, not just saying 'yes'.

1.3   E.g. yes, because the mean number of buttercups in Area 1 is lower than the mean number of buttercups in Area 2 *[1 mark]*. / No, because there could be other factors affecting the growth of the buttercups, that haven't been investigated *[1 mark]*.

1.4   total number of buttercups = mean per quadrat × total area
14 × 1750 = **24 500** buttercups *[1 mark]*.

The size of the quadrat is 1 m² so all you have to do is multiply the mean number of buttercups per quadrat by the total area of Area 1. If the quadrat had a different size, then you would first have to divide the area of the habitat by the size of the quadrat.

Pages 81-82 — Using Transects

1.1   B and C *[1 mark]*
1.2   A *[1 mark]*
1.3   E.g. a quadrat / a tape measure *[1 mark]*
2   56 squares are more than half covered by the grass species.
(56 ÷ 100) × 100 = **56%** *[2 marks — otherwise 1 mark for estimating 56 squares covered.]*

You should count a square if it's more than half covered.

3.1   E.g. the ground might be slippery / there might be large waves from the sea / the tide might come in *[1 mark]*.

Any sensible suggestion of a hazard you might find at a beach would get you the mark for this question.

3.2   It will take less time to collect the data *[1 mark]*.
3.3   The percentage cover of bladderwrack increases between 2 m and 18 m from the low tide point / the further the distance from the low tide point, the higher the percentage cover of bladderwrack, up to 18 m *[1 mark]*. The percentage cover then falls between 18 m and 20 m *[1 mark]*.
3.4   E.g. repeat the investigation again and see if they get the same results *[1 mark]*.

Page 83 — The Water Cycle

Warm-up

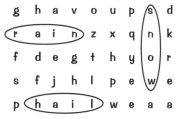

1.1   evaporation *[1 mark]*
1.2   Water that falls from the clouds *[1 mark]*.
1.3   It provides fresh water for plants and animals *[1 mark]*.
1.4   By animals eating the plants *[1 mark]*.

Page 84 — The Carbon Cycle

1   A: decay *[1 mark]*
B: eating *[1 mark]*
C: respiration *[1 mark]*
2.1   Microorganisms break down dead matter *[1 mark]*. As they break it down, they release carbon dioxide back into the air through respiration *[1 mark]*.
2.2   Plants take in carbon dioxide from the air during photosynthesis *[1 mark]*. They use the carbon in carbon dioxide to make glucose *[1 mark]*. This glucose is used to make carbon compounds (e.g. carbohydrates) in the plant *[1 mark]*.

Pages 85-86 — Biodiversity and Waste Management

1   Biodiversity is the variety of different **species** in an ecosystem. An ecosystem with a high biodiversity is **more** stable than an ecosystem with a low biodiversity.
[2 marks — 1 mark for each correct answer.]
2.1   The human population is growing *[1 mark]*.
The standard of living is increasing *[1 mark]*.
2.2   Air — e.g. acidic gases *[1 mark]*
Land — e.g. herbicides / household waste *[1 mark]*
Water — any two from: e.g. sewage / toxic chemicals / fertilisers / pesticides / herbicides *[2 marks — 1 mark for each correct answer]*
2.3   Pollution kills animals and plants *[1 mark]*, therefore it reduces biodiversity *[1 mark]*.
3.1   E.g. a bar chart *[1 mark]*.
3.2   River 1 is less polluted than River 2 because there are fewer rat-tailed maggots *[1 mark]*.

Rat-tailed maggots indicate high levels of pollution and there are fewer in River 1, which indicates it is less polluted.

3.3   A short distance downstream of the discharge site *[1 mark]*.
A short distance upstream of the discharge site *[1 mark]*.

Testing in these two locations means that the student can compare the level of pollution before and after the factory has added waste water to the river.

Page 87 — Global Warming

Warm-up
carbon dioxide, methane, increasing, heating up

1.1   E.g. the butterfly is present in more places in 2016 compared to 1986 *[1 mark]*. In 2016, the butterfly is present further up Britain/further north than in 1986 *[1 mark]*.
1.2   E.g. data on temperatures between 1986 and 2016 *[1 mark]*.

Page 88 — Deforestation and Land Use

1.1   as a compost *[1 mark]*
1.2   carbon dioxide *[1 mark]*
1.3   global warming *[1 mark]*
2.1   Any two from: e.g. building / quarrying / farming / dumping waste *[2 marks — 1 mark for each correct answer.]*
2.2   E.g. so it can be used to graze cattle / grow rice / grow crops for biofuels. *[1 mark]*
2.3   Effect: it reduces biodiversity *[1 mark]*.
Reason: e.g. forests contain many species of plants and animals, which would no longer be able to live there once the forest had been cut down *[1 mark]*.

Page 89 — Maintaining Ecosystems and Biodiversity

1   Replace the fences around her fields with hedgerows.
Allow wild flowers and grasses to grow around the edges of her fields. *[2 marks — 1 mark for each correct answer.]*
2.1   Reducing deforestation. *[1 mark]*
2.2   E.g. this could reduce the amount of land taken over for landfill *[1 mark]*, leaving ecosystems in place *[1 mark]*.
2.3   E.g. individuals could be bred in zoos, then released into the wild *[1 mark]*. This could increase biodiversity in areas where the species being released has low numbers/has been wiped out *[1 mark]*.

Answers

Topic C1 — Atomic Structure and the Periodic Table

Page 90 — Atoms

Warm-up

Protons and **neutrons** are found in the nucleus of an atom.
Electrons move around the nucleus in shells.
Compared to electrons, protons and neutrons are **heavy**.

1

Particle	Relative Charge
Proton	+1
Neutron	0
Electron	−1

[3 marks — 1 mark for each correct answer]

2   neutral *[1 mark]*
3.1   39 *[1 mark]*
3.2   19 *[1 mark]*
3.3   protons = 19 *[1 mark]*
    neutrons = mass number – atomic number
       = 39 – 19 = **20** *[1 mark]*
    electrons = 19 *[1 mark]*

Page 91 — Elements

1   Atoms are the smallest part of an element that can exist
    [1 mark].
2.1   Number of neutrons for isotope A
    = mass number – number of protons = 79 – 35 = **44** *[1 mark]*
    Number of neutrons for isotope B
    = mass number – number of protons = 81 – 35 = **46** *[1 mark]*
2.2   35 *[1 mark]*
The number of electrons is equal to the number of protons.
2.3   abundance of isotope A × mass number of isotope A
    = 51 × 79 = 4029 *[1 mark]*
    abundance of isotope B × mass number of isotope B
    = 49 × 81 = 3969 *[1 mark]*
2.4   Relative atomic mass
    $= \dfrac{\text{sum of(isotope abundance} \times \text{isotope mass number)}}{\text{sum of abundances of all the isotopes}}$
    $= \dfrac{4029 + 3969}{51 + 49} = \dfrac{7998}{100} = 79.98 = \mathbf{80.0}$ (1 d.p.)
    [2 marks — 1 mark for correct answer, 1 mark for correct number of decimal places]

Page 92 — Compounds

1.1   It contains two elements held together by chemical bonds
    [1 mark].
1.2   4 *[1 mark]*
A molecule of ammonia contains 1 nitrogen atom and 3 hydrogen atoms making a total of 4 atoms altogether.
2.1   sodium chloride *[1 mark]*
2.2   Any two from: B/NaCl *[1 mark]* / C/C₂H₄ *[1 mark]* /
    E/SO₂Cl₂ *[1 mark]*
2.3   1 *[1 mark]*
2.4   S: 1, O: 2, Cl: 2 *[2 marks for all three correct, otherwise 1 mark for two correct]*

Page 93 — Chemical Equations

Warm-up
1) True   2) False   3) True   4) True
1.1   calcium and water *[1 mark]*
1.2   calcium hydroxide and hydrogen *[1 mark]*
2.1   sodium + chlorine → sodium chloride *[1 mark]*
2.2   2Na + Cl₂ → 2NaCl *[1 mark]*
2.3   4Na + O₂ → 2Na₂O *[2 marks — 1 for each correct number]*

Page 94 — Mixtures

1   crude oil *[1 mark]*
2.1   2 *[1 mark]*
2.2   The chemical properties of the different parts in a mixture **don't change** *[1 mark]* when they're added together. The different parts can be separated from the mixture using **physical** *[1 mark]* methods.
3.1   Type of substance: mixture *[1 mark]*.
    Reason: air consists of two or more elements or compounds *[1 mark]* that aren't chemically combined together *[1 mark]*.
3.2   No *[1 mark]*. The chemical properties of argon are not changed by being part of a mixture *[1 mark]*.

Page 95 — Chromatography

1.1   Place the sheet in the solvent so that the solvent is just below the pencil line *[1 mark]*.
1.2   Pencil marks are insoluble (so won't dissolve into the solvent) *[1 mark]*.
2.1   solvent front *[1 mark]*
2.2   The different dyes in the ink move up the paper at different speeds *[1 mark]*
2.3   insoluble *[1 mark]*

Page 96 — More Separation Techniques

1.1   Filtration is used to separate **insoluble** *[1 mark]* solids from **liquids** *[1 mark]*.
1.2   Filter paper *[1 mark]*, funnel *[1 mark]*.
2.1   crystallisation *[1 mark]*
You can't just use evaporation here — the substance would break down if you heated it too much.
2.2   How to grade your answer:
    Level 0:   Nothing written worthy of credit *[No marks]*.
    Level 1:   A brief method is given, but there are steps missing *[1 to 2 marks]*.
    Level 2:   A method is given, but it is lacking in detail, or steps are out of order *[3 to 4 marks]*.
    Level 3:   A clear and detailed method is given *[5 to 6 marks]*.
    Here are some points your answer may include:
    Gently heat the solution in the evaporating dish.
    Stop heating once some of the solvent has evaporated or when crystals start to form.
    Leave the solution to cool until crystals have formed.
    Put the filter paper in the funnel and place the funnel in a beaker.
    Pour the mixture into the filter paper.
    The liquid passes through the filter paper, but the solid crystals will be left behind on the filter paper.
    After all the liquid has passed through the filter paper leave the crystals to dry out.

Pages 97-98 — Distillation

1   Fractional distillation *[1 mark]*
2.1   condenser *[1 mark]*
2.2   It changes from a gas to a liquid / it condenses *[1 mark]*.
2.3   E.g. the thermometer will read 118 °C *[1 mark]*.
2.4   Butanol has a boiling point greater than 100 °C / greater than the boiling point of water *[1 mark]*. So it would not evaporate when heated by a water bath *[1 mark]*.
3.1   In the first step, the temperature that the student heated the solution to was too high *[1 mark]*. Heating the mixture to 120 °C will cause both the ethanol and the water to evaporate *[1 mark]*.
3.2   The student should heat the mixture to a temperature of 78 °C. This will cause the ethanol in the mixture to evaporate, but not the water *[1 mark]*.
3.3   Bismuth iodide is soluble in ethanol but not in water *[1 mark]*. If the student removed the water instead of the ethanol, the bismuth iodide would still be dissolved in the solution and could not be removed by filtration *[1 mark]*.
3.4   The student should stop heating the solution when crystals start to form *[1 mark]*. They should then filter the crystals out of the solution and leave them in a warm place to dry *[1 mark]*.

Answers

Page 99 — The History of The Atom

Warm-up

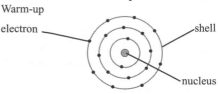

electron — shell
nucleus

1.1 Tiny solid spheres *[1 mark]*.
1.2 Nuclear model: 2, Bohr's nuclear model: 3,
Plum pudding model: 1
[2 marks for all three correct, otherwise 1 mark for one correct]
2.1 Plum pudding model — A positively charged 'ball' with negatively charged electrons in it *[1 mark]*.
Bohr's nuclear model — Electrons in fixed orbits surrounding a small positively charged nucleus *[1 mark]*.
Nuclear model — A small positively charged nucleus surrounded by a 'cloud' of negative electrons *[1 mark]*.
2.2 neutron *[1 mark]*

Page 100 — Electronic Structure

1

Electron shell	Number of electrons it can hold
1st	2
2nd	8
3rd	8

[3 marks — 1 mark for each correct answer]

2.1 2,8,8,2 *[1 mark]*
2.2 E.g. this shell can hold a maximum of two electrons *[1 mark]*.
3.1 Chlorine: 2,8,7 *[1 mark]*
Boron: 2,3 *[1 mark]*
3.2

[1 mark for correct number of electrons, 1 mark for correct arrangement]

You don't have to have the electrons paired up on the diagram. As long as there is the same number of electrons on the same shells you get the marks.

Page 101 — Development of The Periodic Table

1.1 E.g. protons (neutrons and electrons) had not been discovered / atomic numbers weren't known *[1 mark]*.
1.2 E.g. they weren't complete *[1 mark]* / some elements were put in the wrong groups/columns *[1 mark]*.
2.1 So that elements with similar properties were in the same group *[1 mark]*.
2.2 The properties of the elements that were found after Mendeleev made his table fitted with the gaps that he'd left in the table *[1 mark]*.
2.3 isotopes *[1 mark]*

Page 102 — The Modern Periodic Table

1.1 By atomic number / proton number *[1 mark]*.
1.2 groups *[1 mark]*
1.3 non-metals *[1 mark]*
2.1 Group: 2 *[1 mark]*.
Reason: The atom has 2 outer shell electrons. *[1 mark]*.
2.2 Period: 3 *[1 mark]*.
Reason: The atom has 3 shells of electrons *[1 mark]*.
2.3 X and Z *[1 mark]*
Elements X and Z both have 3 shells of electrons, so they're in the same period.
2.4 Element: A *[1 mark]*
Reason: Element A has the same number of outer electrons as element X / element A is in the same group as element X *[1 mark]*.

Page 103 — Metals and Non-Metals

1.1 Metals: Towards the left and bottom *[1 mark]*.
1.2 Conductors of electricity *[1 mark]*. Can be bent or hammered into different shapes *[1 mark]*.
2.1 A^{2+}: metal X^{2-}: non-metal *[1 mark if both correct]*
2.2 When metals react, they **lose** *[1 mark]* electrons. When this happens they end up with a **full** *[1 mark]* outer shell of electrons.
2.3 Any three from: e.g. dull / brittle / poor conductors of electricity / low density / not always solids at room temperature *[1 mark for each]*.

Page 104 — Group 1 Elements

1.1 lithium (least dense), sodium, potassium (most dense) *[1 mark]*
1.2 Melting point — decreases *[1 mark]*
Boiling point — decreases *[1 mark]*
2.1 +1 *[1 mark]*
2.2 ionic *[1 mark]*
3.1 sodium + water → **sodium hydroxide** + **hydrogen**
[2 marks — 1 mark for each correct answer]
3.2 E.g. potassium has more electron shells than sodium so the outer electron of potassium is further away from the nucleus than the outer electron of sodium *[1 mark]*. This means the outer electron of potassium is less attracted to the nucleus *[1 mark]* and more easily lost *[1 mark]*.

Page 105 — Group 7 Elements

1 The Group 7 elements all have **seven** *[1 mark]* electrons in their outer shell. They can react to form ions with a **1−** *[1 mark]* charge. These ions are called **halides** *[1 mark]*.
2.1 They are non-metals that exist as molecules of two atoms *[1 mark]*.
2.2 fluorine *[1 mark]*
3.1 Chlorine is more reactive than bromine *[1 mark]*. This is because chlorine has fewer electron shells than bromine so its outer shell is closer to the nucleus *[1 mark]*. This means it's easier for chlorine to gain an electron when it reacts *[1 mark]*.
Because of the increasing distance between the nucleus and the outer shell, reactivity decreases down the group. Bromine is further down the group than chlorine, it's outer shell is further away from the nucleus and therefore it's less reactive than chlorine.
3.2 H *[1 mark]*
Reason: e.g. hydrogen is a non-metal / halogens form molecular compounds with non-metals *[1 mark]*.

Page 106 — Group 0 Elements

1.1 gases *[1 mark]*
1.2 single atoms *[1 mark]*
1.3 They have a stable electron arrangement / full outer shell of electrons *[1 mark]*.
2.1 Any value above −108 °C and below 25 °C *[1 mark]*.
Boiling point increases down the group, so Radon will boil at a higher temperature than xenon. All the Group 0 elements are gases at room temperature, so radon must have a boiling point below 25 °C.
2.2 E.g. as you go down the group, the elements have more electrons *[1 mark]*. This means the forces between the atoms get stronger *[1 mark]*. So more energy is needed to break the forces / the boiling points increase *[1 mark]*.

Answers

Topic C2 — Bonding, Structure and Properties of Matter

Page 107 — Formation of Ions

1.1 atoms *[1 mark]*
1.2 1 *[1 mark]*
2.1 Metal atoms usually lose electrons to become positive ions *[1 mark]*.
2.2

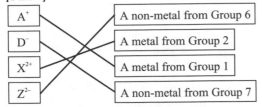

[2 marks if all four correct, otherwise 1 mark if two correct]

Page 108 — Ionic Bonding

1.1 positively *[1 mark]*, negatively *[1 mark]*, opposite *[1 mark]*
1.2 Magnesium ion: Mg^{2+} *[1 mark]*
Oxygen ion: O^{2-} *[1 mark]*
2.1

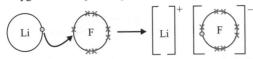

[1 mark for arrow showing electron transfer from Li to F, 1 mark for correct electronic structure of fluoride ion (seven crosses and one dot), 1 mark for correct charges on the ions]
2.2 electrostatic attraction / electrostatic force *[1 mark]*
2.3 E.g. the particles in the compound are oppositely charged ions/ have opposite charges / the bond is formed by electrons being transferred from one atom to another *[1 mark]*.

Page 109 — Ionic Compounds

Warm-up
In an ionic compound, the particles are held together by **strong** forces of attraction. These forces are called ionic bonds and act **in all directions**.
1.1 E.g.

[1 mark for correct structure, with alternating ions]
You'd also get the marks if you labelled all the white circles as Br⁻ and all the grey circles as K⁺.
1.2 Any one from: e.g. the diagram doesn't correctly represent the sizes of ions / it shows gaps between the ions *[1 mark]*.
2.1 conduct electricity in the solid state *[1 mark]*
2.2 giant ionic lattice *[1 mark]*

Page 110 — Covalent Bonding

1 Covalent bonds form between two **non-metal** *[1 mark]* atoms. These bonds form because the atoms **share** *[1 mark]* a pair of **electrons** *[1 mark]*.
2.1

Each line represents one covalent bond.
2.2 A: Cl_2 *[1 mark]*
B: CH_4 *[1 mark]*
C: H_2O *[1 mark]*

Pages 111-112 — Simple Molecular Substances

1.1

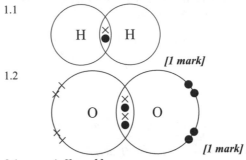

[1 mark]
1.2

2.1 A *[1 mark]*
2.2 E.g. molecule A/HCl has covalent bonding and all simple molecular substances contain covalent bonds *[1 mark]*.
3.1

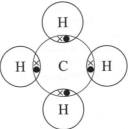

[1 mark for the correct layout of atoms and shells, 1 mark for the correct number of electrons in each bond]
3.2 E.g. they don't show how the atoms are arranged *[1 mark]* / how big the atoms are compared to each other *[1 mark]*.
4.1 The bonds between the atoms are strong *[1 mark]*. The forces between the molecules are weak *[1 mark]*.
4.2 The forces between the molecules / the intermolecular forces *[1 mark]*.
4.3 As these substances get larger, the forces between molecules/ intermolecular forces get stronger *[1 mark]*. As methane is larger than hydrogen this means that more energy is needed to break the stronger forces in methane *[1 mark]*, so it will have a higher boiling point than hydrogen *[1 mark]*.

Page 113 — Polymers and Giant Covalent Structures

Warm-up
In a polymer lots of **small** units are joined together to form a **long** molecule.
1 C *[1 mark]*
2.1 ammonia *[1 mark]*
Ammonia has a simple covalent structure — it forms small molecules.
2.2 They don't contain charged particles *[1 mark]*.
3.1 $(C_2H_4)_n$ *[1 mark]*
3.2 covalent bonds *[1 mark]*
3.3 At room temperature there isn't enough energy to break the intermolecular forces between polymer molecules *[1 mark]*.

Answers

Page 114 — Structures of Carbon

1   Buckminsterfullerene: B *[1 mark]*
         Nanotube: C *[1 mark]*
         Graphene: A *[1 mark]*

2.1   4 *[1 mark]*

2.2

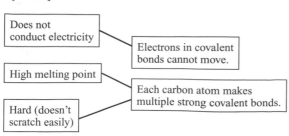

[2 marks if all three correct, otherwise 1 mark if one correct]

2.3   Carbon atoms are arranged in hexagons / rings of six carbon atoms *[1 mark]*.

2.4   Each carbon atom in graphite has one electron that's free to move *[1 mark]*. This means that graphite can conduct electricity, which is useful in electronics *[1 mark]*.

Page 115 — Metallic Bonding

Warm-up

The following should be circled: copper, tin, magnesium, aluminium.

1   Metal X *[1 mark]*. Metal X contains two different sizes of atoms / it doesn't have clear layers of atoms *[1 mark]*.

2.1   electrons *[1 mark]*

2.2   There are strong forces of attraction between the positive metal ions and the negative electrons *[1 mark]*. These forces of attraction hold the ions together in a regular pattern *[1 mark]*.

2.3   Metallic bonds are very strong *[1 mark]* so lots of energy is needed to break them *[1 mark]*.

2.4   E.g. metal A would be easier to bend *[1 mark]*. Metal A is made from layers of atoms that are all the same size *[1 mark]*. This means they can easily slide over each other and allow the metal to bend *[1 mark]*.

Page 116 — States of Matter

1.1   A *[1 mark]*

1.2   C *[1 mark]*

1.3   B *[1 mark]*

2.1   C *[1 mark]*

2.2   The particles in a substance *[1 mark]*

3.1   solid (strongest) → liquid → gas (weakest) *[1 mark]*

3.2   Solids have a fixed shape *[1 mark]*.

Page 117 — Changing State

1.1   freezing *[1 mark]*

1.2   melting *[1 mark]*

2.1   boiling / evaporating *[1 mark]*

2.2   The bonds are strong *[1 mark]*.

3.1   sodium chloride *[1 mark]*
At 900 °C, water would be a gas and copper would be a solid.

3.2   Sodium chloride *[1 mark]* and water *[1 mark]*.
At 1500 °C, copper would be a liquid.

Topic C3 — Quantitative Chemistry

Page 118 — Relative Formula Mass

1.1   relative formula mass of HCl = 35.5 + 1 = **36.5** *[1 mark]*

1.2   relative formula mass of Cl_2 = 35.5 + 35.5 = **71** *[1 mark]*

2

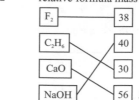

       [2 marks if all four correct, otherwise 1 mark if two correct]

3.1 M_r(MgO) = 24 + 16 = 40 *[1 mark]*

3.2   percentage mass of magnesium = $\dfrac{A_r(\text{Mg}) \times 1}{M_r(\text{MgO})} \times 100$
        $= \dfrac{24 \times 1}{40} \times 100 =$ **60%** *[2 marks for correct answer, otherwise 1 mark for correctly using the equation]*

You still get all the marks for this part if you got the answer to 3.1 wrong, but used it correctly here.

Pages 119-121 — Conservation of Mass

Warm-up

1)   Magnesium and hydrochloric acid should be circled.

2)   Boxes should be drawn around magnesium chloride and hydrogen.

3)   hydrogen

4)   hydrogen

1.1   The mass of the reactants will be the same as the mass of the products *[1 mark]*.

1.2   44 g of iron sulfide *[1 mark]*.

2.1   Total mass of reactants = 80.0 + 73.0 = 153 g
        Mass of sodium chloride = 153 − 36.0 = **117 g** *[1 mark]*

2.2   Total mass of products = 175.5 + 54.00 = 229.5 g
        Mass of sodium hydroxide = 229.5 − 109.5 = **120 g** *[1 mark]*

3.1 $2Mg + O_2 \rightarrow 2MgO$ *[1 mark]*

3.2   Mass of oxygen = 20 − 12 = **8 g** *[1 mark]*

4.1   23.2 − 25.4 = **−2.2 g** *[1 mark]*

4.2   E.g. the student is correct that no mass is lost or gained in a chemical reaction *[1 mark]*. The student isn't correct that the measurements must be wrong *[1 mark]*. Carbon dioxide has escaped from the reaction container *[1 mark]* so hasn't been counted in the final measurement *[1 mark]*.

5.1   Repeat 4 *[1 mark]*

5.2   The percentage uncertainty is greater for the data in Table 1 *[1 mark]*, which suggests that the data in Table 2 is more precise *[1 mark]*.

5.3   Table 1: percentage uncertainty = (0.055 ÷ 1.37) × 100%
                              = 4.0% (to 2 s.f.) *[1 mark]*
        Table 2: percentage uncertainty = (0.045 ÷ 2.71) × 100%
                              = 1.7% (to 2 s.f.) *[1 mark]*

5.4   They should increase the initial mass of Compound X *[1 mark]*.

Page 122 — Concentrations of Solutions

Warm-up

Unit	Mass	Volume
g	✓	
cm³		✓
dm³		✓
kg	✓	

1   When a solid is **dissolved** *[1 mark]* in a liquid, a solution is formed. The greater the mass of the solid, the **more** *[1 mark]* concentrated the solution. The larger the volume of liquid, the **less** *[1 mark]* concentrated the solution.

2.1   Conc. of calcium chloride = 28 g ÷ 0.4 dm³ = **70 g/dm³**
        [1 mark for correct answer and 1 mark for correct units]

2.2   The concentration of a solution is the amount of a substance in a given volume of a solution *[1 mark]*.

2.3   Mass = conc. × volume = 50 g/dm³ × 0.2 dm³ = **10 g** *[2 marks for correct answer, otherwise 1 mark for using the correct equation]*

Answers

Topic C4 — Chemical Changes

Page 123 — Acids and Bases

Warm-up

Substances with a pH of less than 7 are **acids**.
Substances with a pH of more than 7 are **bases**.
Substances with a pH of 7 are **neutral**.

1.1   beer *[1 mark]*
1.2   blue / blue-green *[1 mark]*
2.1 H^+ *[1 mark]*
2.2   0 *[1 mark]* – 14 *[1 mark]*
3.1   acid + alkali → salt + water *[1 mark]*
3.2 $H^+_{(aq)} + OH^-_{(aq)} \rightarrow H_2O_{(l)}$ *[1 mark]*
You still get the mark if you didn't include state symbols.
3.3   7 *[1 mark]*

Pages 124-125 — Reactions of Acids

1   Hydrochloric acid — chloride
     Nitric acid — nitrate
     Sulfuric acid — sulfate *[2 marks for all three correct, otherwise 1 mark for one correct]*
2.1   hydrogen *[1 mark]*
2.2   carbon dioxide *[1 mark]*
3.1   water *[1 mark]*
3.2 $2LiOH + H_2SO_4 \rightarrow Li_2SO_4 + 2H_2O$ *[1 mark]*
4.1

		Acid	
		Hydrochloric acid	Sulfuric acid
Metal hydroxide	Calcium hydroxide	Calcium chloride	**Calcium sulfate**
	Copper hydroxide	**Copper chloride**	Copper sulfate
	Magnesium hydroxide	**Magnesium chloride**	**Magnesium sulfate**

[2 marks for five correct answers, otherwise 1 mark for three correct answers]

4.2   hydrochloric acid + calcium hydroxide
     → calcium chloride + water *[1 mark]*
4.3 $Ca(OH)_2 + 2HCl \rightarrow CaCl_2 + 2H_2O$ *[1 mark for correct formulas, 1 mark for correct balancing]*
5.1   zinc chloride *[1 mark]*
5.2   Add zinc oxide to hydrochloric acid until the reaction stops/ the excess metal oxide sinks to the bottom *[1 mark]*. Filter the excess solid from the solution using a filter funnel *[1 mark]*. Heat the zinc chloride solution to evaporate some of the water and then leave to cool *[1 mark]*. Filter and dry the crystals that form *[1 mark]*.

Page 126 — The Reactivity Series and Extracting Metals

1.1   potassium *[1 mark]*
1.2   copper *[1 mark]*
Metals below carbon in the reactivity series can be extracted by reduction with carbon.
1.3   potassium *[1 mark]*
2.1   Reduction is the loss of oxygen *[1 mark]*.
2.2   Element: carbon *[1 mark]*
     Reason: It gains oxygen during the reaction *[1 mark]*.
2.3   Magnesium is more reactive than carbon *[1 mark]*.

Page 127 — Reactions of Metals

1   metal + acid → salt + hydrogen *[1 mark]*
2.1   calcium + water → calcium hydroxide + hydrogen *[1 mark]*
2.2   Lithium, calcium, magnesium, copper *[2 marks for correct answer, otherwise 1 mark for two metals in the correct places]*
2.3   E.g. use the same volume of water / use the same amount of metal / use the same surface area of metal *[1 mark]*.
2.4   Magnesium chloride *[1 mark]* and copper *[1 mark]*
2.5   A more reactive metal will displace a less reactive metal from its compound *[1 mark]*.

Pages 128-129 — Electrolysis

Warm-up

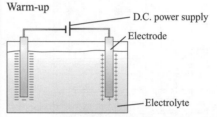

1.1   So the ions can move to the electrodes *[1 mark]*.
1.2   In electrolysis, the anode is the **positive** *[1 mark]* electrode. **Negative** *[1 mark]* ions move towards the anode and **lose** *[1 mark]* electrons. The cathode is the **negative** *[1 mark]* electrode. **Positive** *[1 mark]* ions move towards the cathode and **gain** *[1 mark]* electrons.
2.1   A liquid or solution that can conduct electricity *[1 mark]*.
2.2   lead bromide → lead + bromine *[1 mark]*
3.1   molten aluminium *[1 mark]*
3.2   To lower the melting point of the electrolyte *[1 mark]*.
3.3   Carbon in the electrode reacts with oxygen to form carbon dioxide *[1 mark]*, so it breaks down over time *[1 mark]*.
4.1 O^{2-} *[1 mark]*
4.2   Iron is more reactive than hydrogen *[1 mark]*.
4.3   chlorine *[1 mark]*

Answers

Topic C5 — Energy Changes

Pages 130-131 — Exothermic and Endothermic Reactions

1   An exothermic reaction is one that **gives out** *[1 mark]* energy. This is shown by a **rise** *[1 mark]* in the temperature of the surroundings.

2.1   The products have less energy than the reactants *[1 mark]*.

2.2   thermal decomposition *[1 mark]*

3.1   The temperature of the surroundings goes down *[1 mark]*.

3.2   From the surroundings *[1 mark]*.

3.3   It stays the same *[1 mark]*.

3.4   E.g. a sports injury pack *[1 mark]*.

4.1

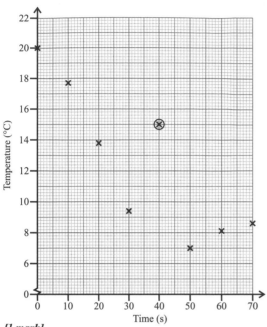

[1 mark]

4.2

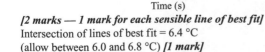

[2 marks — 1 mark for each sensible line of best fit]

4.3   Intersection of lines of best fit = 6.4 °C (allow between 6.0 and 6.8 °C) *[1 mark]*

4.4   Maximum temperature change = 20.0 – 6.4 = **13.6 °C** (allow between 13.2 and 14.0 °C) *[1 mark]*

Page 132 — Measuring Energy Changes

1.1   Change: e.g. put the polystyrene cup in a beaker filled with cotton wool / add a lid to the polystyrene cup *[1 mark]*. Reason: e.g. to reduce the amount of energy lost to the surroundings *[1 mark]*.

1.2   4, 2, 1, 3 *[2 marks for all four correct, otherwise 1 mark for two correct answers]*

1.3   31 – 18 = **13 °C** *[1 mark]*

1.4   Independent: concentration of acid *[1 mark]*
Dependent: temperature change *[1 mark]*

Page 133 — Reaction Profiles

1.1   activation energy *[1 mark]*

1.2   A *[1 mark]*

2.1

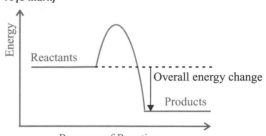

[1 mark]

2.2   Type of reaction: exothermic *[1 mark]*
Reason: e.g. the products have less energy than the reactants / the reaction gives out energy to the surroundings *[1 mark]*.

Topic C6 — The Rate and Extent of Chemical Change

Page 134 — Rates of Reaction

1.1   The particles colliding more often *[1 mark]*.
The particles colliding with more energy *[1 mark]*.

1.2   At the start *[1 mark]*

2.1   reaction B *[1 mark]*

2.2   The reaction has finished / no more product is being formed *[1 mark]*.

Page 135 — Factors Affecting Rates of Reaction

Warm-up
You should have circled the reaction that uses the lump of calcium carbonate.

1   Decreasing the pressure of the reaction will cause the rate of reaction to **decrease** *[1 mark]*. This is because the same number of particles are in a **larger** *[1 mark]* space, so they will collide **less** *[1 mark]* frequently.

2.1   Using a larger volume of the solution, but keeping the concentration the same *[1 mark]*.

2.2   Adding a catalyst decreases the activation energy needed for the reaction to occur *[1 mark]*.

Page 136 — Measuring Rates of Reaction

1   Gas syringe *[1 mark]*
Mass balance *[1 mark]*

2.1   Concentration: B *[1 mark]*
Reason: More gas was produced in the same period of time *[1 mark]*.

2.2   Dependent variable: volume of gas produced *[1 mark]*
Independent variable: concentration of acid *[1 mark]*

2.3   Any one from: e.g. the volume of the acid / the mass of the marble chips / the surface area of the marble chips / the temperature *[1 mark]*.

Answers

Page 137 — More on Measuring Rates

1 If the rate is higher than the rate of the original reaction, the cross will disappear **more quickly** *[1 mark]*.
If the rate is lower than the rate of the original reaction, the cross will disappear **more slowly** *[1 mark]*.

2.1

Concentration of hydrochloric acid (g/dm^3)	15	30	45	**60**	75
Time taken for mark to disappear (s)	**194**	187	**181**	174	168

[3 marks — 1 mark for each correct answer]

2.2 The results are subjective / they may not have agreed over the exact point when the mark disappears *[1 mark]*.

Page 138 — Graphs of Reaction Rate Experiments

1.1

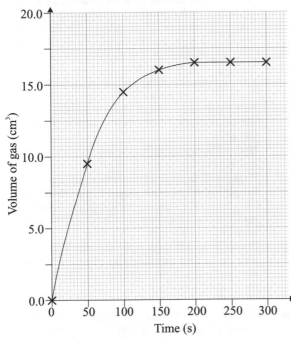

[2 marks for all points plotted correctly, or 1 mark for at least five points plotted correctly, 1 mark for line of best fit]

1.2

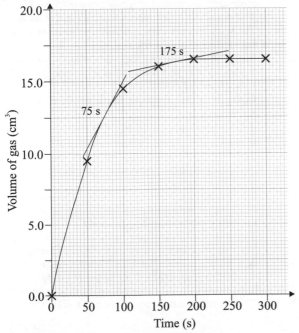

[2 marks — 1 mark for each correct tangent]

1.3 Time: 75 s *[1 mark]*
Reason: The tangent at 75 s is steeper than the tangent at 175 s *[1 mark]*.

Page 139 — Working Out Reaction Rates

1.1 $40 \div 125 = $ **0.32** units *[2 marks for correct answer, otherwise 1 mark for correct working]*

1.2 cm^3/s *[1 mark]*

2.1

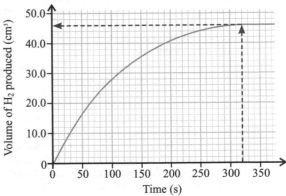

mean rate = amount of product formed ÷ time
= $46.0 \div 320 = 0.14375 = $ **0.144 cm^3/s**

[2 marks for correct answer, otherwise 1 mark for correct working]

You can work out from a graph when a reaction has finished by finding the point where the line goes flat.

2.2

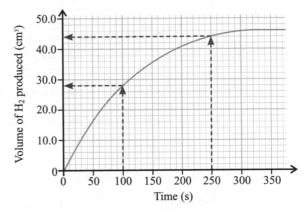

volume of H$_2$ produced $= 44.0 - 28.0 = 16$ cm^3
time difference $= 250 - 100 = 150$ s
mean rate = amount of product formed ÷ time
$= 16.0 \div 150 = 0.10666... = $ **0.107 cm^3/s**

[4 marks for correct answer, otherwise 1 mark for working out the volume of H$_2$ produced, 1 mark for calculating the time difference and 1 mark for correct working when calculating the mean rate]

Answers

Pages 140-141 — Reversible Reactions

1 ⇌ *[1 mark]*

2 1 When the reaction is heated, it moves in the forward direction and the amount of **products** *[1 mark]* increases.

   2 The energy **taken in** *[1 mark]* by the endothermic reaction is **the same as** *[1 mark]* the amount **given out** *[1 mark]* during the exothermic reaction.

3.1 At equilibrium, the rate of the forward reaction is equal to the rate of the backwards reaction *[1 mark]*.

3.2 A closed system stops the reactants and products from escaping and prevents anything else getting in *[1 mark]*.

4.1 Line 1 represents the concentration of methanol *[1 mark]*. At the start of the reaction, there is no methanol present in the reaction mixture, but the concentration increases as the reaction takes place *[1 mark]*.

4.2 The reaction reached equilibrium at time C *[1 mark]*. At time C, both lines are flat, meaning the concentrations of the reactants and the products are constant *[1 mark]*.

4.3 The scientist could produce methanol by cooling/decreasing the temperature of the reaction mixture *[1 mark]*.

4.4 E.g.

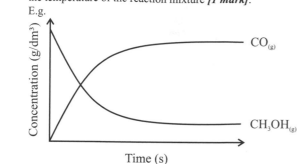

Time (s)

[1 mark for the correct curves, 1 mark for the correct labels]

It's also correct if your curves don't cross, as long as you show the concentration of carbon monoxide increasing and the concentration of methanol decreasing.

Topic C7 — Organic Chemistry

Page 142 — Hydrocarbons

1.1 **A** *[1 mark]*

1.2 **B** *[1 mark]*

2.1 A compound that is formed from hydrogen and carbon atoms *[1 mark]* only *[1 mark]*.

2.2 alkane + oxygen → **carbon dioxide** + **water** *[1 mark]*

2.3 oxidation *[1 mark]*

3.1 **B, D,** and **E** *[1 mark]*. They fit the general formula for the alkanes / of C_nH_{2n+2} *[1 mark]*.

3.2 butane *[1 mark]*

3.3 $C_5H_{12} + 8O_2 \rightarrow 5CO_2 + 6H_2O$ *[3 marks — 1 mark for each correct number]*

Page 143 — Crude Oil

Warm-up

diesel oil, petrol, liquefied petroleum gas and kerosene should be circled.

1.1 Crude oil is formed from **plankton** *[1 mark]* and the remains of other plants and animals that were buried in **mud** *[1 mark]* millions of years ago. Crude oil is being used up much more quickly than it's being made, so it's a **finite** *[1 mark]* resource.

1.2 Any two from: e.g. polymers / solvents / lubricants / detergents *[1 mark for each]*.

2.1 Carbon atoms bond together to form different groups of compounds *[1 mark]*.

2.2 it increases *[1 mark]*

2.3 E.g. how flammable it is / how viscous it is *[1 mark]*.

Page 144 — Fractional Distillation

1.1 A *[1 mark]*

1.2 E *[1 mark]*

1.3 B *[1 mark]*

2.1 Change of state: condensation / the vapour turns from a gas to a liquid *[1 mark]*.

Explanation: fractionating column becomes cooler as you go up it so the gases condense / change from a gas to a liquid *[1 mark]*.

2.2 How to grade your answer:

Level 0: Nothing written that answers the question *[No marks]*.

Level 1: Basic outline of how fractional distillation works is given but it lacks detail. No link is made between the boiling points and the chain lengths of hydrocarbons *[1 to 2 marks]*.

Level 2: Some explanation of how the separation of hydrocarbons is linked to their chain length is given. The explanation is not complete *[3 to 4 marks]*.

Level 3: A full explanation of why hydrocarbons separate into fractions depending on chain length is given. The explanation includes details of the change in temperature in the fractionating column, the link between chain length and boiling point, and the changes of state in the fractionating column *[5 to 6 marks]*.

Here are some points your answer may include:

The fractionating column is hot at the bottom and gets cooler as you go up.

Hydrocarbons of similar chain lengths have similar boiling points.

So they will condense at similar temperatures.

Longer hydrocarbons have high boiling points.

They'll only stay a gas when it's very hot. So they condense and drain out of the fractionating column near the bottom where the temperature is still high.

Shorter hydrocarbons have low boiling points.

They stay gases even at lower temperatures. So they condense and drain out of the fractionating column near the top where the temperature is cooler.

Pages 145-146 — Cracking

1.1 cracking *[1 mark]*

1.2 alkanes *[1 mark]*, alkenes *[1 mark]*

1.3 E.g. shorter chain hydrocarbons are more useful/can be used for more applications than long chain hydrocarbons *[1 mark]*.

2.1 The long-chain hydrocarbons are vaporised *[1 mark]*. The hydrocarbon vapour is mixed with steam and heated to a high temperature *[1 mark]*.

2.2 E.g. in catalytic cracking the hydrocarbon vapour is passed over a catalyst rather than being mixed with steam *[1 mark]*.

2.3 C_5H_{10} *[1 mark]*

2.4 $C_{12}H_{26} \rightarrow C_6H_{14} + 2C_3H_6$ *[2 marks — 1 mark for each correct number]*

2.5 Add orange bromine water to each sample you are testing *[1 mark]*. If the sample is an alkene (pentene), it will react with the bromine water and turn colourless *[1 mark]*. If the sample is an alkane (hexane), it won't react with the bromine water and it will remain orange *[1 mark]*.

3.1 The hydrocarbon vapour is flammable *[1 mark]*. The bung prevents the vapour from escaping the boiling tube and igniting *[1 mark]*.

3.2 The volume of gas produced by the reaction is measured by how much water is pushed out of the test tube *[1 mark]*.

3.3 A measuring cylinder has a scale which could be used to more accurately measure the volume of gas *[1 mark]*.

3.4 The cold water could cause the boiling tube to crack *[1 mark]*.

3.5 E.g. the temperature of the reaction *[1 mark]*.

Answers

Topic C8 — Chemical Analysis

Page 147 — Purity and Formulations

1.1 The mixture is made up of less than five parts *[1 mark]*.
1.2 Any one from: e.g. medicines / cleaning products / fuels / cosmetics / fertilisers / metal alloys *[1 mark]*.
2.1 A single element or compound not mixed with any other substance *[1 mark]*.
2.2 Sample **A** *[1 mark]* because it melts at a specific temperature whereas sample B melts over a range of temperatures / sample A melts at a higher temperature than sample B *[1 mark]*.
2.3 It will increase the boiling point *[1 mark]*.

Pages 148-150 — Using Paper Chromatography

Warm-up

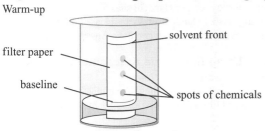

filter paper
baseline
solvent front
spots of chemicals

1.1 The dyes moved in the mobile phase *[1 mark]*.
1.2 E.g. different substances are dissolved in the solvent/mobile phase for different amounts of time *[1 mark]*.
1.3 They're all pure substances *[1 mark]*.
2.1 A *[1 mark]*
2.2 C *[1 mark]*
2.3 Repeat the experiment in different solvents *[1 mark]*. If they are made of the same substances, the spots on the chromatograms for the two food colourings will have matching R_f values in each solvent *[1 mark]*.
2.4 R_f = distance moved by substance ÷ distance moved by solvent
$R_f = 9.0 ÷ 12.0 = $ **0.75**
[2 marks for correct answer, otherwise 1 mark for correct working]
2.5 The scientist could run a reference/pure sample of the substance against food colouring A in different solvents *[1 mark]*. If a chemical spot in food colouring A matches the R_f of the substance in more than one solvent, then the substance is probably in food colouring A *[1 mark]*.
3.1 The student could conclude that at least one compound in the ink is insoluble in the solvent *[1 mark]*.
3.2 There could be more than five compounds in the ink *[1 mark]*. Several compounds in the ink could have similar R_f values/ solubilities in the mobile phase (solvent), which would cause their spots to overlap/merge *[1 mark]*.
3.3 Arrow A: The student drew the arrow from the baseline to the top of the spot *[1 mark]*. They should have drawn the arrow to the centre of the spot *[1 mark]*.
Arrow B: The student drew the arrow from the baseline to the top of the paper *[1 mark]*. They should have drawn the arrow from the baseline to the solvent front *[1 mark]*.

Page 151 — Tests for Gases

1.1 litmus paper *[1 mark]*
1.2 chlorine/Cl_2 *[1 mark]*
2.1 E.g. the gas could be toxic/an irritant *[1 mark]*.
2.2 carbon dioxide *[1 mark]*
2.3 The gas was not hydrogen *[1 mark]*.
2.4 oxygen *[1 mark]*

Topic C9 — Chemistry of the Atmosphere

Page 152 — The Evolution of the Atmosphere

Warm-up
Animals evolved — 4
The early atmosphere formed — 1
The oceans formed — 2
Plants evolved — 3
1.1 One-fifth oxygen and four-fifths nitrogen *[1 mark]*.
1.2 Any two from: e.g. carbon dioxide / water vapour / named noble gas *[2 marks — 1 mark for each correct answer]*
1.3 By algae and plants photosynthesising *[1 mark]*.
1.4 By volcanic activity *[1 mark]*.
2 How to grade your answer:
Level 0: There is no relevant information. *[No marks]*
Level 1 There is a brief description of how carbon dioxide was originally released into the atmosphere and one point briefly describing how it was later removed. *[1 to 2 marks]*
Level 2: There is some description of how carbon dioxide was originally released into the atmosphere and at least two points describing how it was later removed. *[3 to 4 marks]*
Level 3: There is a good description of how carbon dioxide was originally released into the atmosphere and detailed points describing how it was later removed. *[5 to 6 marks]*
Here are some points your answer may include:
In the first billion years of Earth, carbon dioxide was released by erupting volcanoes that covered the Earth's surface.
The early atmosphere contained mostly carbon dioxide.
Over time, carbon dioxide was removed from the atmosphere.
Much of the carbon dioxide dissolved in the oceans.
Dissolved carbon dioxide formed carbonates that precipitated as sediments.
As sedimentary rocks, oil and gas were formed, carbon was trapped within them.
Green plants and algae took in carbon dioxide through photosynthesis.
There is now less than 1% carbon dioxide in the atmosphere.

Pages 153-154 — Greenhouse Gases and Climate Change

1.1 Nitrogen *[1 mark]*
1.2 The sun gives out **short** *[1 mark]* wavelength radiation.
The Earth reflects this as **long** *[1 mark]* wavelength radiation.
This radiation is **absorbed** *[1 mark]* by greenhouse gases and then given out in all directions.
Some heads back to Earth and **warms** *[1 mark]* the Earth's surface.
2.1 The graph shows an increase in carbon dioxide levels in the atmosphere between 1960 and 2015 *[1 mark]*.
2.2 E.g. deforestation / burning fossil fuels / agriculture / producing waste *[1 mark]*
2.3 The Earth's climate is very complex so it's hard to make models that aren't oversimplified *[1 mark]*.
2.4 E.g. rising sea levels / certain areas getting too much or too little rain / more frequent and severe storms / temperature and rainfall changes affecting food production *[1 mark]*.
3.1 As carbon dioxide levels increased, the global temperature also increased *[1 mark]*.
3.2 E.g. the table doesn't include data from before 1960 *[1 mark]* so you cannot tell from the table what was happening to CO_2 levels before that date *[1 mark]*. / The table doesn't include data in the years between the ones given *[1 mark]* so you cannot tell from the table what was happening to CO_2 levels in the years in between *[1 mark]*.
3.3 Higher temperatures may cause ice caps to melt *[1 mark]*, reducing the amount of ice available for scientists to collect *[1 mark]*.

Answers

Page 155 — Carbon Footprints

1.1 Governments are worried that reducing carbon footprints could lead to sea levels rising *[1 mark]*.

1.2 Producing more waste — increase.
Using more renewable energy resources — decrease.
Using more fossil fuels — increase.
Using processes that require more energy — increase.
Capturing carbon dioxide and storing it underground — decrease.
[3 marks for all 5 correct, otherwise 2 marks for 4 correct and 1 mark for 2 correct]

2.1 A measure of the amount of carbon dioxide and other greenhouse gases *[1 mark]* released over the full life cycle of something *[1 mark]*.

2.2 Any two from: e.g. lack of education / reluctance to change their lifestyle / cost of changing lifestyle *[2 marks — 1 mark for each correct answer]*.

Page 156 — Air Pollution

1 Sulfur dioxide — combustion of fossil fuels that contain sulfur impurities.
Nitrogen oxides — reaction of gases in the air caused by the heat of burning fossil fuels.
Particulates — incomplete combustion of hydrocarbons.
[2 marks, otherwise 1 mark for one correct answer]

2.1 Sulfur dioxide / nitrogen oxides/nitrogen monoxide/nitrogen dioxide/dinitrogen monoxide *[1 mark]*

2.2 Any two from: e.g. damage to plants / buildings / statues / metals *[2 marks — 1 mark for each correct answer]*.

3.1 Nitrogen oxides cause respiratory problems *[1 mark]* and contribute to acid rain *[1 mark]*.

3.2 E.g. they can cause respiratory problems *[1 mark]*.

3.3 Name: carbon monoxide *[1 mark]*.
Reason: it is colourless and odourless *[1 mark]*.

Topic C10 — Using Resources

Page 157 — Finite and Renewable Resources

1.1 Resource: coal *[1 mark]*
Reason: e.g. it does not form as fast as humans can use it *[1 mark]*.

1.2 A resource that can be remade/replaced as fast it is being used *[1 mark]*.

1.3 E.g. natural rubber / wool / fresh water / food *[1 mark]*

2.1 E.g. the development of fertilisers has meant more crops can be grown in a given area *[1 mark]*.

2.2 E.g. synthetic rubber has replaced natural rubber / poly(ester) has replaced cotton in clothes / bricks are used instead of timber in construction *[1 mark]*.

Page 158 — Reuse and Recycling

1.1 Recycling metals increases the finite amount of metals in the Earth *[1 mark]*.

1.2 Glass products are **crushed** *[1 mark]* and then **melted** *[1 mark]*. They are then **reshaped** *[1 mark]* to make other products for a different use. This process uses **less** *[1 mark]* energy than making new glass.

2.1 Raw material: paper *[1 mark]*
Reason: e.g. plant fibre is a renewable source *[1 mark]*.

2.2 Any one from: e.g. reusing a stainless steel mug would mean less waste would end up in landfill compared to using paper cups only once / overall less energy would be needed to make one stainless steel mug compared to making lots of paper cups *[1 mark]*.

Page 159 — Life Cycle Assessments

Warm-up
Getting the Raw Materials — Coal being mined from the ground.
Manufacture and Packaging — Books being made from wood pulp.
Using the Product — A car using fuel while driving.
Product Disposal — Plastic bags going to landfill.

1 It looks at every stage of a product's life to assess the impact on the environment *[1 mark]*.

2.1 E.g. mining metals can damage the environment / extracting/ processing metals uses lots of energy / extracting/processing metals causes pollution *[1 mark]*.

2.2 Burning fossil fuels releases greenhouse gases/harmful substances *[1 mark]*.

2.3 E.g. landfill sites take up space / landfill sites pollute land and water / transporting waste to landfill sites takes lots of energy / transporting waste to landfill sites can release pollutants *[2 marks — one mark for each correct answer]*.

Pages 160-161 — Using Life Cycle Assessments

1 selective life cycle assessment *[1 mark]*

2.1 E.g. less waste is produced during the manufacture / they can be reused several times *[2 marks — 1 mark for each correct answer]*.

2.2 Any two from: e.g. energy used in extraction / energy used in manufacture / energy used in transportation of materials/ bags/waste / pollutants produced during extraction / pollutants produced during manufacture / pollutants produced during transportation of materials/bags/waste *[2 marks — 1 mark for each correct answer]*.

3.1 E.g. glass bottles can be reused multiple times *[1 mark]*.

3.2 Less resources are needed to produce the energy needed to recycle a can *[1 mark]*. This means that it is more environmentally friendly to recycle a can than to make a new one *[1 mark]*.

3.3 Sorting and separating the glass makes the recycling process more expensive and time-consuming to complete *[1 mark]*.

3.4 E.g. not all the cans and bottles will be recycled / some might be sent to landfill *[1 mark]*.

Page 162 — Potable Water

Warm-up
rivers, lakes, reservoirs

1.1 Water that is safe to drink *[1 mark]*.

1.2 groundwater/water trapped in rocks underground *[1 mark]*

2.1 passing water through filter beds — solid waste *[1 mark]*
sterilisation — microbes *[1 mark]*

2.2 E.g. chlorine / ozone / ultraviolet light *[3 marks — 1 mark for each correct answer]*.

Page 163 — Desalination

1 **A**: Bunsen burner *[1 mark]*
B: round bottom flask *[1 mark]*
C: thermometer *[1 mark]*
D: condenser *[1 mark]*

2.1 The membrane lets water molecules pass through but traps the salts *[1 mark]*.

2.2 E.g. processing fresh water takes less energy than desalination processes *[1 mark]* which makes it less expensive *[1 mark]*.

Page 164 — Waste Water Treatment

1.1 organic matter *[1 mark]*, harmful microbes *[1 mark]*

1.2 It may contain harmful chemicals which need to be removed *[1 mark]*.

2.1 To remove grit *[1 mark]* and large bits of material/twigs/plastic bags *[1 mark]*.

2.2 Substance **A**: sludge *[1 mark]*
Substance **B**: effluent *[1 mark]*

2.3 anaerobic digestion *[1 mark]*

Answers

Topic P1 — Energy

Page 165 — Energy Stores and Systems

1 A car slowing down without braking. — kinetic energy store
   A mug of hot tea cooling down. — thermal energy store
   A stretched spring returning to its original shape. —
   elastic potential energy store
   A battery in a circuit. — chemical energy store
   *[3 marks for all four correct, otherwise 2 marks for
   two or three correct and 1 mark for one correct]*

2.1 An object or a group of objects *[1 mark]*.

2.2 From top to bottom: false, true, false.
   [1 mark for each correct answer]

Page 166 — Conservation of Energy and Energy Transfers

1 Energy can be created.
   Energy can be destroyed.
   *[1 mark for each correct answer, otherwise no marks if more
   than two boxes have been ticked]*

2.1 Energy is transferred from: the apple's gravitational potential
   energy store *[1 mark]*
   Energy is transferred to: the apple's kinetic energy store *[1 mark]*

2.2 As the apple falls, **work** is done on the apple by the
   gravitational force. This means energy is transferred
   mechanically. *[1 mark for each correct answer]*

3 Energy is transferred mechanically *[1 mark]* from the bicycle's
   kinetic energy store *[1 mark]* to the thermal energy store of the
   brake pads *[1 mark]*.

Page 167 — Kinetic and Potential Energy Stores

1 $E_e = \frac{1}{2}ke^2 = \frac{1}{2} \times 20 \times 0.01^2$ *[1 mark]* = **0.001 J** *[1 mark]*

2.1 $E_p = mgh$ *[1 mark]*

2.2 $E_p = 0.50 \times 9.8 \times 2.0$ *[1 mark]* = **9.8 J** *[1 mark]*

2.3 To rearrange the equation for speed, multiply both sides by 2:
   2 × kinetic energy = mass × (speed)^2
   Then divide both sides by mass:
   (2 × kinetic energy) ÷ mass = (speed)^2
   Then take the square root of both sides to get:
   speed = $\sqrt{(2 \times \text{kinetic energy}) \div \text{mass}}$ *[1 mark]*
   = $\sqrt{(2 \times 9.8) \div 0.50}$ *[1 mark]*
   = 6.260... = **6.3 m/s (to 2 s.f.)** *[1 mark]*

*If you got a different answer in question 2.2, you would still get the marks
here if you used your answer and the correct method.*

Page 168 — Energy Transfers by Heating

Warm-up
The energy needed to raise the temperature of 1 kg of a substance
by 1 °C.

1 An electric kettle is used to heat some water. When the kettle is
   on, energy is transferred **electrically** to the thermal energy store
   of the kettle's heating element. The energy is then transferred
   by heating to the water. The energy is transferred to the water's
   thermal energy store.
   [3 marks —1 mark for each correct answer]

2.1 First convert 200 g into kg:
   200 ÷ 1000 = 0.2 kg *[1 mark]*
   Then rearrange the equation $\Delta E = mc\Delta\theta$ for the change in
   temperature:
   $\Delta\theta = \Delta E \div (mc)$
   = 9000 ÷ (0.2 × 900) *[1 mark]*
   = **50 °C** *[1 mark]*

2.2 The amount of energy needed to heat the copper block is **less
   than** the amount of energy needed to heat the aluminium block.
   [1 mark]

Pages 169-170 — Investigating Specific Heat Capacity

1.1
power supply
thermometer
flask
liquid
immersion heater
ammeter
*[3 marks for all correct labels, otherwise 2 marks for three
correct labels and 1 mark for two correct labels]*

1.2 From top to bottom: liquid C, liquid B, liquid A. *[1 mark]*

1.3 Putting insulation around the flask. *[1 mark]*

2.1 Ticks should be placed in the following columns:
   The mass of the block — Control variable *[1 mark]*
   The temperature of the block — Dependent variable *[1 mark]*
   The temperature of the room — Control variable *[1 mark]*

2.2 systematic error *[1 mark]*

2.3 Subtract 1 °C from all the measurements / repeat the experiment
   and retake all the readings correctly *[1 mark]*.

2.4 mean temperature = (31.0 + 29.5 + 32.5) ÷ 3 *[1 mark]*
   = 31.0 °C *[1 mark]*

Page 171 — Power

Warm-up
Power is the **rate of** energy transfer or **work done**.
It is measured in **watts**.

1 B *[1 mark]*

2.1 Rearrange the equation for work done:
   $W = Pt$ *[1 mark]* = 35 × 600 *[1 mark]* = **21 000 J** *[1 mark]*

2.2 $P = E \div t$ *[1 mark]*
   so $t = E \div P$ *[1 mark]* = 16 800 ÷ 35 *[1 mark]*
   = **480 s** *[1 mark]*

Page 172 — Reducing Unwanted Energy Transfers

1 Energy is **always** wasted when the handle is turned. The bucket
   rises faster when **less** energy is wasted. The speed at which the
   bucket rises will be increased by **lubricating** the **axle**.
   [4 marks — 1 mark for each correct answer]

2 D *[1 mark]*. Bricks that are thicker and with a lower thermal
   conductivity will transfer energy through them more slowly
   [1 mark]. So the rate of cooling of the house is lower, which
   means the house is more efficient *[1 mark]*.

3 Some of the energy transferred to the phone is dissipated/wasted
   [1 mark] to the thermal energy store of the phone *[1 mark]*.

Pages 173-174 — Efficiency

1.1 Whenever energy is transferred, some energy is wasted.
   [1 mark]

1.2 B *[1 mark]*

1.3 Kettle *[1 mark]*

*In order to compare the efficiencies, it's best to convert one of the values so
they're both a percentage, or both a decimal. To find the efficiency of the
kettle as a percentage: 0.75 × 100 = 75%. To find the efficiency of the
toaster as a decimal: 68 ÷ 100 = 0.68.*

2 (16 000 ÷ 20 000) × 100 *[1 mark]*

3.1 Efficiency = Useful power output ÷ Total power input *[1 mark]*

3.2 Efficiency = 75% = 0.75
   Total power input = Useful power output ÷ Efficiency
   [1 mark]
   = 57 ÷ 0.75 *[1 mark]* = **76 W** *[1 mark]*

4.1 E.g. getting an electric shock from the use of electricity
   [1 mark], and getting burnt by the hot water *[1 mark]*.

4.2 The kettle is more efficient for higher masses of water *[1 mark]*.

4.3 E.g. the graph in Figure 2 shows that efficiency increases as the
   mass of water increases *[1 mark]*.

Answers

Page 175 — Energy Resources and Their Uses

Warm-up

Renewable — bio-fuel, solar, tidal, geothermal, wave power, hydro-electricity, wind

Non-renewable — oil, coal, gas, nuclear fuel

1.1   coal, oil, (natural) gas
       [3 marks — 1 mark for each correct answer]

1.2   E.g. generating electricity / heating
       [2 marks — 1 mark for each correct answer]

1.3   Bio-fuel *[1 mark]*

2   E.g. non-renewable energy resources will run out one day
       [1 mark] but renewable energy resources will never run out
       [1 mark].

Page 176 — Wind, Solar and Geothermal

1.1   Advantage:
       Any one from: e.g. they produce no pollution once they're built / they do no permanent damage to the landscape
       [1 mark for a correct answer].
       Disadvantage:
       Any one from: e.g. they're not reliable as they don't produce electricity when there's no wind/if it's too windy / supply of electricity can't be increased when there's extra demand
       [1 mark for a correct answer].

1.2   E.g. geothermal power is reliable as the hot rocks are always hot
       [1 mark].

2   How to grade your answer:
       Level 0:   There is no relevant information. *[No marks]*
       Level 1:   There is a brief description of how the reliability of each energy resource varies throughout the year. The answer uses at least one piece of data from the table. *[1 to 2 marks]*
       Level 2:   There is a detailed description of how the reliability of each energy resource varies throughout the year. A sensible conclusion as to why the university would choose both options has been made. At least two pieces of data from the table are used to provide evidence for the answer. *[3 to 4 marks]*

       Here are some points your answer may include:
       The average wind speed between October and March was higher than the average wind speed between April and September.
       So wind turbines will be able to generate more electricity between October and March than between April and September.
       Between April and September, the average number of daylight hours was higher than the average number of daylight hours between October and March.
       So solar panels will be able to generate more electricity between April and September than between October and March.
       So when one of the methods of generating electricity is producing less, the other method will be producing more.
       By installing both, the university will have a more constant and reliable electricity supply throughout the year.

Page 177 — Hydro-electricity, Waves and Tides

1.1   They must be built near the coast. *[1 mark]*
       They can disturb the habitats of animals. *[1 mark]*

1.2   Any one from: e.g. they can't respond straight away when there's extra demand for electricity / they're not as reliable because the waves die down when the wind drops.
       [1 mark for one correct answer]

2   How to grade your answer:
       Level 0:   There is no relevant information. *[No marks]*
       Level 1:   There is a brief description of the reliability or environmental impact of one of the energy resources. *[1 to 2 marks]*
       Level 2:   There is a clear and detailed comparison of the reliability and environmental impacts of both energy resources, including similarities and differences between them. *[3 to 4 marks]*

       Here are some points your answer may include:
       Both energy resources are reliable.
       We can predict the tides as the tides come in and out at known times.
       Except in countries where it doesn't rain regularly, there is always water available for a hydro-electric power plant to work. However, rain is less reliable than the tides.
       Hydro-electric power plants can provide a constant supply of electricity.
       There are times during the day when tidal barrages aren't producing electricity, as the water level on both sides of the barrage are the same.
       Hydro-electric power plants can also increase their supply when there's extra demand, but tidal barrages can't.
       Hydro-electric power plants require the flooding of valleys, which causes a loss of habitat for any animals and plants living there.
       Tidal barrages also affect local wildlife — they change the habitat of nearby animals.
       When hydro-electric power plants flood the valley, plants in the valley die and rot.
       This releases gases that contribute to global warming.
       Using tides to generate electricity creates no pollution.

Page 178 — Bio-fuels and Non-renewables

Warm-up

The waste produced is difficult to dispose of.

It is a non-renewable energy resource.

The radiation produced when using nuclear power is dangerous to humans.

1   From top to bottom: both, bio-fuels, fossil fuels.
       [3 marks — 1 mark for each correct answer]

2   How to grade your answer:
       Level 0:   There is no relevant information. *[No marks]*
       Level 1:   There is a brief explanation of an advantage or a disadvantage of fossil fuels. *[1 to 2 marks]*
       Level 2:   There is some explanation of both advantages and disadvantages of fossil fuels. *[3 to 4 marks]*
       Level 3:   There is a clear and detailed explanation of the advantages and disadvantages of using fossil fuels. *[5 to 6 marks]*

       Here are some points your answer may include:
       Advantages:
       Fossil fuels are reliable.
       Power plants can respond quickly to changes in demand.
       Disadvantages:
       Fossil fuels are slowly running out / they are a non-renewable energy resource.
       Burning fossil fuels releases carbon dioxide into the atmosphere.
       Carbon dioxide in the atmosphere contributes to global warming.
       Burning coal and oil also releases sulfur dioxide, which causes acid rain.
       Acid rain can damage soil and trees. This can damage or destroy the habitats of animals.
       Coal used for generating electricity is obtained by coal mining.
       Coal mining can spoil the landscape by damaging it.
       When drilling for oil to use to generate electricity, there is a risk of oil spills. Oil spillages kill sea life, birds and mammals that live near to the sea.

Answers

Page 179 — Trends in Energy Resource Use

1.1   56 + 10 + 16 = 82 %

[2 marks for correct answer, otherwise 1 mark for reading all three values correctly from the graph]

1.2   E.g. the country is using a larger percentage of renewable energy resources to generate electricity in 2015 than 1995 / overall, they are using a smaller percentage of fossil fuels to generate their electricity in 2015 than they were in 1995 / the percentage of electricity generated from nuclear power is lower in 1995 compared to 2015 *[1 mark]*.

2.1   Any one from: e.g. we now know that burning fossil fuels is bad for the environment *[1 mark]*, so more people want to use renewable energy resources that damage the environment less *[1 mark]* / fossil fuel reserves will run out *[1 mark]*, so we have to find an alternative for them *[1 mark]* / pressure from the public and other countries has lead to government targets for the use of renewable energy resources *[1 mark]*, which puts pressure on energy providers to build power plants that use renewable energy resources *[1 mark]*.

2.2   How to grade your answer:

Level 0:   There is no relevant information. *[No marks]*

Level 1:   At least two factors are given that slow down the rate at which renewable energy resource use is increasing. A brief explanation for one of the factors is given. *[1 to 2 marks]*

Level 2:   There is a clear and detailed explanation of at least two factors that slow down the rate at which renewable energy resource use is increasing. *[3 to 4 marks]*

Here are some points your answer may include:

Building new power plants to replace existing fossil fuel powered ones is expensive.

Some renewable energy resources are less reliable than fossil fuels.

So a mixture of different resources would need to be used, which is also more expensive than just using fossil fuels.

Research into improving renewable energy resources costs money and will take time.

Energy companies are unlikely to pay for all these costs, so this extra cost needs to be paid through energy bills or taxes.

Governments may not want to raise taxes as it may make them unpopular with the public.

Some people don't want to or can't afford to pay the extra cost.

Personal products that use renewable energy resources, like hybrid cars, are generally more expensive than similar ones that use fossil fuels.

Topic P2 — Electricity

Page 180 — Current and Circuit Symbols

Warm-up

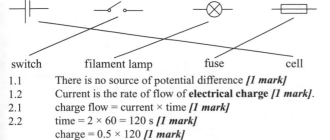

switch   filament lamp   fuse   cell

1.1   There is no source of potential difference *[1 mark]*

1.2   Current is the rate of flow of **electrical charge** *[1 mark]*.

2.1   charge flow = current × time *[1 mark]*

2.2   time = 2 × 60 = 120 s *[1 mark]*

charge = 0.5 × 120 *[1 mark]*

= 60 *[1 mark]* coulombs *[1 mark]*

Page 181 — Resistance and V = IR

1   potential difference = current × resistance

potential difference = 3 × 6 *[1 mark]* = **18 V** *[1 mark]*

2   At a fixed temperature, the **resistance** of an ohmic conductor will remain **constant** as the current though it is **changed**.

[3 marks — 1 mark for each correct answer]

3.1   rearrange potential difference = current × resistance for resistance:

resistance = potential difference ÷ current *[1 mark]*

resistance = 25 ÷ 3 *[1 mark]*

= 8.333...Ω

= **8.3 Ω (to 2 s.f.)** *[1 mark]*

3.2   As the temperature of the filament lamp increases, its resistance increases *[1 mark]*. The higher the resistance, the lower the current through the lamp (for a fixed potential difference) *[1 mark]*.

Page 182 — Investigating Resistance

1.1   To calculate the resistance of each length of wire, the student **divided** the reading on the voltmeter by the reading on the **ammeter**. *[2 marks – 1 mark for each correct answer]*

1.2

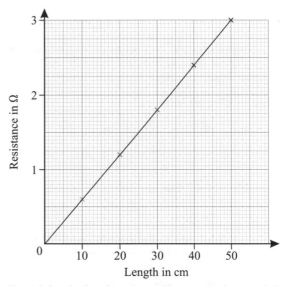

[1 mark for plotting the point at 40 cm correctly, 1 mark for plotting the point at 50 cm correctly, 1 mark for a straight line of best fit passing through all points and the origin]

1.3   Resistance is directly proportional to length. *[1 mark]*

Pages 183-184 — I-V Characteristics

1.1   B *[1 mark]*

B is the only graph that is a straight line, so it must be of the linear component.

1.2   E.g. a fixed resistor *[1 mark]*

2.1   E.g. set the resistance of the variable resistor *[1 mark]*. Take readings of the current through and the potential difference across the component *[1 mark]*. Then change the resistance of the variable resistor and take readings of current and potential difference. Repeat this for a range of values *[1 mark]*.

2.2   Read potential difference, when current is 2.0 A, off the graph

potential difference = 6 V *[1 mark]*

potential difference = current × resistance *[1 mark]*

so, resistance = potential difference ÷ current

= 6 ÷ 2.0 *[1 mark]*

= 3 Ω *[1 mark]*

Answers

3.1   E.g.

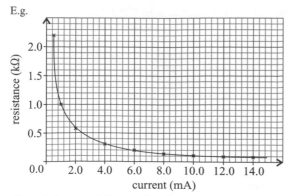

[1 mark for smooth line passing through or close to all points]

3.2   0.4 kΩ (accept between 0.35 and 0.45 kΩ) *[1 mark]*

Read off the value of resistance for a current of 3.0 mA (halfway between the 2.0 mA and 4.0 mA markers) from your curve of best fit.

3.3   The student has only carried out the experiment for positive values of current, and the results may be different for negative values of current *[1 mark]*.

Diodes have a very high resistance for one direction of current flow but not the opposite, so the student's conclusion is not true for negative values of current.

3.4   Have someone else carry out the same experiment using different equipment *[1 mark]*, and if the results are similar to the student's, then the experiment is reproducible *[1 mark]*.

Page 185 — Circuit Devices

1

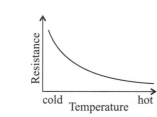

[1 mark]

Thermistors have a high resistance at low temperatures, and their resistance decreases as temperature increases.

2.1   E.g.

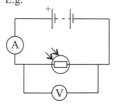

[1 mark for LDR, ammeter and battery in series, 1 mark for voltmeter in parallel across LDR]

2.2   It decreases *[1 mark]*.

2.3   E.g. automatic night lights (turning on a light when it gets dark) / burglar detectors *[1 mark]*

Page 186 — Series Circuits

1

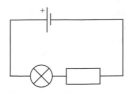

[1 mark]

2.1   60 Ω *[1 mark]*

The total resistance in a series circuit is the sum of all the resistances in the circuit ($R_{total} = R_1 + R_2$).

2.2   Current = 0.05 A *[1 mark]*

The current is the same everywhere in a series circuit.

2.3   total potential difference = 3 V
       potential difference = 3 − (1.2 + 0.6) *[1 mark]*
       = **1.2 V** *[1 mark]*

Page 187 — Parallel Circuits

Warm-up
B

1.1   6 A *[1 mark]*

The total current in the circuit is split between the two branches, so the current through A_1 is found by adding the current through R_1 and R_2.

1.2   9 V *[1 mark]*

The total potential difference across each branch of a parallel circuit is the same.

1.3   The total resistance of the circuit in Figure 1 is smaller than in Figure 2. *[1 mark]*

Adding resistors in parallel decreases the total resistance of a circuit, so removing a resistor increases the resistance.

Page 188 — Investigating Circuits

1.1

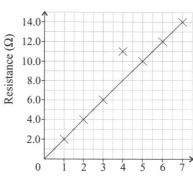

[1 mark for straight line going through the origin and through all points except the anomalous result]

1.2   Resistance = 8.0 Ω

[1 mark for any correct answer read from your line of best fit for four resistors]

2   How to grade your answer:

Level 0:   There is no relevant information. *[No marks]*

Level 1:   There is a brief description of the method used to measure resistance of the circuit. The steps mentioned are not in a logical order. *[1 to 2 marks]*

Level 2:   There is a good description of the method used to measure the resistance of the circuit. Most steps are given in a logical order. A correct circuit diagram may be included. *[3 to 4 marks]*

Level 3:   A logical and detailed description is given. The method for investigating the effect of adding resistors in parallel is fully described. A correct circuit diagram may be included. *[5 to 6 marks]*

Here are some points your answer may include:

Assume the potential difference is the same as the potential difference of the battery.

Measure the current through the circuit using the ammeter.

Calculate the resistance of the circuit using $R = V \div I$.

Connect a second identical resistor in parallel with the first resistor.

The second resistor should not be in parallel with the ammeter.

Measure the current and use this to calculate the resistance of the circuit.

Repeat this for several identical resistors.

A correct circuit diagram, similar to:

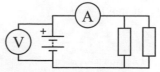

A correct diagram with at least two resistors in parallel is correct. You could also draw your circuit with several resistors in parallel, all separated with switches.

Answers

Answers

Page 189 — Electricity in the Home

Warm-up

Mains electricity is a supply of **alternating** current.

It is at **230** V and has a frequency of **50 Hz**.

1.1   three-core cable *[1 mark]*

1.2   neutral — blue

         earth — green and yellow

         live — brown

         [2 marks for all three correct, 1 mark for one or two correct]

1.3   When an appliance is working normally, **current** flows to the appliance through the **live** wire and the **neutral** wire.

         The **earth** wire will only carry current if there is a fault.

         [4 marks – 1 mark for each correct answer]

1.4   They could get an electric shock *[1 mark]*.

Pages 190-191 — Power of Electrical Appliances

1   Electrically to the kinetic energy store of the car's motor. *[1 mark]*

2   The **power** of an appliance is the energy transferred **per second**. Energy is transferred because the **charges** do work against the appliance's resistance.

         [3 marks – 1 mark for each correct answer]

3.1   energy transferred = power × time *[1 mark]*

3.2   rearrange energy transferred = power × time for time:

         time = energy transferred ÷ power *[1 mark]*

         so time = 140 000 ÷ 700 *[1 mark]* = **200 s** *[1 mark]*

3.3   Power is the rate of energy transfer, so the larger the power, the more energy it transfers per second *[1 mark]*. So the 900 W microwave will transfer the same amount of energy in less time than the 700 W microwave *[1 mark]*.

4.1   The motor used *[1 mark]*.

4.2   Timing how long it takes the mass to travel 30 cm rather than 60 cm *[1 mark]*.

The marker would help the student to see more accurately when the mass has passed a certain point on the ruler, making it easier to see when the mass has moved through 60 cm. Two light gates would measure the time taken more accurately as they would remove any errors introduced from the student's reaction time.

4.3   Mean time taken = (5.1 + 4.8 + 4.5) ÷ 3 *[1 mark]*

         = 4.8 s *[1 mark]*

4.4   Motor A *[1 mark]*. This motor takes the least amount of time to transfer the same amount of energy *[1 mark]*, and as power output is equal to energy transferred over time, a shorter time means a larger power output *[1 mark]*.

Page 192 — More on Power

1.1   power = 6 × 2 *[1 mark]* = **12 W** *[1 mark]*

1.2   energy transferred = charge flow × potential difference *[1 mark]*

1.3   energy transferred = 4 × 6 *[1 mark]* = **24 J** *[1 mark]*

2   current = $\sqrt{\dfrac{1500}{70}}$ *[1 mark]*

Remember, 1.5 kW is equal to 1500 W.

Page 193 — The National Grid

Warm-up

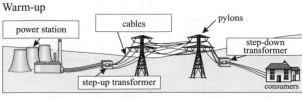

1   It increases the output current and decreases the output potential difference. *[1 mark]*

2   Transmitting electricity with a high current causes a lot of energy to be wasted due to heating *[1 mark]*. The national grid uses step-up transformers to increase the potential difference of the electricity *[1 mark]*. For a given power, increasing the potential difference decreases the current *[1 mark]*. This decreases the energy lost by heating which increases the efficiency of the national grid *[1 mark]*.

Topic P3 — Particle Model of Matter

Page 194 — The Particle Model and Motion in Gases

Warm-up

From left to right: liquid, solid, gas

1   The energy stored by the particles *[1 mark]*.

2   The tyre pressure on a hot day will be higher than the tyre pressure on a cold day *[1 mark]*.

3   The average energy in the kinetic energy stores of the gas particles decreases *[1 mark]*. This decreases the average speed of the gas particles *[1 mark]*.

Page 195 — Density of Materials

1   a eureka can *[1 mark]*

2.1 $\rho = m \div v$ *[1 mark]*

2.2 ρ = 28 875 ÷ 1.5 *[1 mark]* = 19 250

         = **19 000 kg/m³ (to 2 s.f.)** *[1 mark]*

3   Level 0:   There is no relevant information. *[No marks]*

         Level 1:   There is some reference to finding the mass and volume of the liquid. There is no mention of how to calculate density. *[1 to 2 marks]*

         Level 2:   There is a description of how to measure the volume and mass using the equipment given. There is a description of how these are used to find the density. *[3 to 4 marks]*

         Here are some points your answer may include:

         Place the empty measuring cylinder on the mass balance.

         Zero the mass balance.

         Pour some acid into the measuring cylinder.

         Write down the mass of the acid shown on the mass balance.

         Read the volume of the acid from the scale on the measuring cylinder.

         Use the equation density = mass ÷ volume to calculate the density of the acid.

Page 196 — Internal Energy and Changes of State

1   When a system is heated, the internal energy of the system **increases**. This either increases the **temperature** of the system or causes a change of state. During a change of state the temperature and the **mass** of the substance remain constant.

         [3 marks — 1 mark for each correct answer]

2.1   Gas to liquid: condensing *[1 mark]*

         Liquid to gas: evaporating/boiling *[1 mark]*

2.2   E.g. a change where you don't end up with a new material / you end up with the same material in a different form *[1 mark]*.

3.1   E.g. the energy stored in a system by its particles. / The total energy in the kinetic and potential energy stores of the particles of a system *[1 mark]*.

3.2   30 − 20 = 10 g *[1 mark]*. E.g. because when a substance changes state, its mass doesn't change. So the mass of the water vapour equals the mass of the water that is no longer a liquid *[1 mark]*.

Answers

Pages 197-198 — Specific Latent Heat

1.1 Between 3 and 8 minutes. — Substance is melting. *[1 mark]*
Between 24 and 35 minutes. — Substance is boiling. *[1 mark]*
Between 8 and 24 minutes. — Substance is a liquid being heated. *[1 mark]*

1.2 $E = mL$ so $L = E \div m$ *[1 mark]*
$L = 34\,000 \div 0.50$ *[1 mark]* = **68 000 J/kg** *[1 mark]*

2.1 The graph first hits 0 °C at time = 4 minutes,
and stays at 0 °C until time = 142 minutes.
So the total time at 0 °C = 142 − 4 = 138 minutes *[1 mark]*
So, average rate of energy transfer =
total energy transferred ÷ time taken for energy transfer
$$= 83\,500 \div 138 \text{ [1 mark]}$$
$$= 605.072...$$
$$= \textbf{605 J/min (to 3 s.f)}$$
[1 mark]

2.2 Taking temperature measurements every 30 s instead of every minute. *[1 mark]*
This will allow the student to more accurately determine the time at which the ice first reaches 0 °C and when its temperature increases from 0 °C. Insulation would change the experiment, as it would interfere with the energy transferred to the ice from the room. A thermometer with a lower minimum temperature wouldn't help, as the student is only interested in when the ice is at 0 °C.

2.3 E.g. remove the solid ice from the liquid water in the beaker *[1 mark]*. Measure the mass of the remaining liquid water to find the mass of ice that actually melted. / Measure the mass of the solid ice and subtract this mass from 250 g *[1 mark]*.

Topic P4 — Atomic Structure

Page 199 — The Current Model of the Atom

Warm-up
1×10^{-10} m

1.1 An atom is made of a **positively**-charged nucleus, surrounded by **electrons**. The nucleus contains **protons** and **neutrons**. The nucleus takes up most of the **mass** of the atom.
[5 marks — 1 mark for each correct answer]
You can swap protons and neutrons in the answer and you will still get the marks.

1.2 10 000 *[1 mark]*

2.1 If an atom absorbs electromagnetic radiation an electron moves to a higher energy level/away from the nucleus *[1 mark]*. If an atom emits electromagnetic radiation an electron moves to a lower energy level/closer to the nucleus *[1 mark]*. If an outer electron absorbs enough energy it can leave the atom *[1 mark]*.

2.2 Positively-charged *[1 mark]*. There are now more positively-charged protons than negatively-charged electrons *[1 mark]*.

Pages 200-201 — Isotopes and Nuclear Radiation

1.1 Isotopes — Atoms with the same number of protons but different numbers of neutrons.
Gamma — Nuclear radiation made up of electromagnetic waves.
Alpha particles — Particles made up of two neutrons and two protons.
[2 marks — 1 mark for one correct line drawn, 2 marks for all 3 correct lines drawn]

1.2 beta decay *[1 mark]*

2.1 23 *[1 mark]*
Remember that the mass number is the top number. It's the total number of protons and neutrons in the nucleus.

2.2 23 − 11 = 12 neutrons *[1 mark]*
The number of neutrons is the difference between the mass number and the atomic number.

2.3 $^{24}_{11}$Na *[1 mark]*
An isotope has the same number of protons (so the same atomic number, the bottom number), but a different number of neutrons (so a different mass number).

3 E.g. alpha particles can't pass through paper *[1 mark]*. Gamma rays can pass through paper easily so the count-rate would not change much with the thickness of the paper *[1 mark]*.

4.1 The (use of) lead blocks *[1 mark]*. These will absorb radiation emitted from the beta source, preventing it from reaching, and potentially harming, the engineer *[1 mark]*.

4.2 uncertainty = range ÷ 2 = (122 − 101) ÷ 2 *[1 mark]*
$$= \textbf{10.5} \text{ [1 mark]}$$

4.3 The mean is given by the sum of all the values, divided by the number of values, so:
mean = (101 + 122 + 105) ÷ 3 *[1 mark]*
$$= 109.33... = \textbf{109 (to nearest whole number)} \text{ [1 mark]}$$

Page 202 — Nuclear Equations

Warm-up
$^{99}_{44}$Ru → $^{99}_{44}$Ru + $^{0}_{0}\gamma$

1.1 Mass number: Doesn't change *[1 mark]*.
Atomic number: Increases by 1 *[1 mark]*.

1.2 It increases *[1 mark]*.

2.1 $^{4}_{2}$He / alpha particle *[1 mark]*

2.2 a = 226 − 4
= 222 *[1 mark]*
b = 88 − 2
= 86 *[1 mark]*

2.3 $^{222}_{86}$Rn → $^{218}_{84}$Po + $^{4}_{2}$He *[1 mark for correct mass numbers, 1 mark for correct atomic numbers and 1 mark for helium nucleus symbol]*

Page 203 — Half-life

1 The **half-life** is the time taken for the number of nuclei of a radioactive isotope in a sample to halve. The rate of decay of a radioactive isotope is called its **activity** and it is measured in **becquerels**. *[3 marks — 1 mark for each correct answer]*

2.1 75 *[1 mark]*
The initial count-rate is 60 cps. Half of this is 30 cps, which corresponds to 75 seconds on the time axis.

2.2 After 1 half-life, there will be 800 ÷ 2 = 400 undecayed nuclei remaining. After 2 half-lives, there will be
400 ÷ 2 = 200 undecayed nuclei remaining.
So 800 − 200 = **600** nuclei will have decayed.
[2 marks for correct answer, otherwise 1 mark for calculating the number of decayed/undecayed nuclei after one half-life]

Page 204 — Irradiation and Contamination

1 Work behind barriers that absorb radiation *[1 mark]*.

2.1 Contamination is when unwanted radioactive particles get onto or into an object *[1 mark]*. Irradiation is when an object is exposed to radiation *[1 mark]*.

2.2 Any two from: e.g. wearing protective gloves / using tongs / wearing a protective suit or mask *[2 marks]*.

3 Contamination *[1 mark]*. Alpha particles cannot pass through skin, so the irradiation risk is lower *[1 mark]*. However, as they are very ionising they could cause lots of damage inside the clockmaker's body if he was contaminated *[1 mark]*.

Answers

Topic P5 — Forces

Page 205 — Contact and Non-Contact Forces

Warm-up

Scalar — mass, time, temperature

Vector — acceleration, weight, force

1   Vector quantities have both magnitude and direction *[1 mark]*.

2   Contact force: e.g. friction / tension / normal contact force *[1 mark]*

Non-contact force: e.g. weight / gravitational force *[1 mark]*

3

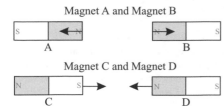

Magnet A and Magnet B

Magnet C and Magnet D

[1 mark for correct arrow length, 1 mark for correct direction]

Pages 206-207 — Weight, Mass and Gravity

1

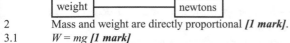

2   Mass and weight are directly proportional *[1 mark]*.

3.1 $W = mg$ *[1 mark]*

3.2 $W = 185 \times 9.8$ *[1 mark]*

       $= 1813 = $ **1800 N (to 2 s.f.)** *[1 mark]*

3.3 $W = mg$ so $g = W \div m$ *[1 mark]*

       $= 703 \div 185$ *[1 mark]*

       $= $ **3.8 N/kg** *[1 mark]*

4.1   E.g. place each disc on a mass balance, and record the mass displayed *[1 mark]*.

4.2   systematic error *[1 mark]*

A systematic error is where all your results are off by the same amount. In this example, each measurement of the weight is too large, because the same weight of the tray has been included in every measurement.

4.3   E.g.

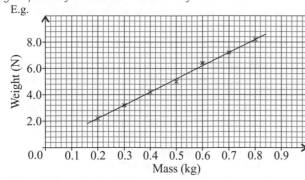

[1 mark for points for 0.3 kg and 0.6 kg plotted correctly. 1 mark for a straight line of best fit drawn through or close to all points]

4.4   E.g. $g = $ gradient $= \dfrac{\text{change in } y}{\text{change in } x} = \dfrac{8.4 - 2.0}{0.82 - 0.18}$ *[1 mark]*

       $= $ **10 N/kg** *[1 mark]*

You'll get the calculation marks here as long as your calculation of the gradient is correct for your line of best fit.

Page 208 — Resultant Forces and Work Done

1   C *[1 mark]*

The resultant force is the sum of the forces acting on each runner. For runner C, the resultant force is 130 N − 100 N = 30 N.

2     $15 - 10 = $ **5 N** *[1 mark]*.

      to the right *[1 mark]*

3.1   Work done $= $ Force $\times$ distance $= 50 \times 15$ *[1 mark]*

      $= $ **750 Nm** *[1 mark]*

3.2   The temperature of the wheels increases *[1 mark]*. This is because doing work causes some energy to be transferred to the thermal energy stores of the wheels *[1 mark]*.

Page 209 — Forces and Elasticity

1.1   One force would just make the spring move not change shape *[1 mark]*.

1.2   Elastic deformation *[1 mark]*

1.3   Inelastic deformation *[1 mark]*

2   force $= $ spring constant $\times$ extension

so spring constant $= $ force $\div$ extension *[1 mark]*

spring constant $= 240 \div 0.2$ *[1 mark]* $= $ **1200** *[1 mark]*

Unit $= $ **N/m** *[1 mark]*

Page 210 — Investigating Springs

1.1

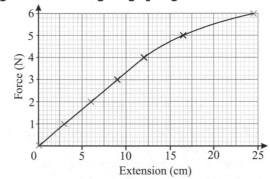

[2 marks for 3 points plotted correctly, otherwise 1 mark for 1-2 points plotted correctly. 1 mark for correct line of best fit.]

1.2   The limit of proportionality *[1 mark]*

2   Work done on spring $= $ energy stored in the spring's elastic potential energy store

8 cm $= 0.08$ m *[1 mark]*

$E = \frac{1}{2}ke^2 = \frac{1}{2} \times 25 \times 0.08^2$ *[1 mark]* $= $ **0.08 J** *[1 mark]*

Page 211 — Distance, Displacement, Speed and Velocity

1.1   7 m *[1 mark]*

1.2   12 m *[1 mark]*

1.3   2 m *[1 mark]*

As the scale is 1 cm = 1 m the number of metres measured is equal to the number of centimetres measured.

2.1   1.5 m/s (accept 1–2 m/s) *[1 mark]*

2.2   Any three from: e.g. fitness / age / distance travelled / terrain *[3 marks — 1 mark for each correct answer]*

2.3 $s = vt$ / distance $= $ speed $\times$ time *[1 mark]*

2.4   time $= $ distance travelled $\div$ speed *[1 mark]*

distance travelled $= 6$ km $= 6000$ m *[1 mark]*

so time $= 6000 \div 1.5$ *[1 mark]*

      $= $ **4000 s (accept 3000–6000 s)** *[1 mark]*

Page 212 — Acceleration

Warm-up

9.8 m/s^2

1   Moving with decreasing velocity *[1 mark]*

2.1 $a = \Delta v \div t$ *[1 mark]*

2.2 $a = \Delta v \div t = 4 \div 1$ *[1 mark]* $= $ **4 m/s^2** *[1 mark]*

3     $v^2 - u^2 = 2as$ so

$a = (v^2 - u^2) \div 2s$ *[1 mark]*

      $= (32^2 - 18^2) \div (2 \times 350)$ *[1 mark]*

      $= $ **1.0 m/s^2** *[1 mark]*

Answers

Page 213 — Distance-Time Graphs

1.1

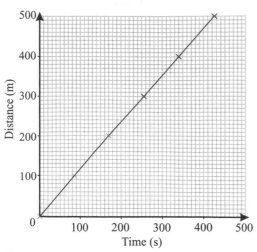

[2 marks for 3 points plotted correctly, otherwise 1 mark for 1-2 points plotted correctly. 1 mark for correctly drawn line.]

1.2   355 m (accept 350–360 m) *[1 mark]*

1.3   215 s (accept 210–220 s) *[1 mark]*

1.4   The boat's speed stays constant *[1 mark]*

Pages 214-215 — Velocity-Time Graphs and Terminal Velocity

1   The resultant vertical force on an object falling at its terminal velocity is zero.
Terminal velocity is the maximum velocity an object can fall at. *[1 mark for both correct]*

2.1   E.g.

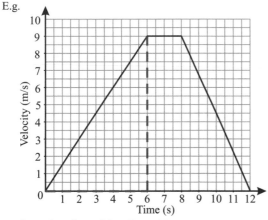

$a = \Delta v \div t$ / gradient of line *[1 mark]*
acceleration = $(9 - 0) \div (6 - 0)$ *[1 mark]* = **1.5 m/s²** *[1 mark]*

2.2   6 s and 8 s *[1 mark]*

3.1   The level of charge of the remote-controlled car *[1 mark]*.

3.2   A set of light gates, connected to a data logger *[1 mark]*.

This is the only option that can calculate speed and record time quickly and accurately.

3.3   The car reaches its maximum speed when its velocity-time graph reaches its maximum value of velocity *[1 mark]*. The graph of the experiment where the car is 100% charged reaches its maximum value of velocity in a shorter time than the other two graphs *[1 mark]*.

Page 216 — Newton's First and Second Laws

1   If the resultant force on a stationary object is zero, the object will remain stationary *[1 mark]*.

2   Newton's Second Law states that the acceleration of an object is directly proportional to the **resultant** force acting on the object. Newton's Second Law also says that the acceleration is inversely proportional to the **mass** of the object.
[2 marks — 1 mark for each correct answer]

3      $F = ma$ so $a = F \div m$ *[1 mark]*
$F = 2400$ N, $m = 400$ kg
so $a = 2400 \div 400$ *[1 mark]* = **6** *[1 mark]*
Unit = **m/s²** *[1 mark]*

Page 217 — Newton's Third Law

Warm-up
When two objects interact, they exert equal and opposite forces on each other.

1   100 N *[1 mark]*

2.1   320 N *[1 mark]*

2.2   640 N *[1 mark]*

Page 218 — Investigating Motion

1.1   The mass of the hook and the trolley *[1 mark]*.

1.2   The acceleration of the trolley is directly proportional to the force acting on it / As force increases, the acceleration of the trolley increases *[1 mark]*.

1.3   E.g. at a force of 2.0 N, the acceleration is 1.0 m/s²
So $m = F \div a$ *[1 mark]* = $2.0 \div 1.0$ *[1 mark]*
= **2 kg** *[1 mark]*

You'll still get the marks if you took readings from a different part of the graph, so long as you get the correct final answer.

1.4   The acceleration will be smaller / The acceleration will decrease *[1 mark]*.

Page 219 — Stopping Distance and Thinking Distance

1   36 m *[1 mark]*

Stopping distance = thinking distance + braking distance

2.1   The distance travelled during the driver's reaction time *[1 mark]*

2.2   The distance travelled under the braking force of the vehicle *[1 mark]*

3   Any three from: tiredness / alcohol / drugs / distractions *[3 marks — 1 mark for each correct answer]*

4   Slower reaction times results in a longer thinking distance / stopping distance *[1 mark]*. This means the car is more likely to hit the object it's trying to avoid before stopping *[1 mark]*.

Page 220 — Braking Distance

Warm-up
Circled answers: Smooth road surface, Ice on the road, Bald tyres
Snow on the road

1   The brakes may overheat *[1 mark]*,
the driver may lose control *[1 mark]*.

2   The temperature of the brakes increases *[1 mark]*. Energy is transferred from the kinetic energy store of the vehicle to the thermal energy stores of the brakes *[1 mark]*.

3   Level 0:   There is no relevant information. *[No marks]*
         Level 1:   There is a brief explanation of why good tyres are important. There is some explanation as to the safety implications of poor tyres. *[1 to 2 marks]*
         Level 2:   A detailed and clear explanation of the importance of having the tyres in good condition. The effects on stopping distance and overall safety are clearly stated. *[3 to 4 marks]*

Here are some points your answer may include:
Bald tyres cannot get rid of water on the road.
This can lead to them skidding on the water.
So having tyres in a good condition helps to stop your car skidding in wet conditions.
Skidding increases the stopping distance.
This decreases the overall safety.
So having tyres in a good condition increases the safety of driving in wet conditions.

Answers

Page 221 — Reaction Times

1   0.2 - 0.9 s *[1 mark]*

2.1 E.g. clicking a mouse when a computer screen changes colour *[1 mark]*

2.2 Student A: (7.0 + 7.1 + 6.9) ÷ 3 = **7.0 cm** *[1 mark]*
     Student B: (8.4 + 8.2 + 8.3) ÷ 3 = **8.3 cm** *[1 mark]*

2.3 Student C *[1 mark]*.

2.4 Any two from: e.g. use the same ruler / always have the same person dropping the ruler / test the students at the same time of day / remove distractions for all students.
     [2 marks — 1 mark for each correct answer]

2.5 Their reaction times are likely to get longer *[1 mark]*.

Topic P6 — Waves

Page 222 — Transverse and Longitudinal Waves

Warm-up
sound waves — L
ripples on water — T
light — T

1.1

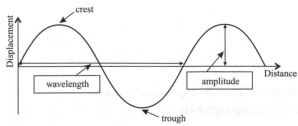

[2 marks — 1 mark for each correct answer]

1.2 The number of complete waves which pass a point in one second *[1 mark]*.

1.3 The vibrations in longitudinal waves are in the same direction as the energy transfer *[1 mark]*. Whereas in transverse waves, the vibration is perpendicular (at right angles) to the direction of energy transfer *[1 mark]*.

2   She's incorrect *[1 mark]*. It is the wave, not the water, that moves so the leaf will just move up and down *[1 mark]*.

Page 223 — Frequency, Period and Wave Speed

1   frequency = 1 ÷ period
           = 1 ÷ 2 *[1 mark]*
           = **0.5 Hz** *[1 mark]*

2.1 Correct order = D, E, B, A, C
     [3 marks for all in correct order, 2 marks for three in correct order, 1 mark for two in correct order.]

2.2 wave speed = frequency × wavelength *[1 mark]*

2.3 wave speed = frequency × wavelength
           = 50.0 × 6.80 *[1 mark]*
           = **340 m/s** *[1 mark]*

Page 224 — Investigating Waves

1.1 3 *[1 mark]*

1.2 The student should divide distance *d* by the number of wavelengths on the string (3) *[1 mark]*

2   E.g. turn on the lamp and set the signal generator to a fixed frequency *[1 mark]*. Then measure the length of 10 waves *[1 mark]*. Divide this distance by 10 to find the wavelength of one water wave *[1 mark]*. Then multiply this wavelength by the frequency of the signal generator (which equals the frequency of the waves) *[1 mark]*.

Page 225 — Refraction

1.1

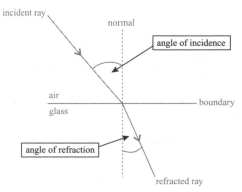

[1 mark for both correct]

1.2 90° *[1 mark]*

2   E.g.

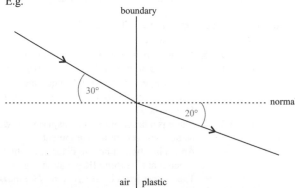

[1 mark for incident ray drawn on the left of the boundary and refracted ray drawn on the right of the boundary with correct arrows on both rays, 1 mark for correctly drawn normal, 1 mark for incident ray at 30° to the normal (on either side of the normal), 1 mark for refracted ray at 20° to the normal on the opposite side of the normal to the incident ray]

You don't need to have labelled the angles in your diagram, we've just included them here to make it clearer.

Page 226 — Electromagnetic Waves

1   gamma rays *[1 mark]*

2.1 In this order: Microwaves *[1 mark]*, X-rays *[1 mark]*.

2.2 Arrow must point to the left (i.e. from gamma rays to radio waves) *[1 mark]*.

2.3 All waves in the electromagnetic spectrum are **transverse** waves. All electromagnetic waves travel at the same speed in **a vacuum**.
     [2 marks — 1 mark for each correct answer]

2.4 gamma rays *[1 mark]*.

Page 227 — Uses of EM Waves

Warm-up
1 - Radio waves can be used to...
2 - ...transmit TV signals...
3 - ...and radio signals.
4 - Some wavelengths...
5 - ...can send signals very long distances.

1.1 When food is cooked in a microwave oven, water in the food **absorbs** microwaves.
     This causes the temperature of the food to **increase**.
     [2 marks — 1 mark for each correct answer]

1.2 E.g. satellite communications *[1 mark]*

2.1 A *[1 mark]*

2.2 E.g. electric heaters, toasters. *[2 marks — 1 mark for each correct answer]*

Answers

Page 228 — More Uses of EM Waves

1.1   fibre-optic cables for communication *[1 mark]*
1.2   energy efficient lamps *[1 mark]*
1.3   Any one from: e.g. suntanning / security marking *[1 mark]*
2.1   X-rays *[1 mark]*, gamma rays *[1 mark]*
2.2   E.g. gamma rays or X-rays in medical imaging / gamma rays as medical tracers / gamma rays to sterilise equipment *[1 mark]*

Page 229 — Investigating IR Radiation

1.1   Suggestion: e.g. bar chart
          Reason: e.g. the independent variable comes in clear categories.
          [1 mark for a sensible suggestion and 1 mark for a valid reason]
1.2   Best emitter   Matt black surface
                         Shiny black surface
                         Matt silver surface
         Worst emitter   Shiny silver surface
         [1 mark for all surfaces in the correct order]

Page 230 — Investigating IR Absorption

1   How to grade your answer:
      Level 0:   There is no relevant information. *[No marks]*
      Level 1:   There is a brief description of an experiment that could be performed with the equipment. The points made are basic and poorly structured. *[1-2 marks]*
      Level 2:   There is a description of an experiment which can be performed with the equipment. An explanation of how to determine which surface is better at absorbing IR radiation is given. The answer has a clear structure. *[3-4 marks]*
      Level 3:   There is a clear and detailed description of an experiment which can be performed with the equipment. An explanation of how to determine which surface is better at absorbing IR radiation is given. The answer has a clear and logical structure. *[5-6 marks]*
     Here are some points your answer may include:
     Place the Bunsen burner in the centre of the heat-proof mat.
     Stand one plate either side of the Bunsen burner.
     Stand the plates so that the side with the ball attached is facing away from the Bunsen burner.
     Make sure that the two plates are an equal distance away from Bunsen burner.
     Light the Bunsen burner.
     Observe which metal ball falls first.
     Make a note of which plate it fell from.
     This plate absorbed more IR radiation.
     So the temperature of this plate increased faster causing the wax to melt faster.
     So the surface facing the flame on this plate is the better absorber.

Page 231 — Dangers of Electromagnetic Waves

Warm-up
1000 mSv
1.1   The type of radiation absorbed *[1 mark]*.
1.2   E.g. skin aging prematurely / increased risk of skin cancer *[2 marks — 1 mark for each correct]*
2   How to grade your answer:
      Level 0:   There is no relevant information. *[No marks]*
      Level 1:   There is a brief description of the health effects of exposure to X-rays. Little or no comparison is made between the two procedures. The points made are basic and poorly structured. *[1-2 marks]*
      Level 2:   There is a full description of the health effects of exposure to X-rays. A detailed comparison is made between the two procedures that is clearly linked to the health risks of each procedure. The answer has a clear and logical structure. *[3-4 marks]*
     Here are some points your answer may include:
     The radiation dose for the lower spine X-ray is 20 times larger than the radiation dose for the skull X-ray.
     This means the risk of harm to the patient from the spine X-ray is twenty times larger than risk caused by the skull X-ray.
     X-rays can cause gene mutations, which can lead to cancer.
     They can also kill off healthy cells in the patient's body.
     The risk of killing cells or causing genes to mutate is larger for the spine X-ray than for the skull X-ray.

Topic P7 — Magnetism and Electromagnetism

Page 232 — Permanent and Induced Magnets

Warm-up
From left to right: attractive, repulsive
1   the force between them is always attractive *[1 mark]*
2   Magnetic forces are examples of **non-contact** forces. The direction of the magnetic field shows the direction that the force would act on a **north** pole at that point. The field is **strongest** at the poles of the magnet.
     [3 marks — 1 mark for each correct answer]
3.1   The magnetic material becomes an induced magnet *[1 mark]* when it's placed in the magnetic field of the permanent bar magnet *[1 mark]*.
3.2   Any one from: e.g. iron / steel / nickel / cobalt *[1 mark]*

Pages 233-234 — Electromagnetism

1.1

     [1 mark for three anticlockwise arrows, one on each field line]
1.2   Y *[1 mark]*
The magnetic field is stronger the closer to the wire you are.
1.3   The wire carrying 0.5 A *[1 mark]*. Its higher current means a stronger magnetic field *[1 mark]*.
2.1   E.g. strong *[1 mark]* and uniform *[1 mark]*.
Uniform means it's the same at any point.
2.2   Change 1 — It reverses *[1 mark]*
              Change 2 — It increases *[1 mark]*
2.3   An electromagnet *[1 mark]*

Answers

3.1 E.g. wearing gloves (when handling the equipment) to protect herself from burns *[1 mark]*.

3.2 Because the experiment is no longer a fair test *[1 mark]*.

The number of turns on the electromagnet has changed, which will change its magnetic field strength. As the experiment is investigating how current affects the strength of the magnet, and something other than current has been changed, it is no longer a fair test.

3.3 The plastic electromagnet would pick up fewer paperclips at each current step than the iron electromagnet *[1 mark]*.

As iron is a magnetic material, it increases the strength of the magnetic field of the coil when used as a core for an electromagnet. Plastic isn't magnetic, so it won't increase the field strength, and the magnet will be weaker and pick up fewer paperclips.

3.4 Increasing the current in steps of 100 mA will give the student more data than in her first experiment *[1 mark]*, so a clearer trend will be seen *[1 mark]*. This means that it will be easier for her to identify results that don't match the trend *[1 mark]*.

Mixed Questions

Pages 235-239 — Biology Mixed Questions

1.1 muscle cell *[1 mark]*

The features of this cell (tissues that contract, lots of mitochondria) suggest it's a muscle cell. If it was a sperm cell, it would have an obvious tail and if it was a nerve cell it would have branched endings to connect it to other cells. It can't be a xylem cell, as that's a plant cell and the question tells you it's an animal cell.

1.2 To provide the energy the cell needs to carry out its function *[1 mark]*.

1.3 E.g. it has got a nucleus / it doesn't have any plasmids *[1 mark]*.

1.4 *E. coli* bacterium *[1 mark]*

2.1 a protein *[1 mark]*

2.2 E.g. making bile / converting excess glucose to glycogen *[1 mark]*.

2.3 kidney *[1 mark]*

3.1 glucose + **oxygen** → **carbon dioxide** + water *[2 marks — 1 mark for each correct answer in bold]*

3.2 plasma *[1 mark]*

3.3 From top to bottom, the steps should be numbered: 2, 4, 3, 1 *[2 marks for all four steps in the correct order, otherwise 1 mark for two steps in the correct order.]*

4.1 photosynthesis *[1 mark]*

The reactants of photosynthesis (carbon dioxide and water) are going into the subcellular structure and the products of photosynthesis (glucose and oxygen) are leaving it — this suggests that photosynthesis is happening inside the subcellular structure.

4.2 chloroplast *[1 mark]*

4.3 45 000 μm *[1 mark]*

Remember, 1 mm = 1000 μm, so 45 mm will equal 45 000 μm.

4.4 Carbon dioxide diffuses into a leaf from the atmosphere *[1 mark]*, through the stomata *[1 mark]*.

4.5 transpiration *[1 mark]*

4.6 translocation *[1 mark]*

5.1 Enzymes speed up chemical reactions in living organisms. *[1 mark]*

5.2 9 *[1 mark]*

5.3 The enzyme will not work *[1 mark]* because the acid will change the shape of its active site/denature the enzyme *[1 mark]* and the substrate will no longer fit *[1 mark]*.

5.4 Alcohol can cause liver damage. *[1 mark]*

5.5 anaerobic respiration / fermentation *[1 mark]*

6.1 A producer produces its own food (using energy from the Sun) *[1 mark]*.

6.2 E.g. increased competition from other plants / increase in grasshopper numbers *[1 mark]*.

6.3 E.g. the population of snakes may decrease *[1 mark]* because they would be competing with the owls for mice *[1 mark]*.

6.4 E.g. the scientist could mark out a transect line across the ecosystem *[1 mark]*. He/she could then place quadrats along the line *[1 mark]* and estimate the percentage cover of grasses in each quadrat *[1 mark]*.

6.5 All the species and environmental factors are in balance *[1 mark]* so the population sizes stay about the same *[1 mark]*.

Pages 240-245 — Chemistry Mixed Questions

1.1 lithium *[1 mark]*

1.2 Any one from: sodium *[1 mark]* / potassium *[1 mark]* / rubidium *[1 mark]* / caesium *[1 mark]* / francium *[1 mark]*

1.3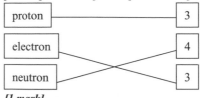

[1 mark]

1.4

[1 mark]

1.5 hydrogen *[1 mark]*

1.6 When a Group 1 element reacts with water a metal **hydroxide** *[1 mark]* is formed.

2.1 mean = (35.60 + 35.90 + 35.75) ÷ 3 = **35.75 cm³** *[2 marks for correct answer, otherwise 1 mark for correct method]*

2.2 range = 35.90 − 35.60 = 0.30
uncertainty = 0.30 ÷ 2 = **0.15 cm³** *[2 marks for correct answer, otherwise 1 mark for calculating range]*

2.3 **HCl** + NaOH → **NaCl** + H_2O *[1 mark for HCl, 1 mark for NaCl]*

2.4 E.g. the pH would start high/above pH 7 *[1 mark]*. As the hydrochloric acid is added it would decrease *[1 mark]* until it reached pH 7/falls below pH 7 *[1 mark]*.

2.5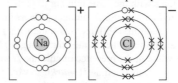

[1 mark for adding seven crosses and one dot to outer shell of Cl⁻ ion, 1 mark for correct charge on both ions]

2.6 ionic *[1 mark]*

3.1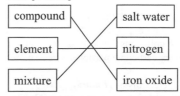

[2 marks if all three correct, otherwise 1 mark if one correct]

3.2 Calcium, carbon and oxygen *[2 marks for all three correct, 1 mark for two correct]*

3.3 Pure water contains only water molecules *[1 mark]* whereas potable water is a mixture containing water and other dissolved substances *[1 mark]*.

3.4 Any two from: e.g. filtration / evaporation / crystallisation / chromatography / simple distillation / fractional distillation *[2 marks — 1 mark for each correct answer]*

Answers

4.1 Group: 6 *[1 mark]*
Explanation: There are 6 electrons in the outer shell *[1 mark]*.

4.2 Charge: 2– *[1 mark]*
Reason: Oxygen atoms need to gain two electrons to get a full outer shell *[1 mark]*.

4.3 oxidation *[1 mark]*

5.1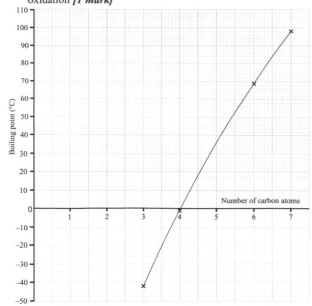

[1 mark for all four points correctly plotted, 1 mark for a smooth curve that passes through all the points]

5.2 **36 °C** *[1 mark for any answer in the range 34-38 °C]*

5.3 C_nH_{2n+2} *[1 mark]*

5.4 M_r of C_3H_8 = (C × 3) + (H × 8) = (12 × 3) + (1 × 8) = 36 + 8
= **44** *[1 mark]*

6.1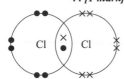

[1 mark for shared pair of electrons, 1 mark for six further electrons in the outer shell of each chlorine atom]

6.2 E.g. isotopes are atoms with the same number of protons / of the same element / with the same atomic number *[1 mark]* that have different numbers of neutrons / different mass numbers *[1 mark]*.

6.3 Hold a piece of damp litmus paper in the unknown gas *[1 mark]*. It will be bleached white in the presence of chlorine *[1 mark]*.

6.4 Chlorine is more reactive than iodine *[1 mark]*, so would displace iodine from sodium iodide solution / the solution would go from colourless to brown *[1 mark]*.

7.1 endothermic *[1 mark]*

7.2 higher *[1 mark]*

7.3 Effect: the rate of reaction will increase *[1 mark]*.
Reason: there will be more particles of ethanoic acid in the same volume *[1 mark]* so collisions between the reactant/ethanoic acid and sodium hydrogen carbonate particles will be more frequent *[1 mark]*.

8.1 Extraction process: electrolysis *[1 mark]*
Reason: electrolysis uses lots of energy *[1 mark]*. This energy often comes from burning fossil fuels *[1 mark]* which releases greenhouse gases *[1 mark]*.

8.2 Any two from: e.g. it helps save some of the finite amount of metal in the earth / it cuts down on the waste getting sent to landfill *[2 marks]*.

9 How to grade your answer:
Level 0:   There is no relevant information. *[No marks]*
Level 1:   A brief attempt is made to explain one or two of the properties in terms of structure and/or bonding. *[1 to 2 marks]*
Level 2:   Some explanation of all three properties, in terms of structure and/or bonding, is given, or a complete explanation of one or two of these properties is given. *[3 to 4 marks]*
Level 3:   Clear and detailed explanation of all three properties, in terms of both structure and bonding, is given. *[5 to 6 marks]*

Here are some points your answer may include:
Diamond
Each carbon atom in diamond forms four covalent bonds in a rigid giant covalent structure, making it very hard.
Because it is made up of lots of covalent bonds, which take a lot of energy to break, diamond has a very high melting point.
There are no free/delocalised electrons in the structure of diamond, so it can't conduct electricity.
Graphite
Each carbon atom in graphite forms three covalent bonds.
The carbon atoms are arranged in layers of hexagons.
There are no covalent bonds between layers, so the layers can slide over each other.
This makes graphite soft and slippery.
The covalent bonds between the carbon atoms take a lot of energy to break, giving graphite a very high melting point.
Each carbon atom has one electron which is free to move, so graphite has lots of free/delocalised electrons and can conduct electricity.

Pages 246-251 — Physics Mixed Questions

1.1 solid to liquid — melting *[1 mark]*
liquid to solid — freezing *[1 mark]*

1.2 Gases are usually **less dense than** liquids. *[1 mark]*

2.1 3 cm *[1 mark]*

2.2 330 m/s *[1 mark]*

3.1 6 m/s *[1 mark]*

3.2 Change in velocity = 6 m/s – 0 m/s = 6 m/s
so, acceleration = 6 ÷ 10 *[1 mark]* = **0.6 m/s²** *[1 mark]*

If you ticked a different answer for 3.1 you will still get the marks if your calculation is correct.

4.1 E.g. a quantity that only has a size / a quantity that has a size but not a direction *[1 mark]*.

4.2 The force on an object due to gravity is called its **weight**. It is measured in **newtons**. You can think of weight as acting from a single point on an object. This point is called the centre of **mass**.
[3 marks — 1 mark for each correct answer]

4.3 newtonmeter *[1 mark]*

4.4 No, she is incorrect. A smaller gravitational field strength will lead to a smaller weight of the pencil case *[1 mark]*.

5.1 speed *[1 mark]*

5.2 5 mins = 5 × 60 = 300 seconds *[1 mark]*
speed = 420 ÷ 300 *[1 mark]* = **1.4 m/s** *[1 mark]*

5.3 mechanically *[1 mark]*

6.1 E.g. medical imaging / medical tracers / killing cancer / sterilising medical equipment *[1 mark]*

6.2 A = 99 *[1 mark]*
B = 0 *[1 mark]*

When a gamma ray is emitted, it doesn't change the charge or mass of the nucleus. Emitting a gamma ray is a way of getting rid of excess energy.

6.3 lead / concrete *[1 mark]*

Answers

7.1

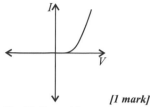

[1 mark]

7.2 $V = IR$ *[1 mark]*

7.3 $R = V \div I$ *[1 mark]*
        $= 2.4 \div 0.4$ *[1 mark]*
        $= 6\ \Omega$ *[1 mark]*

8.1   Heater B *[1 mark]*. It transfers the same amount of energy in half the time so has twice the power *[1 mark]*.

8.2   change in thermal energy = mass × specific heat capacity × temperature change
    Change in temperature = 50 °C – 20 °C = 30 °C *[1 mark]*
    Change in thermal energy = 0.50 × 4200 × 30 *[1 mark]*
                   = **63 000 J** *[1 mark]*

9.1   gravitational potential energy = mass × gravitational field strength × height *[1 mark]*

9.2   mass = gravitational potential energy
             ÷ (gravitational field strength × height) *[1 mark]*
        = 440 ÷ (9.8 × 9.0) *[1 mark]*
        = 4.988... kg
        = **5.0 kg (to 2 s.f.)** *[1 mark]*

9.3

[1 mark for correct shape, 1 mark for arrows pointing from north to south]

9.4   The Earth has a magnetic field *[1 mark]*. The needle points in the direction of the Earth's north pole *[1 mark]*.

9.5   E.g. permanent magnet always have a magnetic field around them *[1 mark]*. Induced magnets only have one when in another magnetic field *[1 mark]*.

10.1

[1 mark for an arrow in the right direction, 1 mark for it being the same length as the driving force arrow]

10.2   kinetic energy = 0.5 × mass × (speed)² *[1 mark]*

10.3   kinetic energy = 0.5 × mass × (speed)²
    so mass = (2 × kinetic energy) ÷ (speed)² *[1 mark]*
    mass = (2 × 7.5) ÷ (5.0)² *[1 mark]*
         = 0.6 kg *[1 mark]*

10.4   Energy is transferred (mechanically) from the kinetic energy store *[1 mark]* of the car to it's gravitational potential energy store *[1 mark]*.

10.5   efficiency = useful output energy transfer ÷ total input energy transfer
    so useful output energy transfer =
    efficiency × total input energy transfer *[1 mark]*
    useful output energy transfer = 0.65 × 700 *[1 mark]*
                   = 455 J *[1 mark]*
    energy wasted = 700 – 455 = **245 J** *[1 mark]*

The Periodic Table

Periods

1

Group 0

	1
	H
	Hydrogen
	1

	4
	He
	Helium
	2

Relative atomic mass

Atomic (proton) number

Group 1   Group 2

Group 3   Group 4   Group 5   Group 6   Group 7

7	9
Li	Be
Lithium	Beryllium
3	4

11	12	14	16	19	20
B	C	N	O	F	Ne
Boron	Carbon	Nitrogen	Oxygen	Fluorine	Neon
5	6	7	8	9	10

2

23	24
Na	Mg
Sodium	Magnesium
11	12

27	28	31	32	35.5	40
Al	Si	P	S	Cl	Ar
Aluminium	Silicon	Phosphorus	Sulfur	Chlorine	Argon
13	14	15	16	17	18

3

39	40	45	48	51	52	55	56	59	59	63.5	65	70	73	75	79	80	84
K	Ca	Sc	Ti	V	Cr	Mn	Fe	Co	Ni	Cu	Zn	Ga	Ge	As	Se	Br	Kr
Potassium	Calcium	Scandium	Titanium	Vanadium	Chromium	Manganese	Iron	Cobalt	Nickel	Copper	Zinc	Gallium	Germanium	Arsenic	Selenium	Bromine	Krypton
19	20	21	22	23	24	25	26	27	28	29	30	31	32	33	34	35	36

4

85	88	89	91	93	96	[98]	101	103	106	108	112	115	119	122	128	127	131
Rb	Sr	Y	Zr	Nb	Mo	Tc	Ru	Rh	Pd	Ag	Cd	In	Sn	Sb	Te	I	Xe
Rubidium	Strontium	Yttrium	Zirconium	Niobium	Molybdenum	Technetium	Ruthenium	Rhodium	Palladium	Silver	Cadmium	Indium	Tin	Antimony	Tellurium	Iodine	Xenon
37	38	39	40	41	42	43	44	45	46	47	48	49	50	51	52	53	54

5

133	137	139	178	181	184	186	190	192	195	197	201	204	207	209	[209]	[210]	[222]
Cs	Ba	La	Hf	Ta	W	Re	Os	Ir	Pt	Au	Hg	Tl	Pb	Bi	Po	At	Rn
Caesium	Barium	Lanthanum	Hafnium	Tantalum	Tungsten	Rhenium	Osmium	Iridium	Platinum	Gold	Mercury	Thallium	Lead	Bismuth	Polonium	Astatine	Radon
55	56	57	72	73	74	75	76	77	78	79	80	81	82	83	84	85	86

6

[223]	[226]	[227]	[261]	[262]	[266]	[264]	[277]	[268]	[271]	[272]	[285]	[286]	[289]	[289]	[293]	[294]	[294]
Fr	Ra	Ac	Rf	Db	Sg	Bh	Hs	Mt	Ds	Rg	Cn	Nh	Fl	Mc	Lv	Ts	Og
Francium	Radium	Actinium	Rutherfordium	Dubnium	Seaborgium	Bohrium	Hassium	Meitnerium	Darmstadtium	Roentgenium	Copernicium	Nihonium	Flerovium	Moscovium	Livermorium	Tennessine	Oganesson
87	88	89	104	105	106	107	108	109	110	111	112	113	114	115	116	117	118

7

The Lanthanides (atomic numbers 58-71) and the Actinides (atomic numbers 90-103) are not shown in this table.

Physics Equations List

Topic P1 — Energy

$E_e = \frac{1}{2}ke^2$	elastic potential energy = 0.5 × spring constant × (extension)^2
$\Delta E = mc\Delta\theta$	change in thermal energy = mass × specific heat capacity × temperature change
$E = mL$	thermal energy for a change of state = mass × specific latent heat

Topic P5 — Forces

$v^2 - u^2 = 2as$	(final velocity)^2 – (initial velocity)^2 = 2 × acceleration × distance

Topic P6 — Waves

$$\text{period} = \frac{1}{\text{frequency}}$$